Tioga F.F.A.

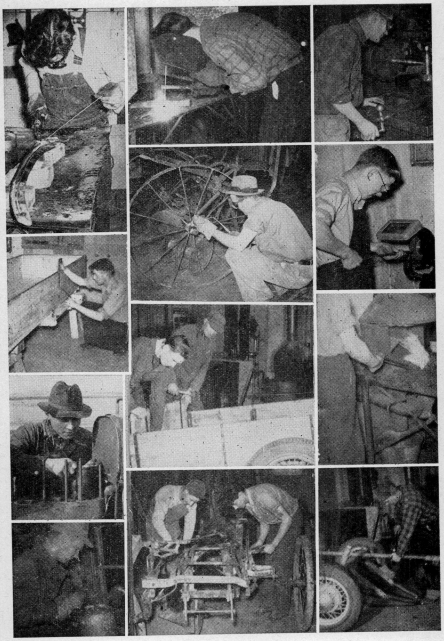

FARM METAL WORK

500...
MORE THINGS TO MAKE
FOR FARM AND HOME

VOL. II*

Compiled by

GLEN CHARLES COOK

Assistant Professor of Education
Michigan State College of Agriculture
and Applied Science

(At the present time on leave of absence
working as Special Representative,
Food Production War Training, U. S.
Office of Education.)

1 9 4 4

* Volume I, *380 Things to Make for Farm and Home*
can be secured from the Interstate.

PREFACE...

In 1941 the author published a book entitled, *380 Things to Make for Farm and Home,* in which a comprehensive list of plans of shop projects and jobs needed on the farm and in the home were included. This book was so enthusiastically received that the author decided a further contribution to farm mechanics in this field could be made by the publication of another book with additional plans and ideas. Teachers stated it was just the kind of a book they had been looking for and requested that a Volume II of such a book be published. These teachers and other interested persons, expressed a desire to have a number of projects included involving metal work. Consequently, special emphasis has been given metal work in this volume.

The primary aim has been to select a practical list of plans and ideas which have been tested and proved successful by State universities and agricultural colleges, farmers, teachers of vocational agriculture, teachers of general shop, in-school and out-of-school youth, county agents, and others interested in shop activities. It is not the purpose of this book to furnish a supply of informational materials on such jobs as tinning coppers, mixing concrete, sharpening a saw, and splicing a belt. This type of information can be secured by obtaining a copy of a *Farm Mechanics Text and Handbook* by Cook, Scranton, and McColly from the publishers of this edition.

Most persons before deciding on a particular type of a project to build, prefer to have a variety of plans to study and evaluate in terms of meeting their particular situation and local needs. In order to meet this need, the author has compiled a number of plans for each type of project where it has been possible to secure a variety of plans. This has been accomplished by evaluating materials furnished by practically every State, various government agencies, numerous commercial concerns, teachers, teacher trainers, and State supervisors.

During the past two years the author has had the opportunity to visit many classes in metal work under the Food Production War Training Program in twelve States. Numerous pictures have been taken of projects constructed and jobs performed by these classes, many of which are included in this book. Many ideas have been discovered for making use of salvage and scrap materials such as a forge from a binder bull wheel, feeders from old oil drums, punches, chisels, and wrecking bars from bridge reenforcing steel, cultivator shovels and gate hinges from old car springs, and numerous projects made from auto drive shafts, steering posts, hay rake teeth, and auto bumpers. These ideas have been included in this volume.

Home-farm shops are recognized as being essential on the farm. Consequently, several plans of homemade equipment have been included. Most of this equipment can be made at a conservative cost. It is hoped that these plans and ideas will stimulate farmers to plan and put into operation a home-farm shop on their farms.

The author is desirous that this book will be found useful to all those engaged in shop activities and that it will be found on the reference shelves of teachers, supervisors, farmers, in-school and out-of-school youth, county agents, agricultural engineers, and others interested in homemade equipment and labor saving devices for the farm and home.

THE AUTHOR.

ACKNOWLEDGMENTS...

The author wishes to express his appreciation and indebtedness to all those who granted permission to have reproductions made from their plans and statements quoted from their publications. The author also wishes to thank all those who furnished pictures and cuts for this publication. Many plans have been furnished by teachers, teacher trainers and supervisors whose cooperation is greatly appreciated. Credit has been given for these reproductions and quotations throughout the book.

The author is especially indebted to the following thirty-nine State colleges and universities which granted permission to reproduce plans from their publications:

Alabama	Montana
Arizona	Nebraska
Arkansas	New Hampshire
California	New York
Colorado	North Carolina
Florida	North Dakota
Georgia	Ohio
Idaho	Oklahoma
Illinois	Oregon
Indiana	Pennsylvania
Iowa	South Carolina
Kansas	South Dakota
Kentucky	Texas
Louisiana	Tennessee
Maine	Vermont
Maryland	Washington
Michigan	West Virginia
Minnesota	Wisconsin
Mississippi	Wyoming
Missouri	

The following is a list of governmental agencies and commercial organizations which furnished materials:

Agricultural Leaders Digest
American Farm Youth Magazine
Bethlehem Steel Corporation

California Redwood Association
Continental Steel Corporation
Douglas Fir Plywood Association
General Electric
International Harvester Company
Morton Salt Company
Portland Cement Association
Red Cedar Shingle Bureau
Rural Electrification Administration
Successful Farming, Meredith Publishing Company
The Linde Air Products Company
United States Department of Agriculture
United States Department of Commerce
United States Office of Education
Westinghouse Electric and Manufacturing Company
Weyerhaeuser Sales Company

The publication of this book would have been impossible had it not been for the splendid cooperation of all persons who so kindly granted permission to use their materials.

TABLE OF CONTENTS

. . .

PART I

EQUIPMENT

... FOR ..

THE HOME-FARM SHOP

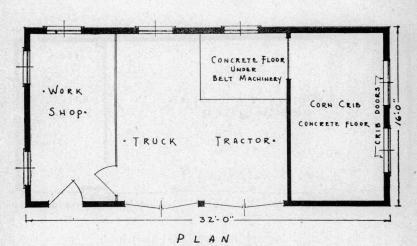

WORK SHOP.

CONCRETE FLOOR UNDER BELT MACHINERY

CORN CRIB CONCRETE FLOOR

CRIB DOORS

• TRUCK   TRACTOR •

16'-0"

32'-0"

P L A N

Fig. 1—Shop, garage and mill house.*

* Figures 1 and 2 courtesy Extension Division, University of Kentucky.

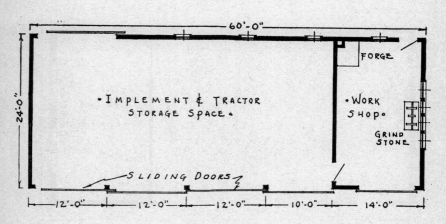

Fig. 2—Machine shed and shop plan.

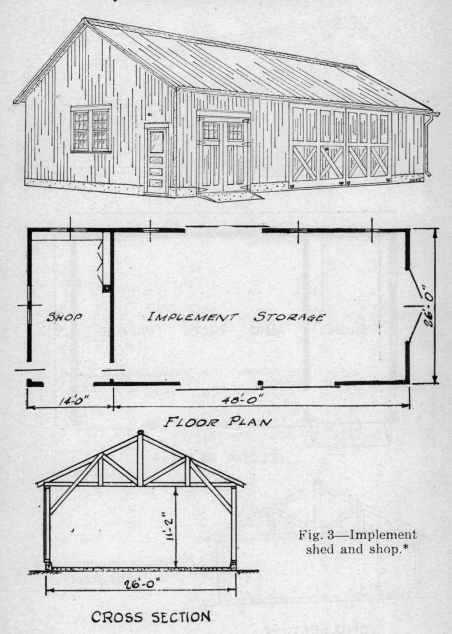

SHOP   IMPLEMENT STORAGE

26'-0"

14'-0"   48'-0"

FLOOR PLAN

11'-2"

26'-0"

CROSS SECTION

Fig. 3—Implement shed and shop.*

* Figures 3 and 4 courtesy Continental Steel Corporation.

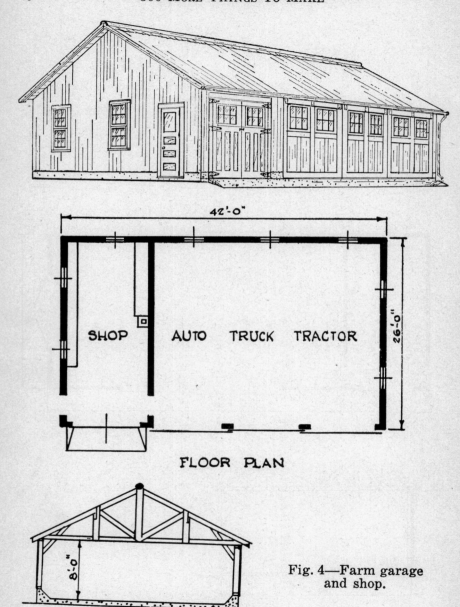

SHOP   AUTO   TRUCK   TRACTOR

42'-0"

26'-0"

FLOOR PLAN

8'-0"

END SECTION

Fig. 4—Farm garage
and shop.

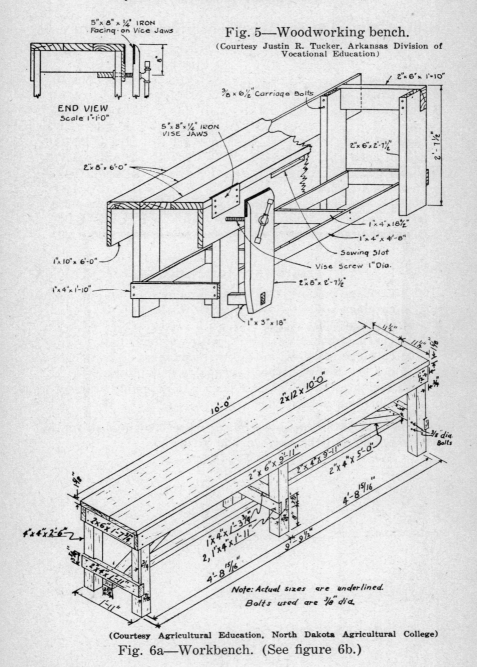

5"x 8"x ¼" IRON
Facing on Vice Jaws

END VIEW
Scale 1"-1'-0"

Fig. 5—Woodworking bench.
(Courtesy Justin R. Tucker, Arkansas Division of
Vocational Education)

⅜ x 6½" Carriage Bolts

2"x 6'x 1'-10"

5"x 8"x ¼" IRON
VISE JAWS

2"x 6"x 2'-7½"

2'-7½"

2"x 8"x 6'-0"

1"x 4"x 18½"

1"x 4"x 4'-8"

Sawing Slot

Vise Screw 1" Dia.

1"x 10"x 6'-0"

1"x 4"x 1'-10"

2"x 8"x 2'-7½"

1"x 3"x 18"

11½"

11½"

2x12 x 10'0"

10'-0"

⅜ dia.
Bolts

2"x 6"x 9'-11"

2"x 4"x 9'-11"

2"x 4"x 5'-0"

4'-8¹⁵/₁₆"

2x6"x 1'-7½"

1"x 4"x 1'-3¾"

4"x 4"x 2'-6"

2, 1"x 4"x 1'-11"

9'-9½"

2"x 4"x 1'-11"

4'-8¹⁵/₁₆"

1'-11"

Note: Actual sizes are underlined.
Bolts used are ⅜ dia.

(Courtesy Agricultural Education, North Dakota Agricultural College)
Fig. 6a—Workbench. (See figure 6b.)

Bill of Materials for Workbench Shown in Figure 6a

Use	No. of Pieces	Size
Bench top	2	2″ x 12″ x 10′
Side rails	2	2″ x 6″ x 9′11″
End rails—top	2	2″ x 6″ x 1′7¾″
Legs	6	4″ x 4″ x 2′6″
Long bracing	1	2″ x 4″ x 9′11″
End bracing	2	2″ x 4″ x 1′11″
Upper center bracing	2	2″ x 4″ x 1′4¾″
Lower center bracing—sides	2	1″ x 4″ x 1′11″
Lower center bracing—top	1	1″ x 4″ x 1′3¾″
Lower center bracing—bottom	1	1″ x 1⅞″ x 1′3¾″
Diagonal bracing	2	2″ x 4″ x 5′0″

Hardware for Bench

4 carriage bolts, ⅜″ x 7″, with washers
4 carriage bolts, ⅜″ x 6½″, with washers
16 carriage bolts, ⅜″ x 5½″, with washers
12 carriage bolts, ⅜″ x 4¾″, with washers
8 carriage bolts, ⅜″ x 4¼″, with washers
5 doz. 3″, No. 14 flathead screws to fasten top
2 doz. 2″, No. 10 flathead screws to assemble bracing
Glue and linseed oil

The lumber in the above bill of material will cost approximately $14.00 and the hardware about $2.50.

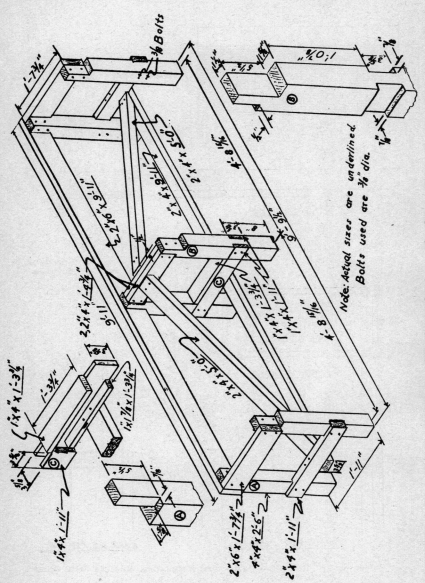

Fig. 6b—Workbench shown in figure 6a.

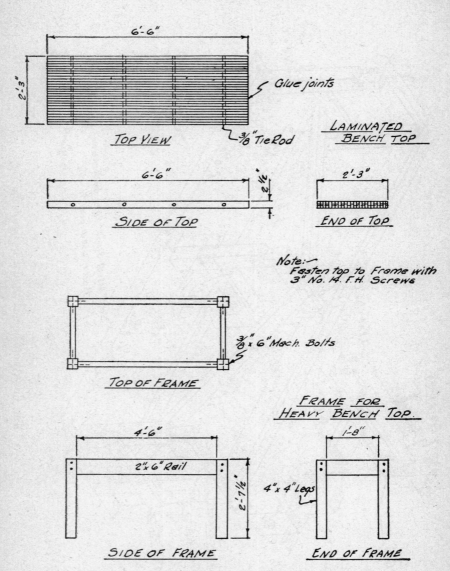

TOP VIEW

LAMINATED BENCH TOP

SIDE OF TOP

END OF TOP

Note:—
Fasten top to Frame with
3" No. 14 F.H. Screws

TOP OF FRAME

FRAME FOR
HEAVY BENCH TOP.

SIDE OF FRAME

END OF FRAME

(Courtesy W. H. Sheldon, Agricultural Engineering, Michigan State College)

Fig. 7—Workbench.

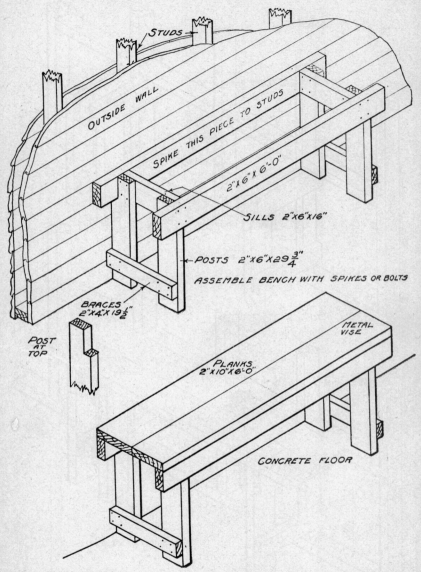

Fig. 8—Framing of metal working bench to be spiked to an outside wall (above), and the completed bench (below).*

* Figures 8 and 9 courtesy L. M. Roehl, Cornell University.

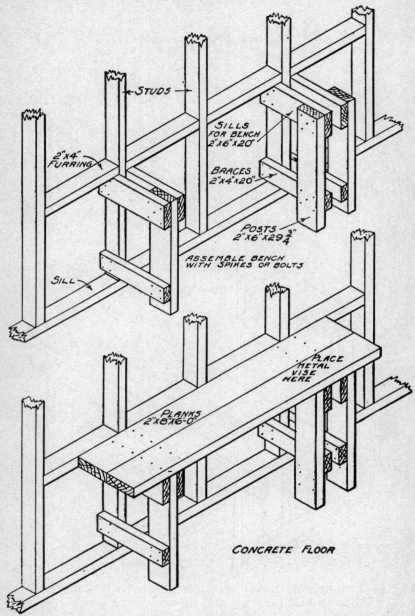

Fig. 9—Framing for metal working bench (above), and top planks of bench in place (below).

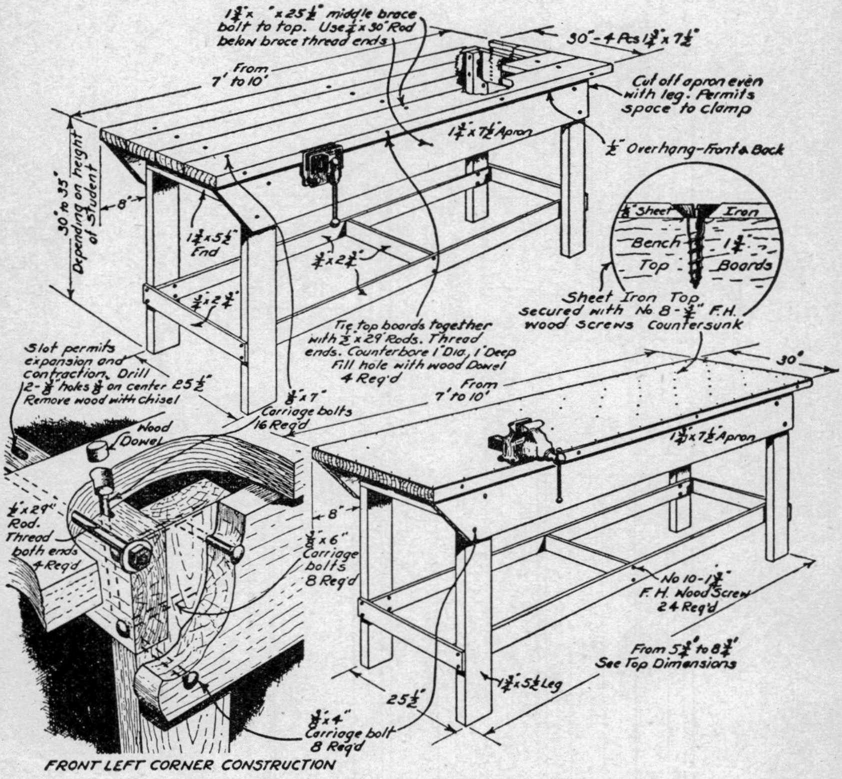

1¾" x " x 25½" middle brace bolt to top. Use ¼" x 30" Rod below brace thread ends
30" - 4 Pcs 1¾" x 7½"
From 7' to 10'
Cut off apron even with leg. Permits space to clamp
1¾" x 7½" Apron
½" Overhang-Front & Back
30" to 35" Depending on height of Student
8"
1¾" x 5½" End
¾" x 2¾"
¾" x 2¾"
Sheet Iron
Bench Top
1¾" Boards
Sheet Iron Top secured with No 8 - ¾" F.H. wood screws Countersunk
Tie top boards together with ½" x 29" Rods. Thread ends. Counterbore 1" Dia, 1" Deep Fill hole with wood Dowel 4 Req'd
Slot permits expansion and contraction. Drill 2 - ⅜" holes ⅜" on center 25½" Remove wood with chisel
⅜" x 7" Carriage bolts 16 Req'd
30"
From 7' to 10'
1¾" x 7½" Apron
Wood Dowel
½" x 29" Rod. Thread both ends 4 Req'd
⅜" x 6" Carriage bolts 8 Req'd
8"
No 10 - 1¾" F.H. Wood Screw 24 Req'd
From 5⅞" to 8¾" See Top Dimensions
1¾" x 5½" Leg
25½"
⅜" x 4" Carriage bolt 8 Req'd
FRONT LEFT CORNER CONSTRUCTION

MATERIALS REQUIRED

Quantity	Description	Size	Grade and Material
4	Top	1¾" x 7½" x (-')	1st choice
2	Aprons	1¾" x 7½" x (-')	Select B hardwood
1	Sills	1¾" x 5½" x 8'	Air dried or kiln dried
1	Legs	1¾" x 5½" x 12'	2nd choice
1	Short braces	¾" x 2¾" x 8'	B or better yellow pine
2	Long braces	¾" x 2¾" x (-')	Air dried or kiln dried
1	Top tension rods	½" x 10' round	Hot rolled mild steel
1	Center sill rod	¼" x 30" round	Hot rolled mild steel
12	Carriage bolts	⅜" x 7"—with nuts	
8	Carriage bolts	⅜" x 6"—with nuts	
8	Carriage bolts	⅜" x 4"—with nuts	
24	Wood screws	No. 10—1¾"	Flat head steel
28	Steel washers	⅜"	
8	Nuts and steel washers	½"	
2	Nuts and steel washers	¼"	
	Add for Metal Working Bench		
1	Metal top	⅛" x 30" x (-')	Hot rolled sheet iron
80	Wood screws	No. 8—¾"	Flat head steel

(Courtesy Coggin and Giles, Bulletin 5, "Farm Shop Activities and Equipment," North Carolina State College of Agriculture)

Fig. 9a—Workbenches.

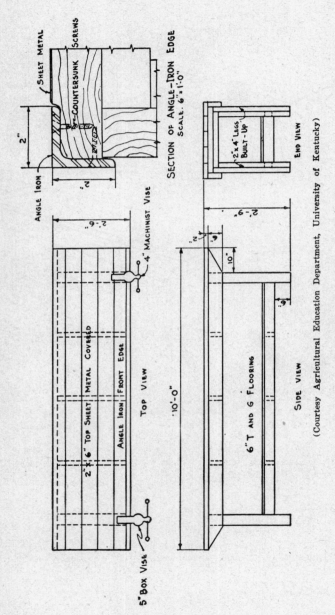

SECTION OF ANGLE-IRON EDGE
SCALE, 6" = 1'-0"

SHEET METAL
COUNTERSUNK
SCREWS
2"
ANGLE IRON
2"

END VIEW
2 x 4" LEGS
BUILT-UP

TOP VIEW
2'-6"
4" MACHINIST VISE
2" x 6" TOP SHEET METAL COVERED
ANGLE IRON FRONT EDGE
5" BOX VISE

SIDE VIEW
2'-9"
10"
2"
6"
6"
10'-0"
6" T AND G FLOORING

(Courtesy Agricultural Education Department, University of Kentucky)

Fig. 10—Metal working bench.

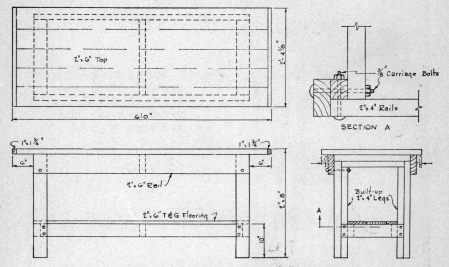

(Courtesy Agricultural Education Department, University of Kentucky)

Fig. 11—Tool sharpening bench. Angle iron may be placed around the edges of the top.

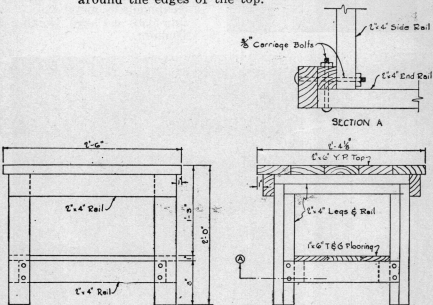

(Courtesy Agricultural Education Department, University of Kentucky)

Fig. 12—Bench saw stand

Fig. 13—Stand for electric
    grinder. Made from
    scrap materials by
    metal working class
    at Fargo, N. D.*

Fig. 14—Coal bin for forge
    coal made by metal work-
    ing class at Fargo, North
    Dakota.

* O. S. Burr was instructor of the class.

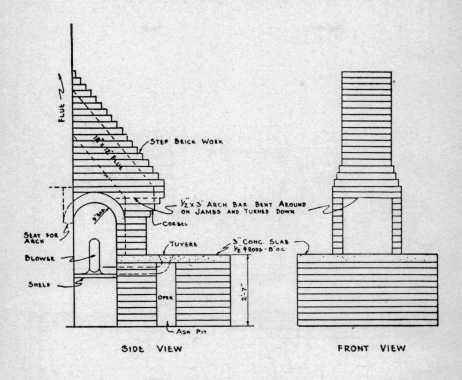

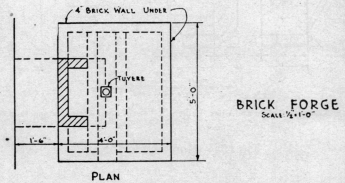

(Courtesy Agricultural Education Department, University of Kentucky)

Fig. 15.—Homemade forge.

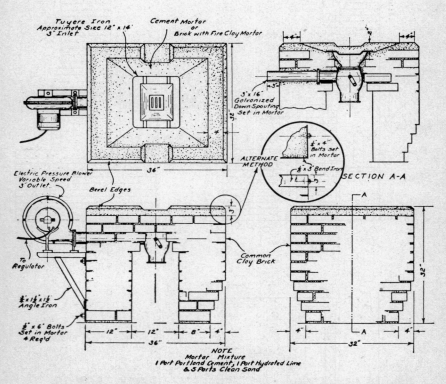

(Courtesy Coggin and Giles, Bulletin 5, "Farm Shop Activities and Equipment,"
North Carolina State College of Agriculture)

Fig.15a—Homemade forge.

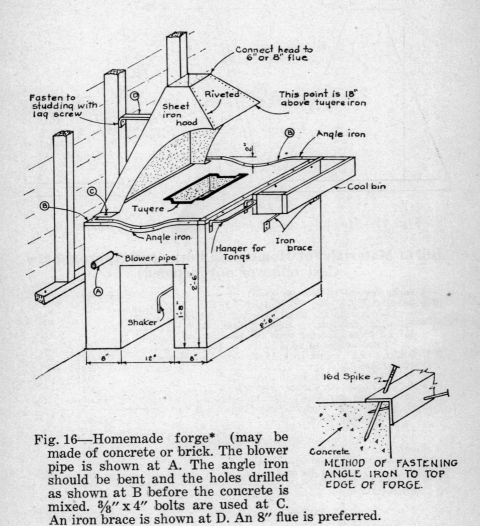

Connect head to
6" or 8" flue

Riveted

This point is 18"
above tuyere iron

Fasten to
studding with
lag screw

Sheet
iron
hood

Angle iron

2"

Coal bin

Tuyere

Angle iron.

Hanger for
Tongs

Iron
brace

Blower pipe

2'-6"

Shaker

1'-8"

8"   12"   8"

2'-6"

16d Spike

Concrete

METHOD OF FASTENING
ANGLE IRON TO TOP
EDGE OF FORGE.

Fig. 16—Homemade forge* (may be
made of concrete or brick. The blower
pipe is shown at A. The angle iron
should be bent and the holes drilled
as shown at B before the concrete is
mixed. 3/8" x 4" bolts are used at C.
An iron brace is shown at D. An 8" flue is preferred.

───────
* Figures 16 and 17 courtesy Extension Division, Nebraska Agricultural
College.

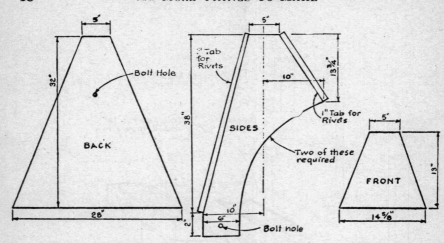

Fig. 17—Hood for homemade forge shown in figure 16.

Bill of Materials for Homemade Forge and Approximate Cost (Blower not included)

4 sacks cement @ 85c per sack	$ 3.40	
1040 pounds sand-gravel @ 10c per 100 lbs.	1.04	
(concrete for anvil base not included)		
4 ½" x 2'6" reinforcing rods for foundation		
4 ½" x 2'4" reinforcing rods for foundation		
Total weight of rods 15 lbs. @ 4c per lb.	.60	
9'8" x 2" x 2" angle iron 16 lbs. @ 4½c per lb.	.72	
28 16d spikes	.05	
2 ⅜" x 4" bolts for hood	.04	
6 ½" x 6" bolts for hanger and bin	.24	
1 tuyere iron complete with shaker and blower	10.00	to 15.00
1 sheet (30" x 96") of 20-gauge galv. iron for hood @ $2.60 per sheet	2.60	
36 rivets for hood	.15	
1'6" x ¼" x 1" strap iron for hood brace	.12	
1 bolt for hood brace	.02	
1 lag screw for hood brace	.02	
1½ ft. ½" rod for hanger	.05	
6 ft. 1" x 8" for bin	.17	
2 brackets for bin	.10	
TOTAL	$19.32	to $24.32

Form Material:

43 ft. 2" x 4" @ $43.00 per M. bd. ft.	1.25
5 ft. 2" x 2" @ $43.00 per M. bd. ft.	.10
77 ft. 8" shiplap @ $43.00 per M. bd. ft.	2.25

Nails:

2 lbs. 8d common, ½ lb. 10d common	.15
TOTAL	$ 3.75

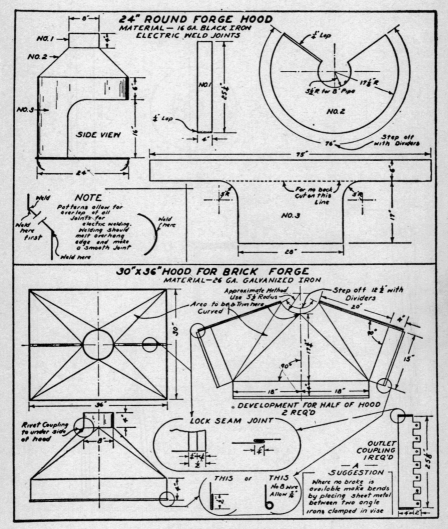

Fig. 17a—Hood layouts for forges.

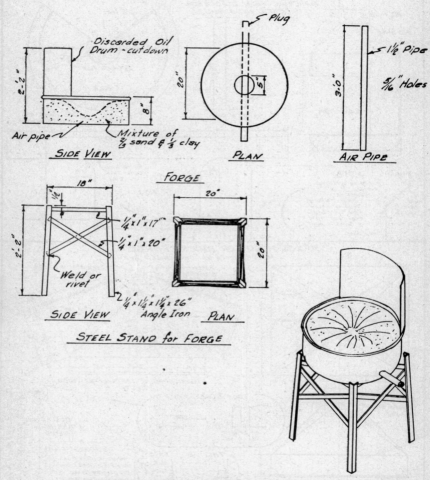

Discorded Oil Drum - cut down

2'-2"

Air pipe

8"

Mixture of ⅔ sand & ⅓ clay

SIDE VIEW

Plug

20"

5"

PLAN

3'-0"

1⅛" Pipe

5/16" Holes

AIR PIPE

FORGE

18"

2'-2"

¼" x 1" x 17"

¼" x 1" x 20"

Weld or rivet

SIDE VIEW

2 ¼" x 1¼" x 1¼" x 26" Angle Iron

20"

20"

PLAN

STEEL STAND for FORGE

(Courtesy W. H. Sheldon, Agricultural Engineering, Michigan State College)

Fig. 18—Homemade forge.

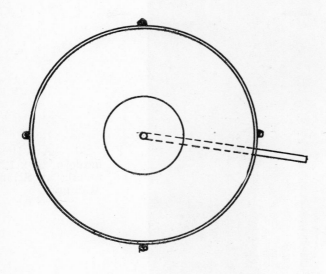

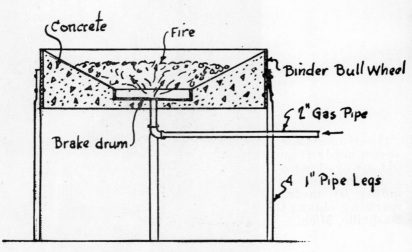

Fig. 19—Homemade forge.

Fig. 20 — Anvil stand made of 2" x 12" materials at St. Johns, Michigan.

Fig. 21—Homemade forge made from oil barrel and vacuum cleaner motor by metal working class at Nashville, Mich.

Fig. 22—Forge made from 3″ rim from wagon wheel. Truck brake drum used for fire box. Angle iron and scrap iron used for base. Made by metal working class at Hector, Minnesota.

Fig. 23—Barrel filled with concrete and used for vise stand. Made by metal working class at Fargo, N. D.

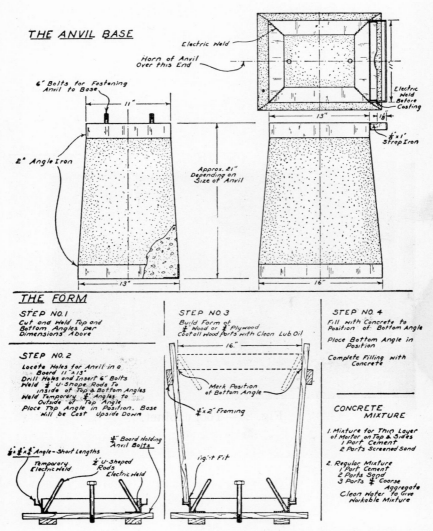

(Courtesy Coggin and Giles, Bulletin 5, "Farm Shop Activities and Equipment," North Carolina State College of Agriculture)

Fig. 23a—Anvil base.

Fig. 24—Tool cabinet.

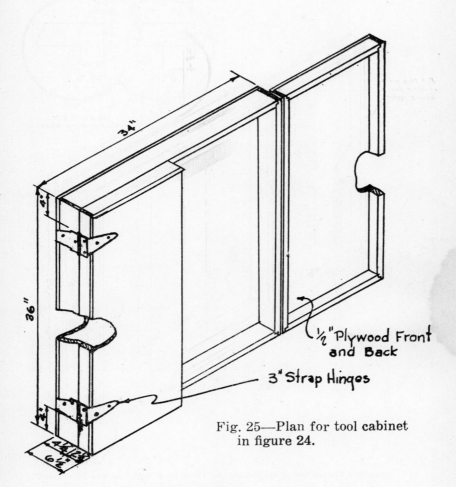

34"

36"

4"

4"

3"

4½"

6½"

½" Plywood Front
and Back

3" Strap Hinges

Fig. 25—Plan for tool cabinet
in figure 24.

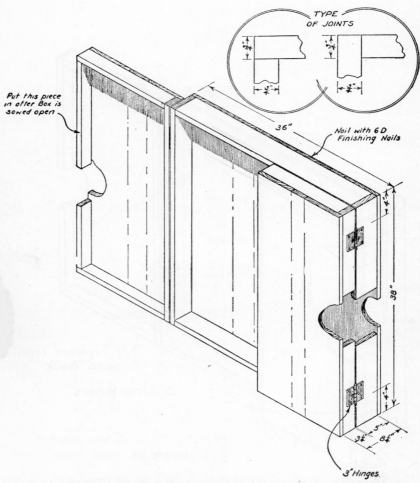

Put this piece
in after Box is
sawed open

TYPE
OF JOINTS

36"

Nail with 6 D
Finishing Nails

38"

3 Hinges.

(Courtesy Coggin and Giles, Bulletin 5, "Farm Shop Activities and Equipment,"
North Carolina State College of Agriculture)

Fig 25a—Tool cabinet to be constructed with hand tools.

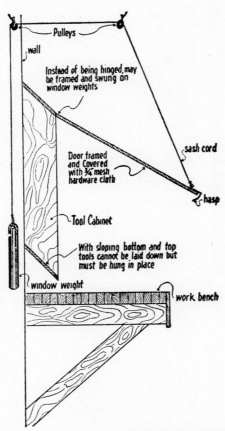

Pulleys

wall

Instead of being hinged, may
be framed and swung on
window weights

sash cord

Door framed
and Covered
with ¾ mesh
hardware cloth

hasp

Tool Cabinet

With sloping bottom and top
tools cannot be laid down but
must be hung in place

window weight

work bench

(Courtesy Agricultural Leaders' Digest)

Fig. 26—End view of workbench with tool cabinet above made
    by vocational agricultural shop students at Washington
    Union High School, Centerville, Calif.

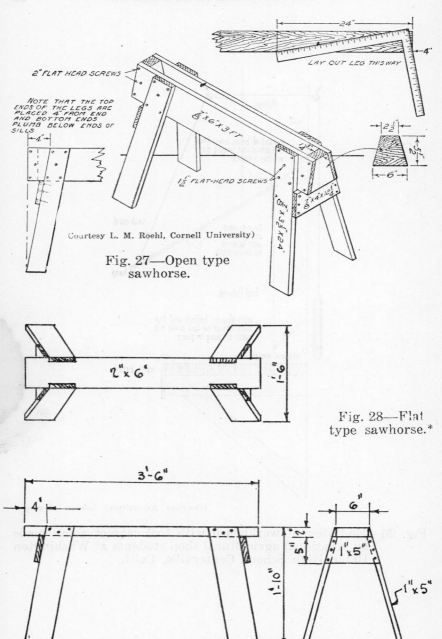

2" FLAT HEAD SCREWS

NOTE THAT THE TOP
ENDS OF THE LEGS ARE
PLACED 4" FROM END
AND BOTTOM ENDS
PLUMB BELOW ENDS OF
SILLS

24"

LAY OUT LEG THIS WAY

4"

2"x6"x3 FT

2½"

5½"

6"

1½" FLAT-HEAD SCREWS

1"x4"x12¾"

8"x3¾"x24"

Courtesy L. M. Roehl, Cornell University)

Fig. 27—Open type
sawhorse.

2" x 6"

1'-6"

Fig. 28—Flat
type sawhorse.*

3'-6"

4"

6"

2"

5"

1"x5"

1'-0"

1"x5"

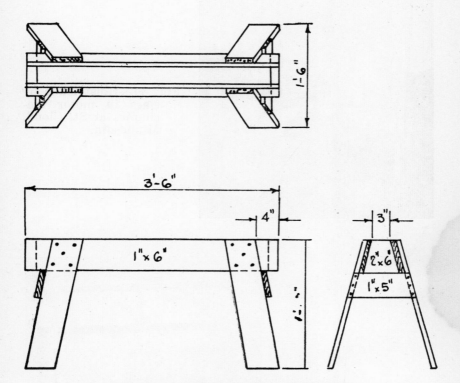

Fig. 29—Open type sawhorse 22″ tall.

* Figures 28 and 29 courtesy Department of Agricultural Education, University of Kentucky.

Fig. 30—Hoist made by class in motor mechanics at St. Cloud, Minnesota.

Fig. 31—Hoist made from an old windmill frame by metal working class at Manchester, Kentucky.

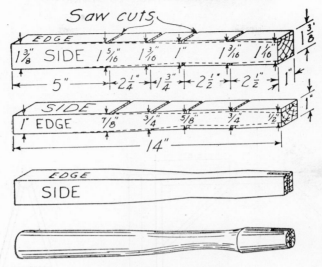

Fig. 32—Hammer handle.*

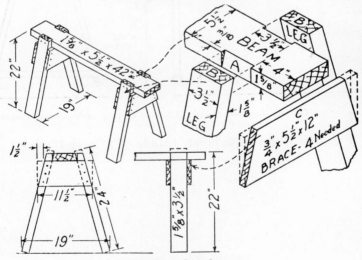

Fig. 33—Sawhorse.

Materials Needed

1 pc. 1⅝″ x 5½″ x 42″ for beam
4 pcs. 1⅝″ x 3½″ x 24″ for legs
4 pcs. ¾″ x 5½″ x 12″ for braces
2 doz. 1¾″, No. 10, flat-head wood screws
8, 3″, No. 14, flat-head wood screws

---

* Figures 32 and 33 courtesy Extension Division, Univ. of Kentucky.

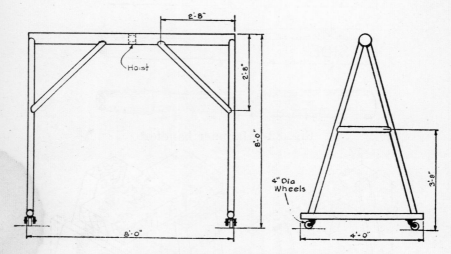

(Courtesy Justin R. Tucker, Arkansas Division of Vocational Education)

Fig. 34—Homemade hoist. (Made of 2″ and 4″ pipe.)

Fig. 35—Power grindstone. Stand made from scrap materials. Power transmitted from motor to grindstone through worm steering gear from old car. Made by metal working class at Fargo, North Dakota.

Fig. 36—Sander made from old gas pipe for the frame, pulleys purchased. Made by Paul Franklin, Melrose, Minnesota.

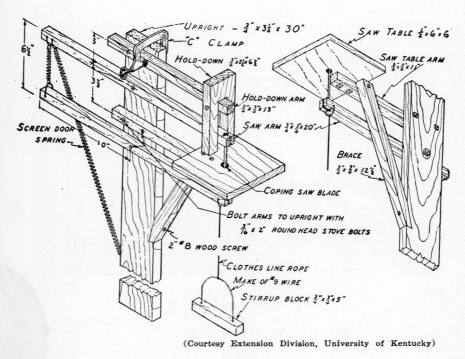

(Courtesy Extension Division, University of Kentucky)

Fig. 37—Homemade jig saw.

Bill of Materials for Homemade Jig Saw

1 pc. ¾″ x 3½″ x 30″ upright
1 pc. ¾″ x ¾″ x 13″ hold-down arm
1 pc. ¾″ x ¾″ x 20″ saw arm
1 pc. ¾″ x ¾″ x 11″ saw table arm
1 pc. ½″ x 6″ x 6″ saw table
1 pc. ¾″ x 2½″ x 6½″ hold down
1 pc. ¾″ x ¾″ x 12½″ saw table brace
1 pc. ¾″ x ¾″ x 5″ stirrup

1, 4″, iron "C" clamp
8, ³⁄₁₆″ x 2″ stove bolts
1, ³⁄₁₆″ x 3″ stove bolt
1, 2″, No. 8, wood screw
1, 18″, No. 9, wire
1, 12″ baling wire
1, 30″ clothes line rope
1, 6½″ coping saw blade
1, screen door spring

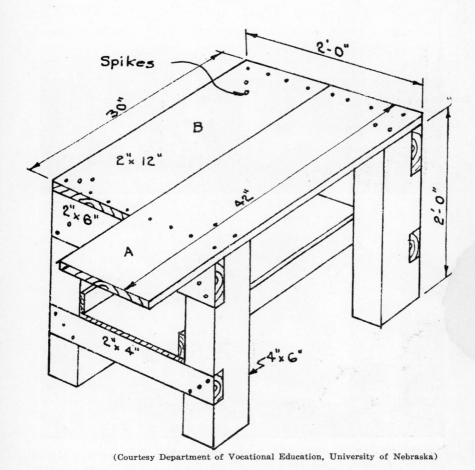

(Courtesy Department of Vocational Education, University of Nebraska)

Fig. 38—Bench for grinding equipment. (A, location of mandrel. B, location of motor.)

Fig. 39—Holder for use in holding disks while sharpening. Made from scrap parts by metal working class at Fargo, North Dakota.

Fig. 40—Homemade grinder made by metal working class at West Salem, Wisconsin. Stones to be purchased.

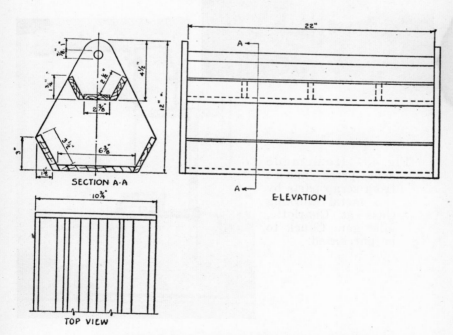

(Courtesy Justin R. Tucker, Arkansas Division of Vocational Education)

Fig. 41—Tool box (all material ½" thick).

Fig. 42—Homemade
stand for electric
drill. Made by metal
working class at
Fargo, North Dako-
ta.

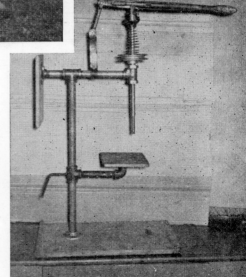

Fig. 43—Homemade
drill press m a d e
from scrap parts by
the metal working
class at Charlotte,
Michigan. Chuck to
be purchased.

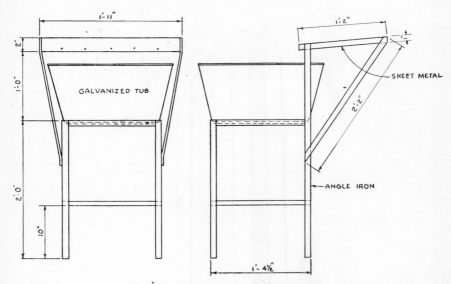

(Courtesy Justin R. Tucker, Arkansas Division of Vocational Education)

Fig. 44—Homemade sink and drain for washing farm machinery repair parts.

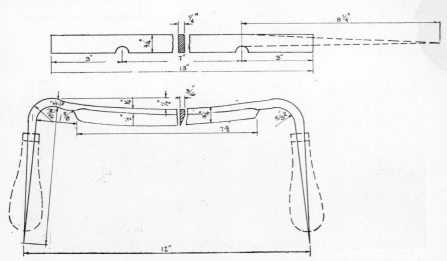

(Courtesy Shop Practice Department, Kansas State Agricultural College)

Fig. 45—Draw knife (Stock may be old auto spring).

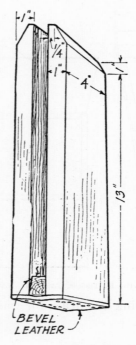

1"

1/4"

1"

4°

13"

BEVEL
LEATHER

(Courtesy Bethlehem Steel Company)

Fig. 46—Homemade harness clamp.

Fig. 47—An easy way to jack up the front end of a truck or car
by driving on to this trough made by Motor Mechanics
class at Manchester, Kentucky.

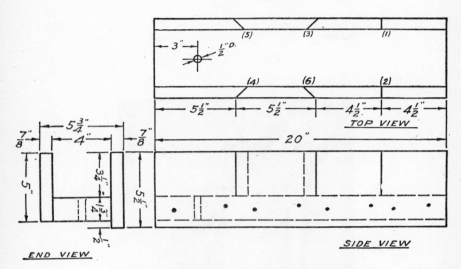

Fig. 48—Miter box.

Fig. 49—Tank truck made at Boys' Training School, Plainfield, Indiana.

Fig. 50—Tank truck made from scrap parts by metal working
class, Fargo, North Dakota.

Fig. 51—Welding stand made from scrap parts by metal working
class in Kentucky.

Fig. 52—Wash tub for cleaning farm machinery parts made from
old oil barrel by metal working class at Fargo, North
Dakota.

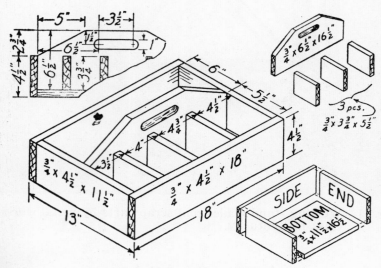

Fig. 53—Tool, nail, and bolt box.

Bill of Materials for Tool, Nail and Bolt Box

2 pcs. ¾" x 4½" x 11½" ends
2 pcs. ¾" x 4½" x 18" sides
1 pc. ¾" x 11½" x 16½" bottom
1 pc. ¾" x 6½" x 16½" center piece with handle
3 pcs. ¾" x 3¾" x 5½" partitions for nails, etc.
4 doz. 6-penny finishing nails

PART II

METAL WORK

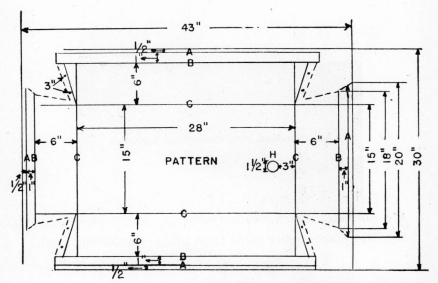

(Courtesy Mississippi State College for Women)

Fig. 54—Pattern for sheet metal sink.

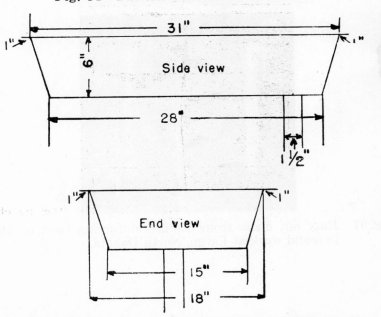

Fig. 55—Views of sheet metal sink shown in Figure 54

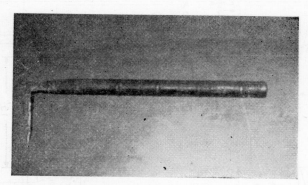

Fig. 56—Staple puller made from bridge reinforcing steel.

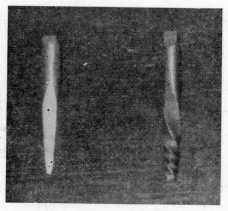

Fig. 57—Easy out made from bridge reinforcing steel by class in metal work at Fargo, North Dakota.

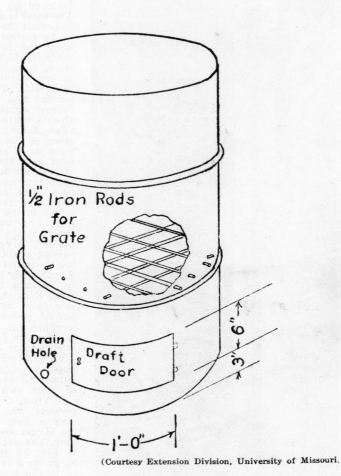

½" Iron Rods for Grate

Drain Hole

Draft Door

3"

6"

1'-0"

(Courtesy Extension Division, University of Missouri.

Fig. 58—Incinerator, made from old oil drum.

(Courtesy Experiment Station,
Colorado State College)

Fig. 59—Livestock cannot rub open the gate
equipped with this safety latch; the gate
rest at the bottom holds the gate in its
original shape and position.

"The ⅛-inch band iron, indicated by the arrow numbered 1, can easily be bent to the shape of the gatepost to which it is fastened by lag screws. The band is cut at the top to permit the cut portions to be turned back to receive the bolt, 2, which holds the U-latch. The U-latch, 3, is of strap iron ¼ inch in thickness and 1 inch wide. The ends are pointed and turned down to rest against the post, thus keeping the latch from falling down. The strap is doubled back to make the U and should extend past the end frame of the gate to allow for a slight giving of the gatepost which sometimes occurs as a result of frost action in the ground. The pin, 4, secured by the chain, is a cotter key; it prevents livestock from raising the U and allowing the gate to swing open. A cotter key is particularly desirable for this purpose, since the slight tension from its tendency to spread prevents it from working out where there is vibration from wind or other causes.

"A good gate rest is an important feature. Most gates will eventually sag of their own weight; in addition, the weight of persons who may climb over a gate may spring the hinges and cause sagging. The gate rest shown in Fig. 59 and indicated by arrow 5 can be adjusted to the required height by loosening the burs and slipping the clamp up or down on the post. The ends of the ⅛-gauge strap-iron rest are rolled under making a grip for the clamp rod. The surface of the rest is sprung down slightly in the middle, giving the gate a tendency to stay in the proper position."

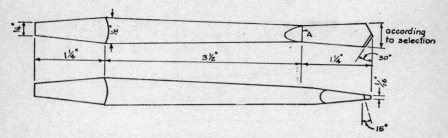

Fig. 60—Diamond point drill (Stock 4½″ x ½″ round tool steel.) *

Step 1—"Lay off ⅞″ from the end for the shank.

Step 2—Decide what size drill to make, then draw out the body to the taper as shown.

Step 3—Draw out the cutting point.

Step 4—Draw out the shank to the size shown.

Step 5—Grind the point to the angles shown.

Step 6—Before tempering be sure that the drill is perfectly straight so that it will run true.

Step 7—Harden and temper to a dark straw."

Table of Sizes

Width at point	¼″	$\frac{5}{16}$″	⅜″	$\frac{7}{16}$″	½″	$\frac{9}{16}$″	⅝″	¾″
Size at A	$\frac{3}{16}$″	$\frac{3}{16}$″	¼″	$\frac{5}{16}$″	⅜″	⅜″	$\frac{7}{16}$″	½″

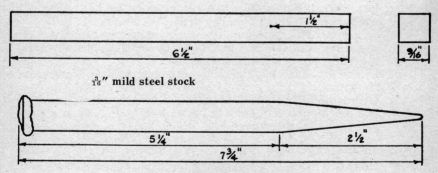

$\frac{3}{16}$″ mild steel stock

The Finished Harrow Tooth

Fig. 61—Harrow tooth.

1. "Mark with center punch 1½″ from end.
2. Upset the head slightly.
3. Draw the point out square to a 2½″ length."

---

* Figures 60 to 64 inclusive, courtesy Department of Agricultural Engineering, Nebraska College of Agriculture.

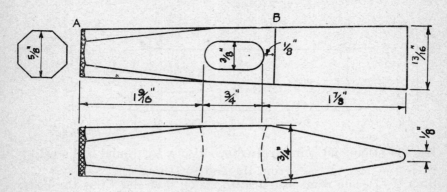

Fig. 62—Cross-peen hammer (Stock ¾″ square x 3¼″ long tool
steel).

Procedure:

1. "On two opposite sides lay off punch marks midway be-
between the ends of the piece.
2. Heat the piece to nearly a bright cherry red and punch
hole for the handle, using an eye-punch the point of
which is some smaller than the required hole. Drive the
punch half way through from one side, then drive it to
meet this hole from the other side. Finish hole by driving large part of punch through from both sides until
the hole is of required size, keeping steel closed around
punch during operation. The stock must be hot enough to
work freely (bright cherry red).
3. Draw out the face end to the form shown, first square
tapering back to 'b' then draw down the corners, making the face octagonal in section.
4. Finish by drawing out the peen end to the dimensions
shown.
5. Grind off all hammer marks and rough places, making
the piece perfectly smooth, then polish with emery cloth
or on a polishing wheel.

Hardening and Tapering:

6. Heat the piece to a medium cherry red, then cool ends in
water, first plunging face end until perfectly cold, then
quickly plunge the peen end, immediately brighten the
ends and look for the colors, which for the face is a light
straw and for the peen a dark straw. If there is not
enough heat remaining in the center of the piece to draw
the temper, heat a pair of special heavy tongs and clamp
them over the center of the hammer, and draw to the
required temper."

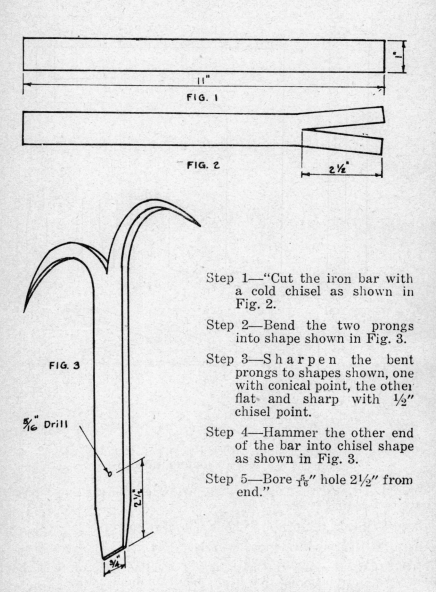

FIG. I

11"

FIG. 2

2½"

FIG. 3

5/16" Drill

2½"

¾"

Step 1—"Cut the iron bar with a cold chisel as shown in Fig. 2.

Step 2—Bend the two prongs into shape shown in Fig. 3.

Step 3—S h a r p e n the bent prongs to shapes shown, one with conical point, the other flat and sharp with ½" chisel point.

Step 4—Hammer the other end of the bar into chisel shape as shown in Fig. 3.

Step 5—Bore $\frac{5}{16}$" hole 2½" from end."

Fig. 63—Horse hoof cleaner (Stock $\frac{5}{16}$" x 1" mild steel)

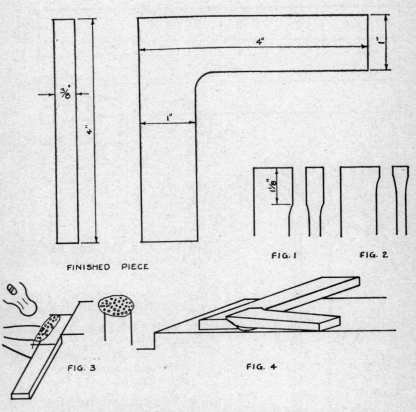

FINISHED PIECE

FIG. 1   FIG. 2

FIG. 3   FIG. 4

Fig. 64—Corner weld (Stock 1 pc. ⅜″ x 1″ x 4½″, 1 pc. ⅜″ x 1″ x 3¾″ common iron).

Step 1—"Upset the long piece as in Fig. 1, and the short piece as in Fig. 2.

Step 2—Scarf the pieces as shown in Fig. 3.

Step 3—Heat and weld as shown in Fig. 4.

NOTE—Go through the operation of welding once or twice before bringing to a heat, thus avoiding mistakes."

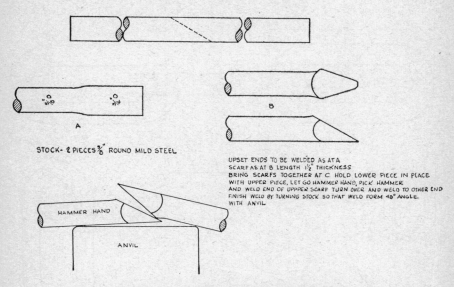

STOCK- 2 PIECES ⅜" ROUND MILD STEEL

A

B

UPSET ENDS TO BE WELDED AS AT A
SCARF AS AT B LENGTH 1½" THICKNESS
BRING SCARFS TOGETHER AT C. HOLD LOWER PIECE IN PLACE
WITH UPPER PIECE, LET GO HAMMER HAND, PICK HAMMER
AND WELD END OF UPPPER SCARF TURN OVER AND WELD TO OTHER END
FINISH WELD BY TURNING STOCK SO THAT WELD FORM 45° ANGLE.
WITH ANVIL

HAMMER HAND

ANVIL

(Courtesy Department of Mechanical Engineering, Michigan State College)

Fig. 65—Welding an iron rod.

Fig. 66—Incinerator made by class in metal work in Kentucky.

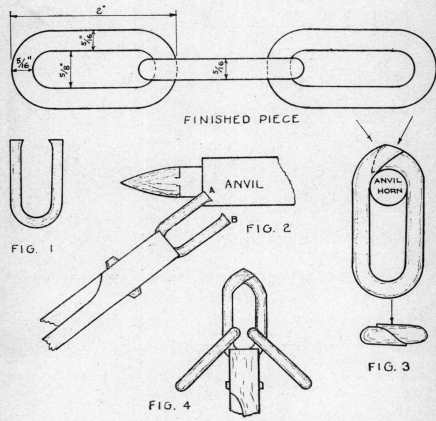

FINISHED PIECE

FIG. 1

ANVIL

FIG. 2

ANVIL HORN

FIG. 3

FIG. 4

(Courtesy Nebraska College of Agriculture)

Fig. 67—Chain making (Stock: 3 pieces $\frac{5}{16}$" round 6" mild steel).

Step 1—"Upset the ends of each piece, and bend to the form of Fig. 1.

Step 2—Bring one end of the piece over the sharp edge of the anvil (Fig. 2) and strike light blows, swinging the piece around, bringing B (Fig. 2) to a sharp edge.

Step 3—Scarf the other end of the piece in the same way.

Step 4—Bend the scarfed ends so that they lap (Fig. 3), then weld.

NOTE—Make two links, then in welding the third hold as shown in Fig. 4."

Fig. 68—Tool for digging holes for use in setting small trees made from an old car spring and a piece of gas pipe at Maustin, Wisconsin.

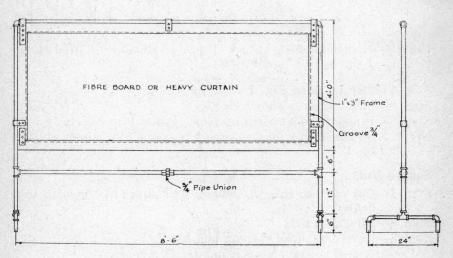

(Courtesy Justin R. Tucker, Arkansas Division of Vocational Education)

Fig. 69—Screen made of ¾″ pipe for use in welding.

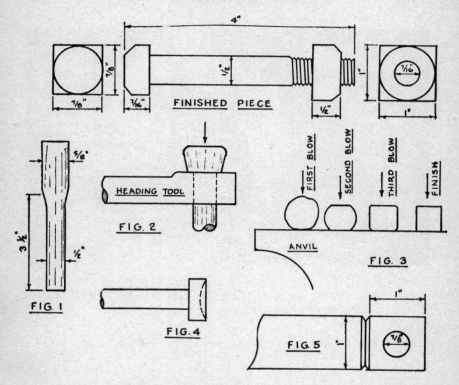

Fig. 70—Homemade bolt (Stock, 1 pc. ½″ round 6½″ mild steel,
    1 pc. ½″ x 1″ mild steel).*

Step 1—"Upset as in Fig. 1.
Step 2—Make head as shown in Fig. 2.
Step 3—Finish head by striking blow as shown in Fig. 3.
NOTE—Do not let the head assume the shape of a cup as shown
    in Fig. 4.

Square Nut:

Step 1—Cut off nut (Fig. 5) square and punch $\frac{7}{16}$″ hole in the
    center.
Step 2—Finish to size.
Step 3—Bevel bolt head corners and nut."

---

* Figures 70 and 71 courtesy Department of Agricultural Engineering,
Nebraska Agricultural College.

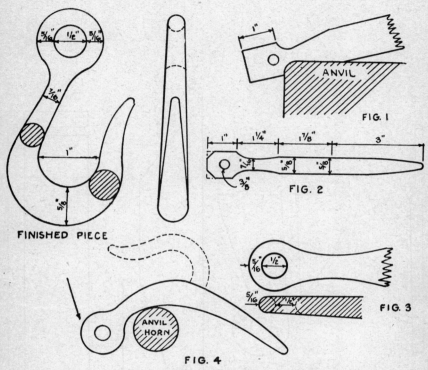

FINISHED PIECE

FIG. I

FIG. 2

FIG. 3

FIG. 4

Fig. 71—Hook (Stock ⅜" x 1" x 4½" mild steel).

Step 1—"Lay off a punch mark 1" from one end of the stock.

Step 2—Heat and draw the piece to the form shown in Fig. 1 and then to the form shown in Fig. 2.

Step 3—Hammer down the corners of the large end of the piece, and bend the small end of the piece as shown by the dotted lines, then punch a ⅜" hole.

Step 4—Make the eye round, and also round in section as in Fig. 3.

Step 5—Bend as shown in Fig. 4 and produce the finished piece."

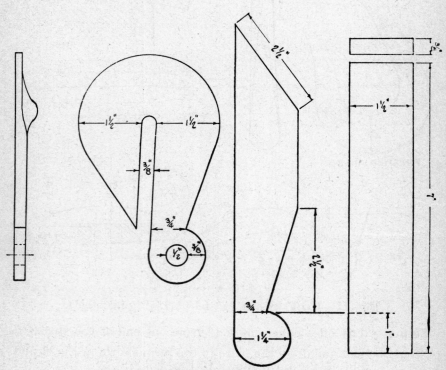

(Courtesy Shop Practice Department, Kansas State Agricultural College)

Fig. 72—Flat grab hook.

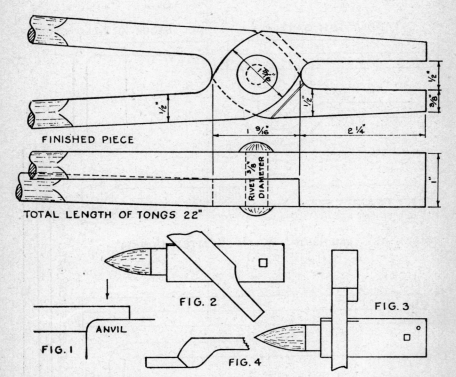

FINISHED PIECE

TOTAL LENGTH OF TONGS 22"

FIG. 2

FIG. 3

ANVIL

FIG. 1

FIG. 4

Fig. 73—Flat tongs (Stock, 1 pc. 1" x 1" x 7"; 2 pcs. ½" x 10" rod mild steel).*

Step 1—"Hold the piece 1⅛" from its end on the corner of the anvil, and with the large hammer draw the piece down to ½" tapered to ⅜" thick x 1" wide x 1½" long. Fig. 1.

Step 2—Hold the piece as in Fig. 2 and draw down to ½" thick, keeping the piece on the square corner of the anvil.

Step 3—Finish the piece (Fig. 3) to the form of Fig. 4, over round corner of anvil.

Step 4—Make the other half of the tongs in a similar manner, being careful to make both pieces exactly alike.

Step 5—Weld on the handles, then punch a ⅜" hole in one of the pieces; hold the two parts together and mark off the second hole by punching through the first."

---

* Figures 73 to 80, inclusive, courtesy Nebraska College of Agriculture.

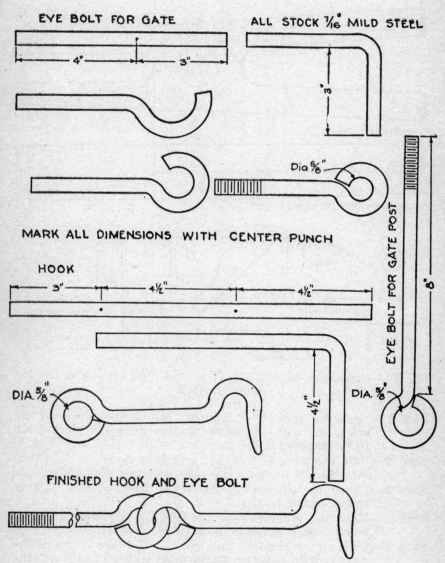

EYE BOLT FOR GATE

ALL STOCK 7/16" MILD STEEL

4"   3"

3"

Dia 5/8"

EYE BOLT FOR GATE POST

8"

MARK ALL DIMENSIONS WITH CENTER PUNCH

HOOK

3"   4½"   4½"

4½"

DIA. 5/8"

DIA. 5/8"

FINISHED HOOK AND EYE BOLT

Fig. 74—Eye bolt and hook.

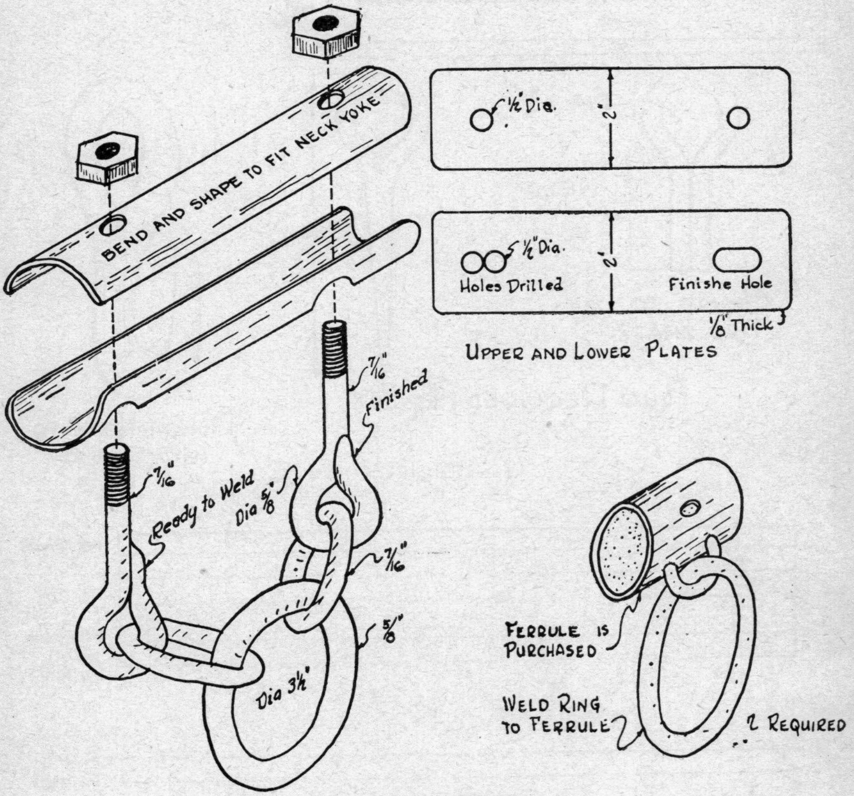
BEND AND SHAPE TO FIT NECK YOKE
1/2" Dia.
2"
1/2" Dia.
Holes Drilled
Finishe Hole
2"
1/8" Thick
UPPER AND LOWER PLATES
7/16"
Finished
7/16"
Ready to Weld
Dia 5/8"
7/16"
5/8"
Dia 3 1/2"
FERRULE IS PURCHASED
WELD RING TO FERRULE
2 REQUIRED

Fig. 75—Neckyoke irons.

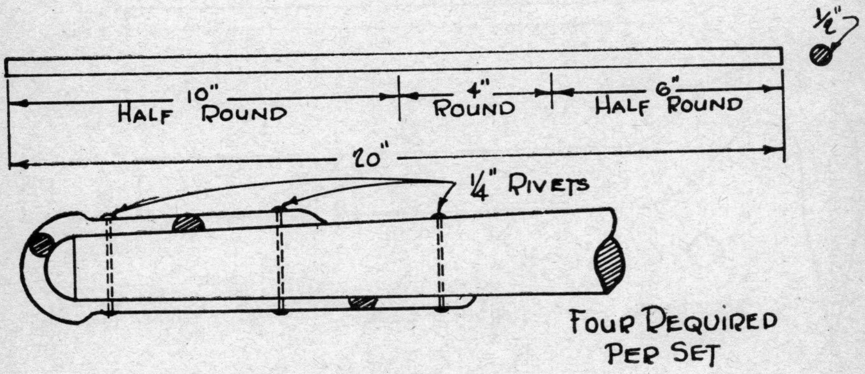
1/2"
10"
HALF ROUND
4"
ROUND
6"
HALF ROUND
20"
1/4" RIVETS
FOUR REQUIRED PER SET

Fig. 76—Singletree irons.

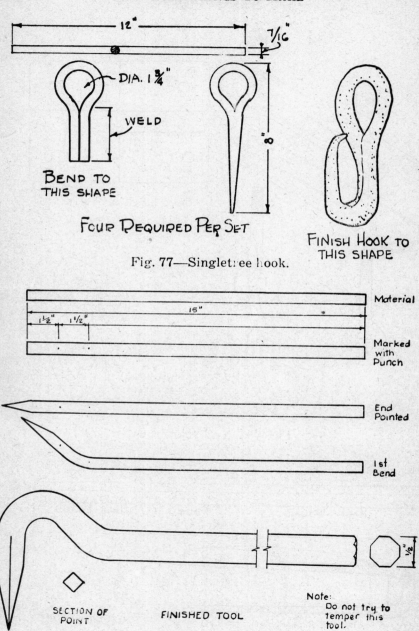

12"

7/16"

DIA. 1¾"

WELD

8"

BEND TO
THIS SHAPE

FOUR REQUIRED PER SET

FINISH HOOK TO
THIS SHAPE

Fig. 77—Singletree hook.

Material

15"

1½" 1½"

Marked
with
Punch

End
Pointed

1st
Bend

½"

SECTION OF
POINT

FINISHED TOOL

Note:
Do not try to
temper this
tool.

Fig. 78—Staple puller made from ½" stock.

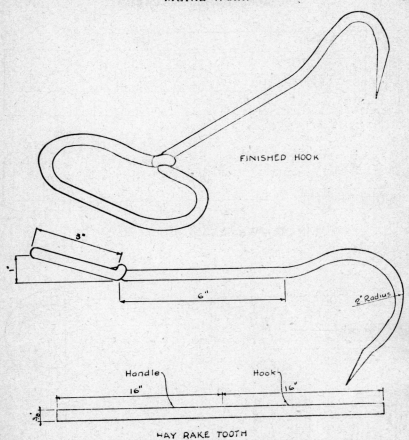

FINISHED HOOK

3"

1"

6"

2" Radius

Handle

Hook

16"

16"

HAY RAKE TOOTH

Fig. 79—Hay hook made from rake tooth.

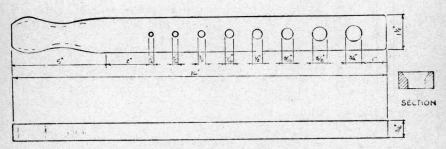

SECTION

Fig. 80—Bolt heading tool (Stock 1½″ x ¾″ x 16″ mild steel).
Tool may be used to make dowels, flat headed bolts and
countersink bolts.

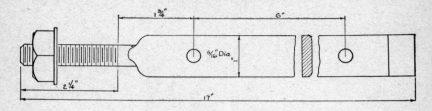

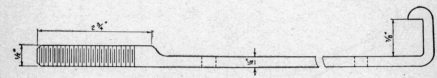

Fig. 81—Wagon box strap bolt.*

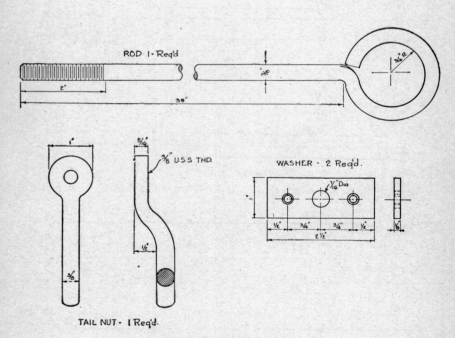

Fig. 82—Wagon box rod.

---

* Figures 81 and 82 courtesy Shop Practice Department, Kansas State Agricultural College.

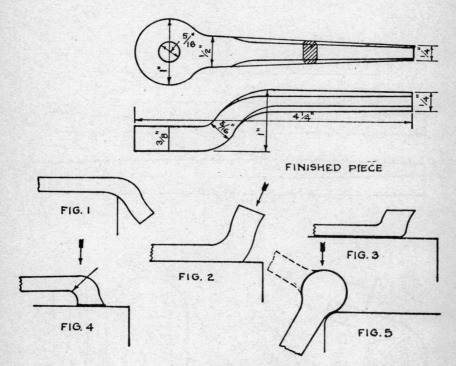

FINISHED PIECE

(Courtesy Nebraska College of Agriculture)

Fig. 83—Endgate rod nut (Stock ½" x 5" round mild steel).

Step 1—"Lay off a mark 2" from one end of piece, upset to $\frac{9}{16}$"
in diameter and bend at mark as shown in Fig. 1.

Step 2—Heat to a white heat and deliver blows as in Fig. 2.

Step 3—Heat to a welding heat and strike as in Fig. 4.

Step 4—Bring to the thickness of finished piece and round as in
Fig. 5. Form handle but do not bend it.

Step 5—Punch hole in center of eye and then bend handle.

NOTE—In punching, drive the punch nearly through on one side.
Turn the piece over and do the same on the other side,
then move the piece over the hole in the anvil and punch
out the chip."

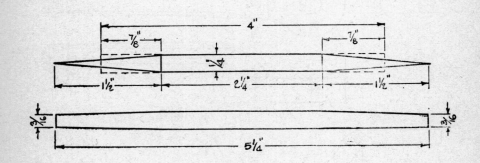

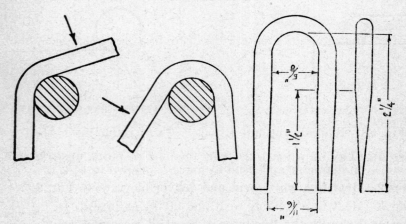

(Courtesy Shop Practice Department, Kansas State Agricultural College)

Fig. 84—Staple (Stock ¼″ x 4″ round iron.)

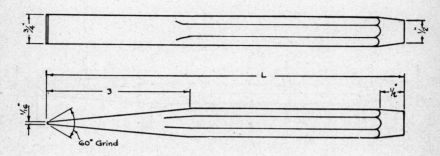

1½" Stock makes 3" length

Fig. 85—Cold chisel (Stock, ⅝" x 7" octagon tool steel).*

1—Forge the piece to the form shown above, being careful not to heat the piece above a cherry red. Do not work piece below a dull red heat.

Hardening and Tempering—

2—Heat the piece to a cherry red, through about 2" from the point.

3—Hold the piece vertically, and dip the point in cold water, chilling it about ¾" back. At the same time move the piece up and down in order to bring the surface in contact with as much cold water as possible, thereby cooling it rapidly. The point will thus be cold and hardened, while at some distance back from the point the piece will still be quite hot.

4—Immediately brighten the surface of the point with emery cloth or a piece of sandstone.

5—Now watch the bright surface very closely. Colors will gradually move down from the heated portion. First will be seen a light straw, then a dark straw, then a light brown, followed by a dark brown. When the dark brown has reached the end of the piece, quickly plunge the cutting edge ¼" back in cold water and the required temper will have been secured. Keep the point cool until the entire piece has come to a black heat, when it may be cooled slowly by dipping it in water. Never cool it rapidly until the body of the punch is above a black heat.

---

* Figures 85 and 86 courtesy Department of Mechanical Engineering, Michigan State College.

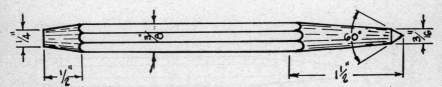

Fig. 86—Center punch (Stock, ⅜" x 4" octagonal tool steel).
Form head. Do not harden. Draw out point 1½" long.
Harden and temper to a purple. Use magnet to deter-
mine hardening heat.

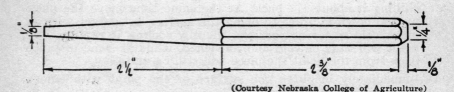

(Courtesy Nebraska College of Agriculture)

Fig. 87—Rivet punch (Stock ⅜" x 4½" octagonal tool steel).
Forge the piece to the form shown above, drawing out
the point, first square and then round, being careful not
to heat the piece above a cherry red. Temper the same
as suggested for a cold chisel, Fig. 85.

Fig. 88—Crow bar made from drive shaft of automobile.

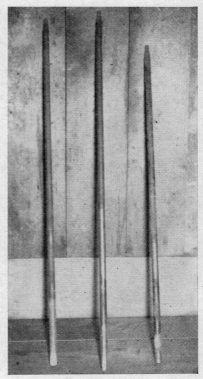

Fig. 89—Steering rods f r o m Model T Fords make good wrecking bars, chisels, rivet cutters, etc.

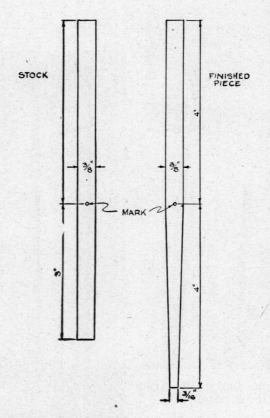

STOCK

FINISHED PIECE

⅜"

⅜"

MARK

3"

4"

4"

3/16"

Fig. 90—Punch (Stock ⅜" rake tooth).*

* Figures 90 and 91 courtesy Nebraska College of Agriculture.

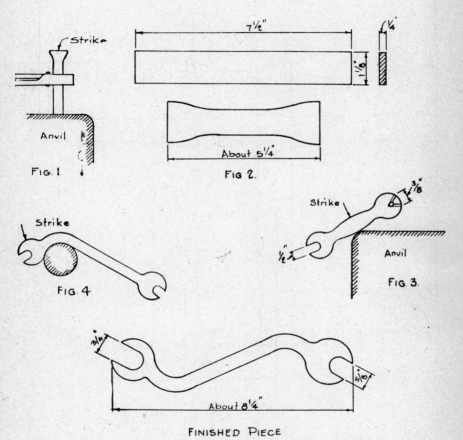

FINISHED PIECE

Fig. 91—S-wrench (Stock ¼″ x 1⅛″ x 7½″ mild steel).

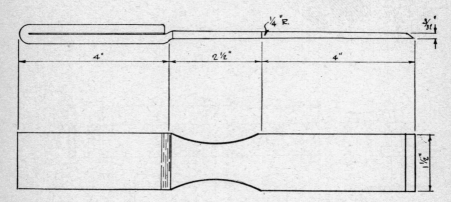

Fig. 91a—Wood chisel made from old auto spring.*

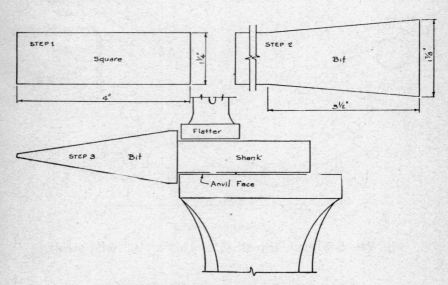

Fig. 91b—Hardie made from old axle.

* Figures 91a and 91b courtesy D. C. Lavergne and C. T. Thompson, State Department of Education, Baton Rouge, Louisiana.

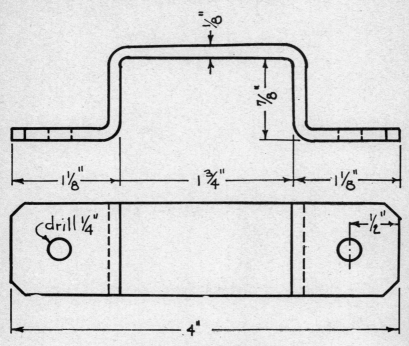

Fig. 92—Wagon box staple.*

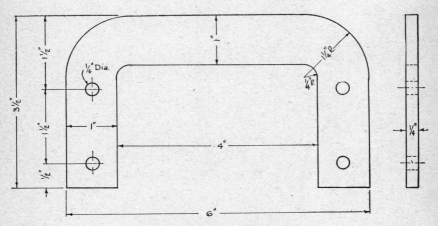

Fig. 93—Wagon box rub iron.

* Figures 92 to 96, inclusive, courtesy Shop Practice Department, Kansas State Agricultural College.

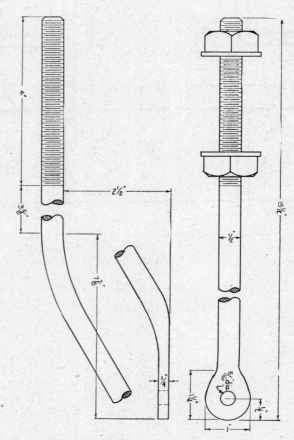

Fig. 94—Wagon box side brace.

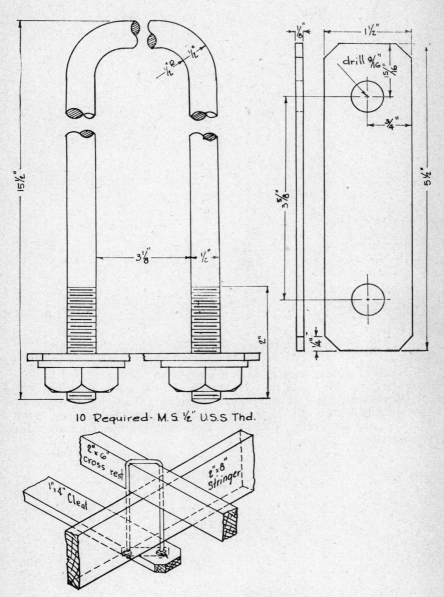

10 Required- M.S. ½" U.S.S Thd.

Fig. 95—Hay rack clamp.

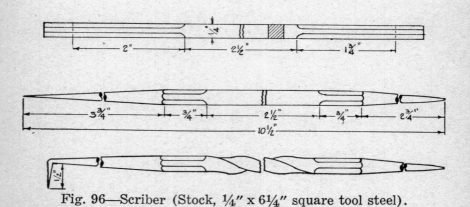

Fig. 96—Scriber (Stock, ¼″ x 6¼″ square tool steel).

"Heat square part to dark orange color, being careful to have a uniform heat. Place in vise at one end of square portion, grip with wrench at the other end of square portion and give one complete twist to the left. In tempering, heat about ½″ of each point slowly and carefully to dark orange color, plunge in water and cool entirely."

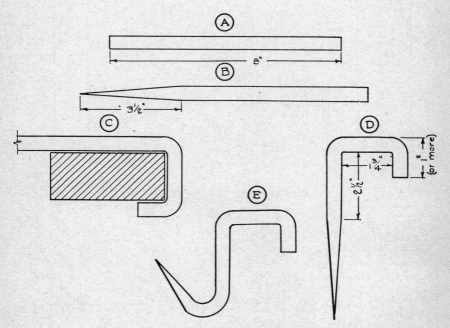

(Courtesy Agricultural Engineering, University of Kentucky)

Fig. 97—Meat hook (Stock, 1 piece ½″ round rod 8″ long, mild
      steel).

1. Start one inch from end and draw out point. Keep cross-section square at first, then finish round as at "B".

2. Mark and bend as shown at "C".

3. Heat carefully and bend as shown at "E".

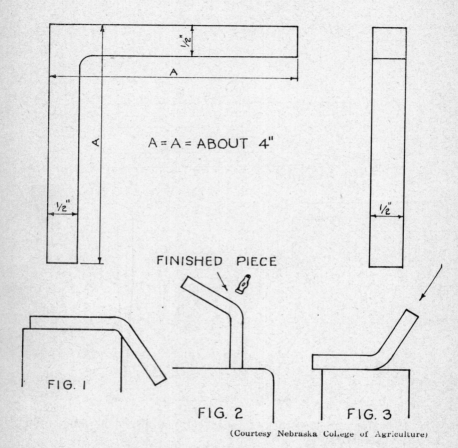

A = A = ABOUT 4"

FINISHED PIECE

FIG. 1

FIG. 2

FIG. 3

(Courtesy Nebraska College of Agriculture)

Fig. 98—Making a corner bend (Stock, ½″ x ½″ x 8″ mild steel).

NOTE—Do not work piece when cooler than a bright red heat.

Step 1—Bend piece in middle until at angle shown in Fig. 1.

Step 2—Heat again and strike blows as in Fig. 2. Change ends of piece very often. As iron works into corner, gradually bend piece to right angle. Do not have the bend a right angle until corner is sharp. If needed, strike blows as in Fig. 3.

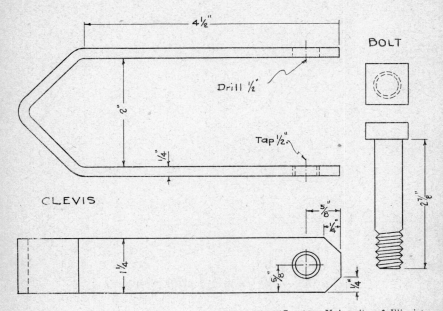

(Courtesy University of Illinois)

Fig. 99—Clevis and bolt.

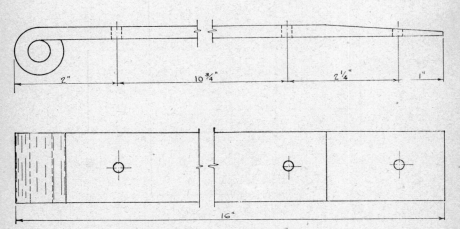

Fig. 99a—Gate hinge made from old auto hinge.

* Figures 99a and 99b courtesy D. C. Lavergne and C. T. Thompson
State Department of Education, Baton Rouge, Louisiana.

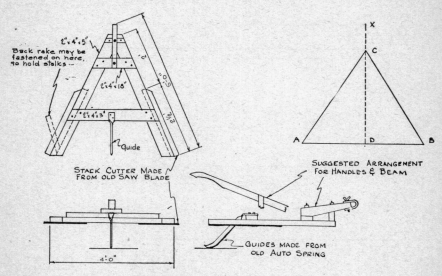

Fig. 99b—Soybean and stalk shaver.

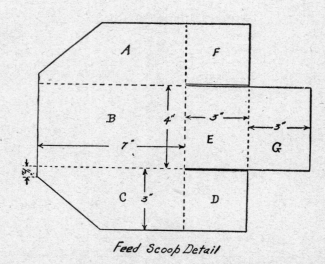

Feed Scoop Detail

(Courtesy Extension Division, University of New Hampshire)

Fig. 100—Feed scoop (A and C are the sides, B the bottom; fold
    AF and CD upward, also fold EG upward at right angles
    to B. A handle is bolted through the end.)

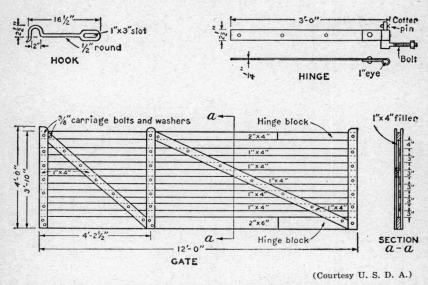

HOOK

HINGE

GATE

SECTION
a-a

(Courtesy U. S. D. A.)

Fig. 101—Farm gate. Hinge may be made from old auto spring.

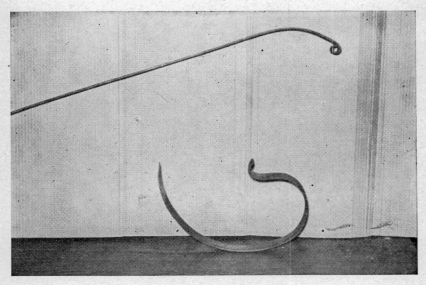

Fig. 102—Harrow spring tooth made from old car bumper by
class in metal work at Charlotte, Michigan.

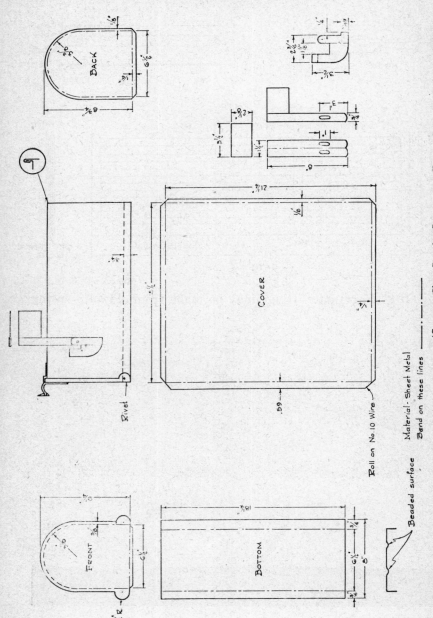

(Courtesy Shop Practice Department, Kansas State Agricultural College)

Fig. 103—Mail box.

F.g. 104—Handy container made from old oil drum by class in metal work at Fargo, North Dakota.

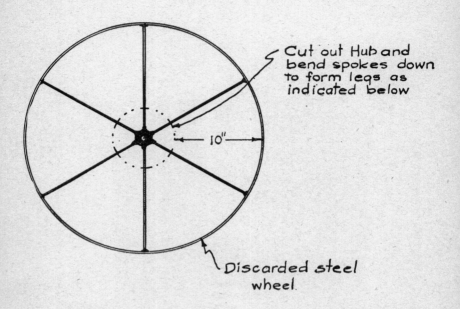

Cut out Hub and
bend spokes down
to form legs as
indicated below

10"

Discarded steel
wheel.

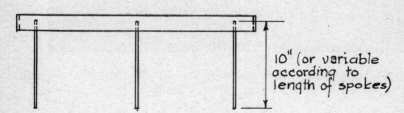

10" (or variable
according to
length of spokes)

Fig. 105—Kettle ring for heating water.

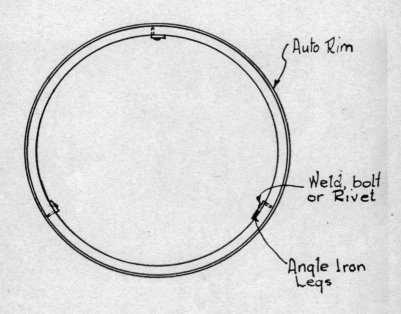

Auto Rim

Weld, bolt or Rivet

Angle Iron Legs

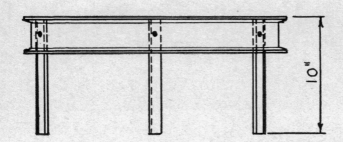

10"

KETTLE RING for HEATING WATER

Fig. 106—Kettle ring for heating water.

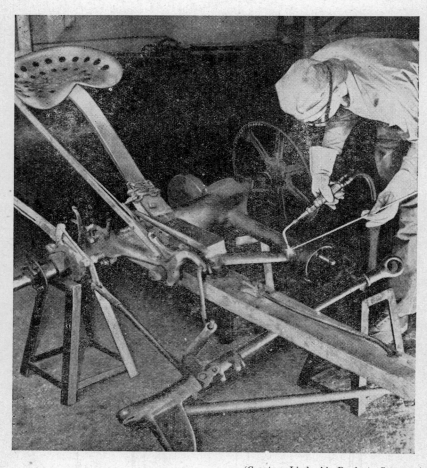

(Courtesy Linde Air Products Company)

Fig. 107—Repairing a cast iron frame of a mowing machine
by bronze-welding.

Fig. 108—"Field cultivator shovels hard-faced with Haynes stellite rod have a life about 500 per cent longer than those not hard-faced."*

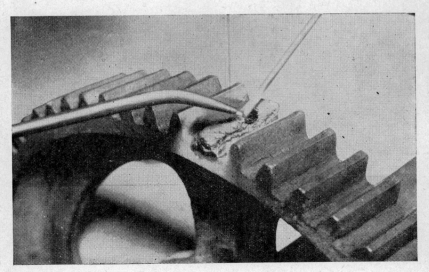

Fig. 109—Broken teeth of a cast iron gear rebuilt by bronze-surfacing.

* Figures 108 to 111, inclusive, courtesy The Linde Air Products Co.

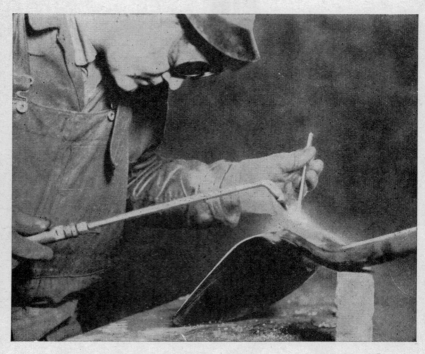

Fig. 110—Bronze-welding a broken shovel strap.

Fig. 111—Changing over tractors from steel wheels to pneumatic-tired wheels by cutting off the steel spokes and welding on new rims.

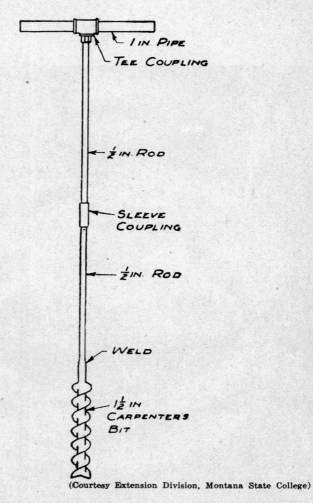

1 IN. PIPE

TEE COUPLING

½ IN. ROD

SLEEVE COUPLING

½ IN. ROD

WELD

1½ IN CARPENTER'S BIT

(Courtesy Extension Division, Montana State College)

Fig. 112—Homemade soil auger. "It consists of a spiral-shaped bit made from a 1½-inch carpenter's standard wood auger-bit welded to a handle made of 2 short pieces of 1-inch pipe fixed to a tee coupling. The screw-point and the side cutting edges of the carpenter's auger are removed in preparing the bit for boring. A post hole type auger also may be used."

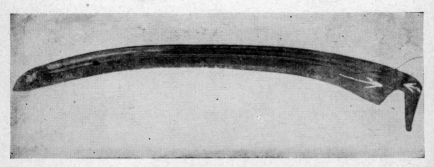

Fig. 113—Broken scythe welded at the point between the arrows by the metal working class at Monroe City, Indiana.

Fig. 114—Draw knife made from old file in metal working class at Charlotte, Michigan.

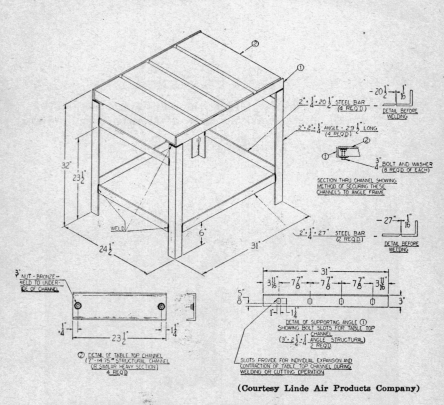

2"·¼"·20½" STEEL BAR
(4 REQ'D)

2"·2"·¼" ANGLE · 29½" LONG
(4 REQ'D)

—20½"—¼"·1/16"
DETAIL BEFORE
WELDING

¾" BOLT AND WASHER
(8 REQ'D OF EACH)

SECTION THRU CHANNEL SHOWING
METHOD OF SECURING THESE
CHANNELS TO ANGLE FRAME

32"

23½"

WELD

6"

24½"

31"

2"·¼"·27" STEEL BAR
(2 REQ'D)

—27"—¼"·1/16"
DETAIL BEFORE
WELDING

¾" NUT · BRONZE
WELD TO UNDER·
SIDE OF CHANNEL

¼"

23½"

¼"

① DETAIL OF TABLE TOP CHANNEL
(7"·14.75" STRUCTURAL CHANNEL
OR SIMILAR HEAVY SECTION)
4 REQ'D

—31"—

3 11/16"   7 7/8"   7 7/8"   7 7/8"   3 11/16"

5/8"

1"   1¼"

3"

DETAIL OF SUPPORTING ANGLE ①
SHOWING BOLT SLOTS FOR TABLE TOP
CHANNEL
(3"·2½"·¼" ANGLE · STRUCTURAL)
2 REQ'D

SLOTS PROVIDE FOR INDIVIDUAL EXPANSION AND
CONTRACTION OF TABLE TOP CHANNEL DURING
WELDING OR CUTTING OPERATION

(Courtesy Linde Air Products Company)

Fig. 115—Welding table. (Scrap materials may be used.)

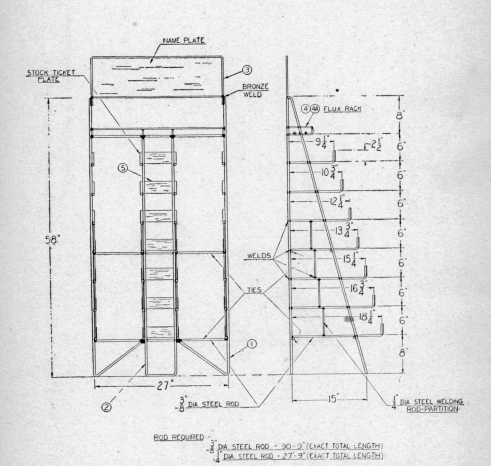

(Courtesy Linde Air Products Company)

Fig. 116—Welding rod rack (may be made of standard reinforcing rods for concrete.) Scrap iron may be used for
numbers 1-4, No. 5 indicates name plate.

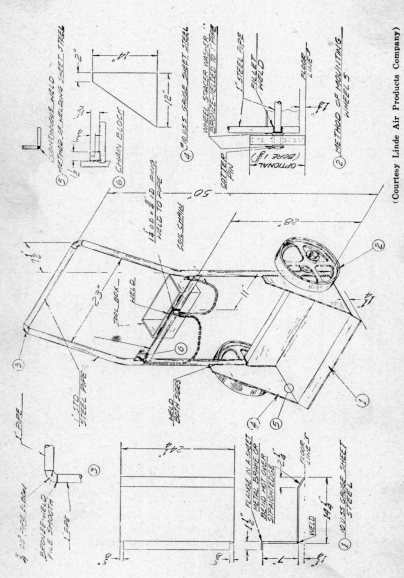

Fig. 117—Two-cylinder welding truck. (Scrap materials may be used.)

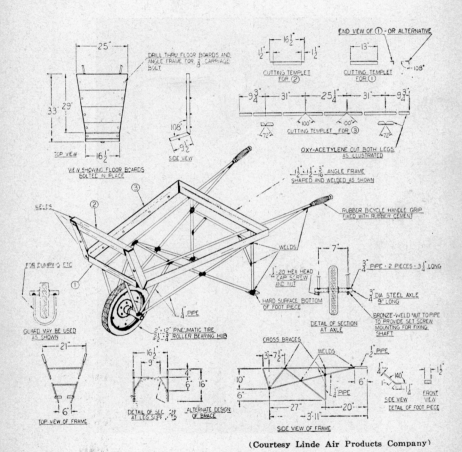

(Courtesy Linde Air Products Company)

Fig. 118—Wheelbarrow. (Scrap materials may be used.)

Fig. 119—Building up a nipple on a plow share at **Monroe**
City, Indiana.

Fig. 120—Welding a broken seat with bailing wire in the metal
working class at Fargo, North Dakota.

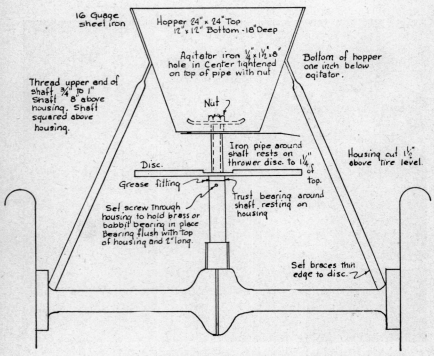

16 Guage sheet iron

Hopper 24" x 24" Top
12" x 12" Bottom - 18" Deep

Agitator iron ¼" x 1½" x 8"
hole in Center tightened
on top of pipe with nut

Bottom of hopper
one inch below
agitator.

Thread upper end of
shaft ¾" to 1"
Shaft 8" above
housing. Shaft
squared above
housing.

Nut

Iron pipe around
shaft rests on
thrower disc. to 1¼"
of top.

Housing cut 1½"
above tire level.

Disc.

Grease fitting

Set screw through
housing to hold brass or
babbit bearing in place.
Bearing flush with top
of housing and 2" long.

Trust bearing around
shaft resting on
housing

Set braces thin
edge to disc.

(Courtesy Agricultural Engineering Department, University of Georgia.
spreader designed by J. M. Everett, Ringgold, Georgia.)

Fig. 121—Lime spreader.

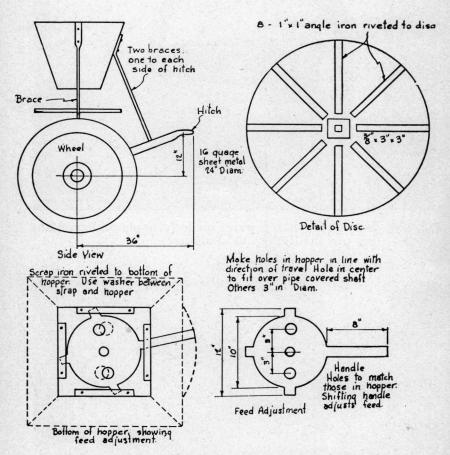

Two braces, one to each side of hitch

Brace

Hitch

Wheel

16 guage sheet metal 24" Diam.

12"

36"

Side View

8 - 1"x1"angle iron riveted to disa

$\frac{3}{8}$"x 3"x 3"

Detail of Disc.

Scrap iron riveted to bottom of hopper. Use washer between strap and hopper

Bottom of hopper, showing feed adjustment.

Make holes in hopper in line with direction of travel. Hole in center to fit over pipe covered shaft. Others 3" in Diam.

12"

10"

3"

3"

8"

Handle Holes to match those in hopper. Shifting handle adjusts feed.

Feed Adjustment

Fig. 122—Lime spreader details from figure 121.

Fig. 123—Kettle for heating water made from old oil barrel and gas pipe at Butlerville, Indiana.

Fig. 124—Various types of carts of this kind may be made for farm use.

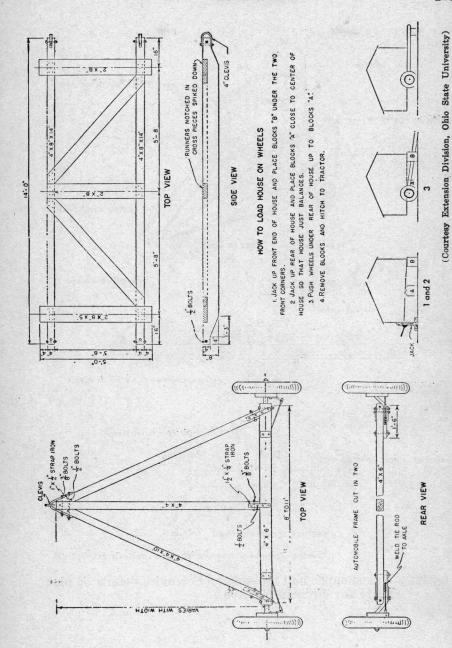

HOW TO LOAD HOUSE ON WHEELS

1. JACK UP FRONT END OF HOUSE AND PLACE BLOCKS "B" UNDER THE TWO FRONT CORNERS.

2. JACK UP REAR OF HOUSE AND PLACE BLOCKS "A" CLOSE TO CENTER OF HOUSE SO THAT HOUSE JUST BALANCES.

3. PUSH WHEELS UNDER REAR OF HOUSE UP TO BLOCKS "A".

4. REMOVE BLOCKS AND HITCH TO TRACTOR.

TOP VIEW

SIDE VIEW

RUNNERS NOTCHED IN CROSS PIECES SPIKED DOWN

4" CLEVIS

4" X 8" X 14'

2" X 8"

2" X 8"

2" X 8" X 5'

14'-0"

5'-8"

5'-8"

16"

16"

3'-8"

5'-0"

½" BOLTS

1 and 2

3

JACK

A   B

A   B

(Courtesy Extension Division, Ohio State University)

CLEVIS

1" X ½" STRAP IRON

⅜" BOLTS

½" BOLTS

1½" X ¼" STRAP IRON

⅜" BOLTS

½" BOLTS

4" X 4"

4" X 6"

4" X 4" X 10'

8'-10"

TOP VIEW

VARIES WITH WIDTH

REAR VIEW

AUTOMOBILE FRAME CUT IN TWO

4" X 6"

1'-6"

WELD TIE ROD TO AXLE

Fig. 125—A set of detached skids and a wheeled portable house mover.

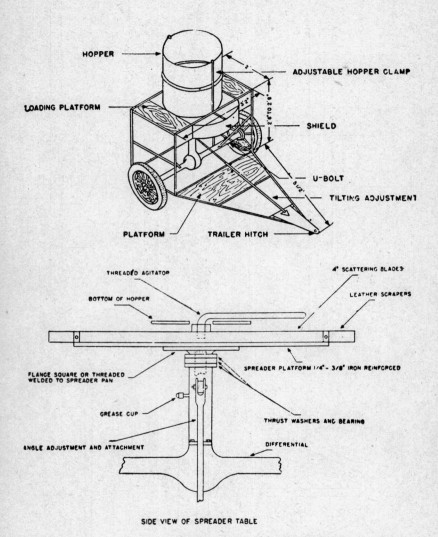

HOPPER

ADJUSTABLE HOPPER CLAMP

LOADING PLATFORM

SHIELD

U-BOLT

TILTING ADJUSTMENT

PLATFORM   TRAILER HITCH

THREADED AGITATOR

4" SCATTERING BLADES

BOTTOM OF HOPPER

LEATHER SCRAPERS

FLANGE SQUARE OR THREADED
WELDED TO SPREADER PAN

SPREADER PLATFORM 1/4" - 3/8" IRON REINFORCED

GREASE CUP

THRUST WASHERS AND BEARING

ANGLE ADJUSTMENT AND ATTACHMENT

DIFFERENTIAL

SIDE VIEW OF SPREADER TABLE

(Courtesy Extension Division, Montana Agricultural College)

Fig. 126—Grasshopper bait spreader. (For more details of plan
write for circular No. 109.)

Fig. 127—Portable sheep dipping tank made by farm shop class at Coopersville, Michigan.

Fig. 128—Box for blacksmith coal constructed of scrap angle iron and lined with tongue and grooved lumber. It is placed on rollers.

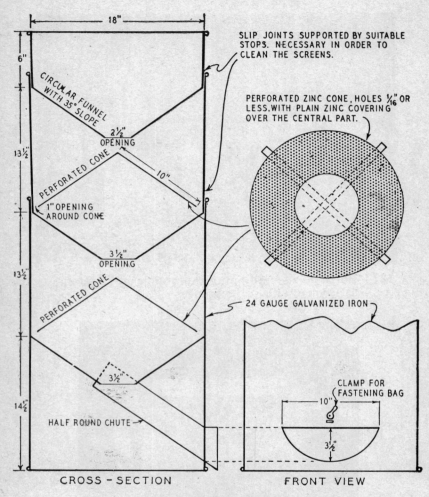

SLIP JOINTS SUPPORTED BY SUITABLE
STOPS. NECESSARY IN ORDER TO
CLEAN THE SCREENS.

PERFORATED ZINC CONE, HOLES ¹⁄₁₆" OR
LESS, WITH PLAIN ZINC COVERING
OVER THE CENTRAL PART.

18"

6"

CIRCULAR FUNNEL
WITH 35° SLOPE

2½"
OPENING

13½"

PERFORATED CONE

10"

1" OPENING
AROUND CONE

3½"
OPENING

13½"

PERFORATED CONE

24 GAUGE GALVANIZED IRON

3½"

14½"

HALF ROUND CHUTE

CLAMP FOR
FASTENING BAG

10"

3½"

CROSS - SECTION   FRONT VIEW

(Courtesy Extension Division, University of Illinois)

Fig. 129—A gravity seed treater suitable for applying Ceresan.
"In operating this treater, one man pours a bushel of
grain slowly into the funnel at the top, while another
gradually pours in a ½-ounce measure of Ceresan directly above the center of the funnel. Treatment can
be applied much more rapidly with this equipment than
with the barrel mixer, and with much less effort. Also
the sack being tightly connected with the spout, there
is less diffusion of dust."

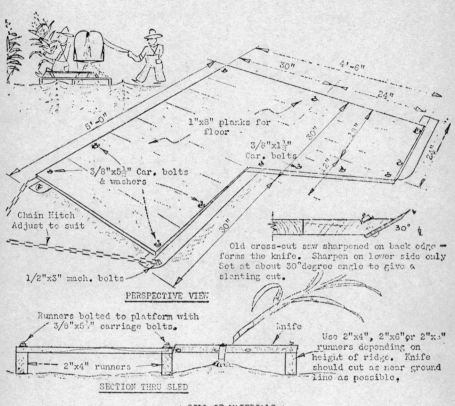

Old cross-cut saw sharpened on back edge — forms the knife. Sharpen on lower side only. Set at about 30°degree angle to give a slanting cut.

PERSPECTIVE VIEW

Runners bolted to platform with 3/8"x5½" carriage bolts.

Knife

Use 2"x4", 2"x6" or 2"x8" runners depending on height of ridge. Knife should cut as near ground line as possible.

SECTION THRU SLED

* BILL OF MATERIALS *
(Rough Lumber)

2 Pcs. 2"x4"(2"x6" or 2"x8")x5'-0"; Runners   4 - 3/8"x1½" Carriage bolts
1 Pc. 2"x4"   "   x2'-0"; Runner   2 - ½"x3" Machine bolts
3 Pcs. 1"x8"x10'-0"; Floor   1 lb. 16 penny common nails
8   3/8"x5½" Carriage bolts   About 5 or 6 feet of trace chain for hitch.

(Courtesy Extension Division, Clemson Agricultural College)

Fig. 130—Corn cutter.

Bill of Materials—(Rough Lumber)

2 pcs. 2"x4" (2"x6" or 2"x8") x 5'0"; runners   4, ⅜"x1½" carriage bolts
1 pc. 2"x4" (2"x6" or 2"x8") x 2'0"; runner   2, ½"x3" machine bolts
3 pcs. 1"x8"x10'0"; floor   1 lb. 16-py. common nails
8. ⅜"x5½" carriage bolts   About 5 or 6 feet of trace chain for hitch.

Fig. 132—Stand made from scrap materials by class in metal work at Fargo, North Dakota.

Fig. 131—Wire reel made from scrap materials by class in metal work at West Salem, Wisconsin.

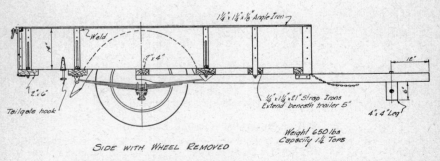

SIDE WITH WHEEL REMOVED

(Courtesy W. H. Sheldon, Agricultural Engineering, Michigan State College)

Fig. 133—Two-wheel trailer. (See figure 134 for top detail.)

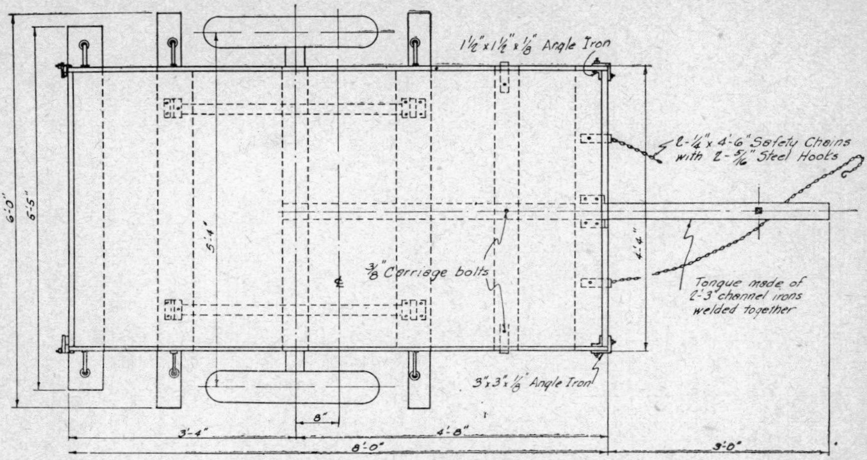

Fig. 134—Top view of trailer shown in figure 133.

Bill of Materials for Two-Wheel Trailer (Fig. 133)

Use	Pcs.	Size	Material
Leg	1	4"x4"x6"	Oak
Sideboard	2	1"x14"x8'0"	"
Endboard	2	1"x14"x4'2"	"
Bed	--	34 bd. ft. 1"	"
Cross brace	2	2"x4"x4'4"	"
" "	2	2"x6"x6'0"	"
" "	1	2"x6"x4'4"	"
" "	1	2"x6"x5'5"	"
Tongue	2	3"x1½"x8'0"	[Irons
Trim	2	1¼"x1¼"x⅛"x8'0"	∠ Iron
"	2	1¼"x1¼"x⅛"x4'2"	" "
Corner brace	2	3"x3"x⅛"x16"	" "
" "	2	1½"x1½"x⅛"x13"	" "
" "	2	1"x1"x⅛"x13"	" "
Tongue brace	2	2"x2"x¼"x5"	" "
Side brace	4	¼"x1¼"x21"	Strap irons
" "	8	¼"x1¼"x14"	" "
Tailgate hinge	3	¼"x1½"x15½"	" "
" "	2	¼"x1½"x3½"	" "
" "	6	¼"x1½"x4½"	" "
Tailgate lock	4	⅛"x½"x2¼"	" "
" "	2	¼"x¾"x4½"	" "
Side brace	60	¼"x1¼"	F.H. bolts
Corner brace	14	¼"x1½"	" "
Tailgate lock	8	3/16"x¾"	" "
" "	2	⅜"x3"	Carriage bolts
Tongue	3	⅜"x6"	" "
Tailgate hinge	3	⅜" dia. x 4½"	Rod
" "	6	⅜" dia. x 1½"	Pipe
Tailgate lock	2	¼" dia. x 1½"	Rod
" "	2	⅜"	Square nuts
Tailgate hinge	18	2" No. 14	Screws
Body braces	6	½"x12"	--------
Bed	96	2" No. 14	Screws
Bed	22	⅜"x3½"	Carriage bolts
Chain	2	¼"x4'6"	--------
Hooks	2	5/16"	--------
Stop and tail light	--	--------	--------
Cable	1	15' 2-wire	--------

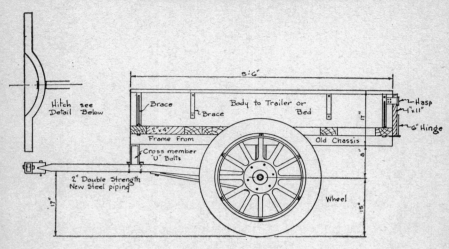

SIDE ELEVATION

(Courtesy Extension Division, Alabama Polytechnic Institute)

Fig. 135—Two-wheeled trailer.

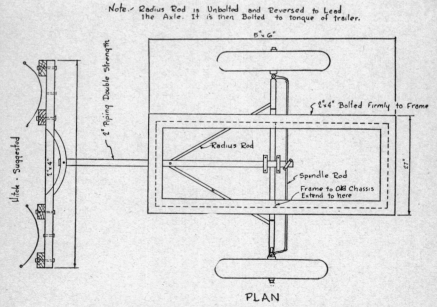

PLAN

Fig. 136—Plan of trailer shown in figure 135.

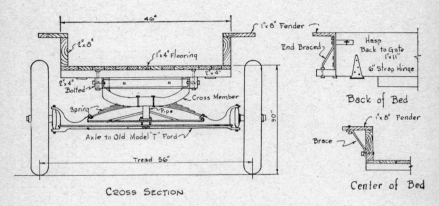

Fig. 137—Trailer shown in figure 135.

Bill of Materials for Trailer in Figure 135

Lumber:

6 1″ x 4″ x 12′ flooring
2 2″ x 8″ x 8′ sides to bed
1 1″ x 8″ x 12′ fenders
1 1″ x 11″ x 4′ gate

3 2″ x 4″ x 12′ frame and joists
Tongue of 2″ x 4″ and iron
  channel

Parts from Old Ford Chassis:

1 front axle, including wheels, radius rods, spindle rod, etc.
14′10″ of old frame or channel of 4″ depth and 5/32 thick
2 cross members to old chassis
1 set of springs. (Front 1¾″)

Hardware:

16 ⅜″ x 2½″ bolts, frame
10 ⅜″ x 6″ bolts, frame
4 ¼″ x 1¼″ strap iron
  braces
4 ¼″ x ¼″ strap iron
  braces for fenders

2 6″ strap hinges for gate
2 4½″ hasps for gate
3 expansion bolts, for connect-
  ing tongue to axle and
  spindle rod

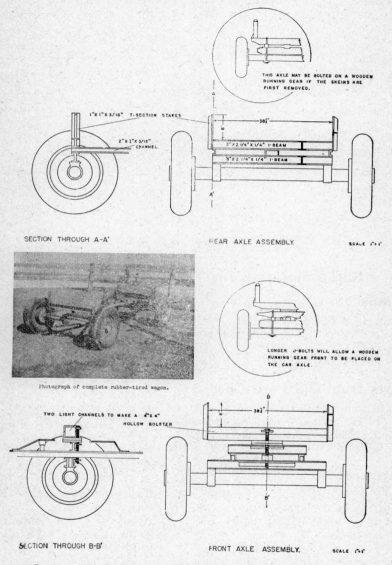

SECTION THROUGH A-A'

REAR AXLE ASSEMBLY.

SCALE 1"=1'

Photograph of complete rubber-tired wagon.

SECTION THROUGH B-B'

FRONT AXLE ASSEMBLY.

SCALE 1"=1'

(Courtesy Agricultural Experiment Station, South Dakota Agricultural College)

Fig. 138a—Rubber-tired farm wagon.

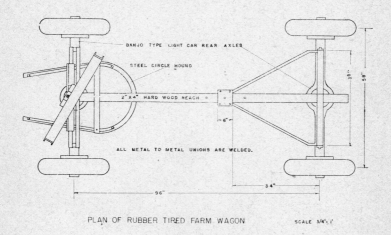

PLAN OF RUBBER TIRED FARM WAGON   SCALE 3/4":1'

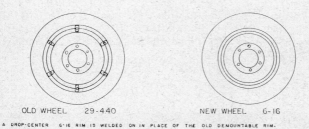

OLD WHEEL   29-4.40   NEW WHEEL   6-16

A DROP-CENTER 6-16 RIM IS WELDED ON IN PLACE OF THE OLD DEMOUNTABLE RIM.

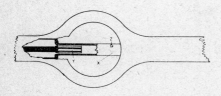

INNER BEARING DETAIL

ALL GEARS ARE REMOVED. PIPE "X" IS WELDED TO
AXLE AND SPLINED END OF AXLE "Y" TURNS IN DIRT
PROOF PLAIN BEARING MADE OF PIPE, WELDED IN.
"Z" IS A ZERK FITTING.

SOUTH DAKOTA
AGRICULTURAL EXPERIMENT STATION

RUBBER TIRED FARM WAGONS.

BUILT BY BILL MITTS
DRAWN BY H. H. DE LONG
AGRICULTURAL ENGINEERING DEPT. 3/18/40

Fig. 138b—South Dakota plan of rubber-tired farm wagon
continued.

Fig. 139—Inside of wheel cut out and welded onto a 6.00 x 16″ rim for use on heavy duty four-wheel rubber tired wagon. Made by class in metal work at Etna Green, Indiana.

Fig. 140—Rubber-tired wagon designed by Harley Hughes, Austin, Indiana. Made from two model A Ford axles, 3-inch pipe, 3½-inch boiler flue, 6-inch channel iron for cross pieces and angle iron.

PART III

WOODWORKING AND FARM CARPENTRY

Plans for Construction Procedures

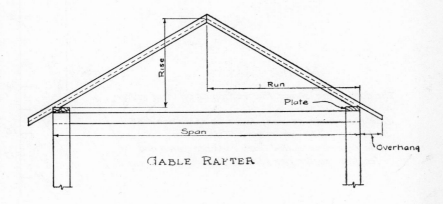

GABLE RAFTER

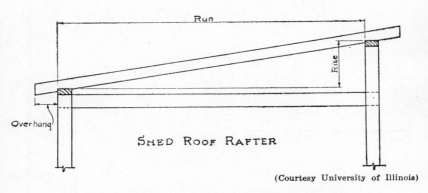

SHED ROOF RAFTER

(Courtesy University of Illinois)

Fig. 141—Some terms used in rafter framing.

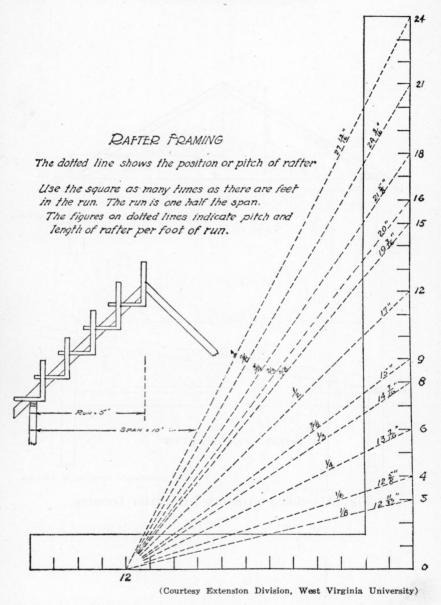

RAFTER FRAMING

The dotted line shows the position or pitch of rafter

Use the square as many times as there are feet
in the run. The run is one half the span.
The figures on dotted lines indicate pitch and
length of rafter per foot of run.

(Courtesy Extension Division, West Virginia University)

Fig. 142—Handy guide for rafter-framing of farm buildings.

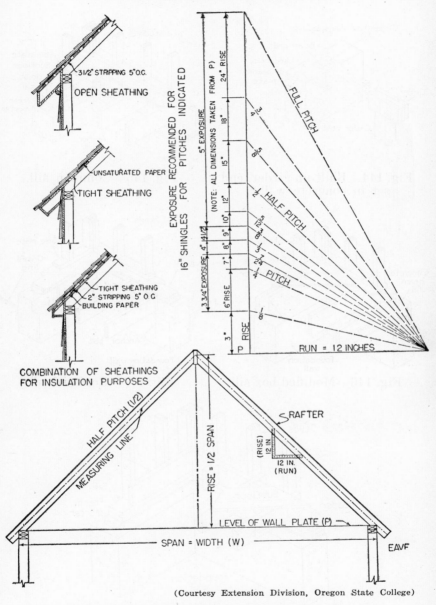

(Courtesy Extension Division, Oregon State College)

Fig. 143—Roof pitches and shingle exposures.

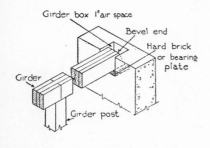

Fig. 144—Built-up girder, end
set in concrete wall.*

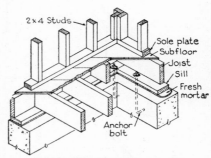

Fig. 145—Common sill.

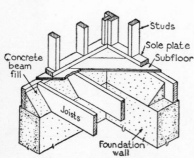

Fig. 146—Modified box sill

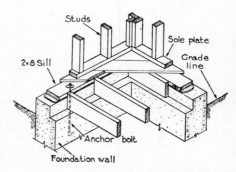

Fig. 147—Recessed sill

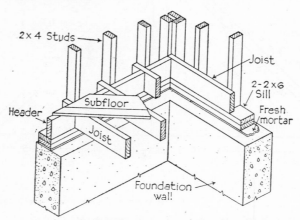

Fig. 148—Eastern sill assembly.

* Figures 144 to 148, inclusive, courtesy Weyerhaeuser Sales Company

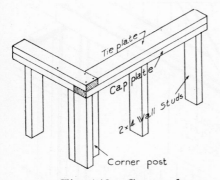

Fig. 149—Cap and
tie plate.*

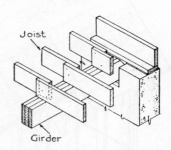

Fig. 150—Framing joist
on top of girder.

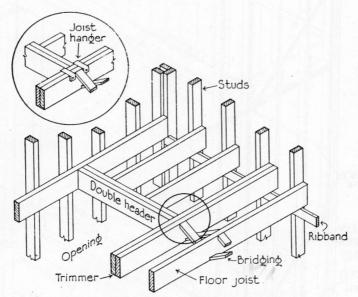

Fig. 151—Framing around floor opening.

* Figures 149 to 151, inclusive, courtesy Weyerhaeuser Sales Company.

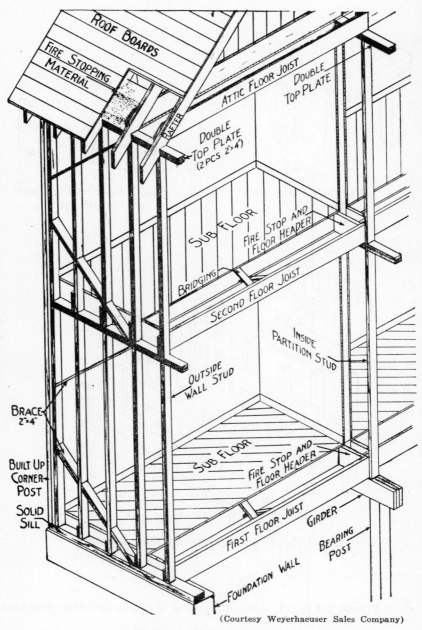

(Courtesy Weyerhaeuser Sales Company)

Fig. 152—House framing.

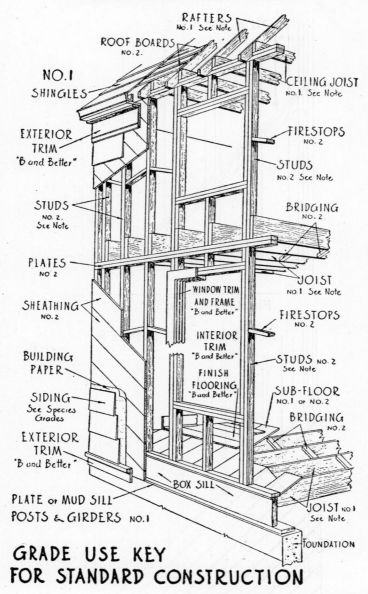

RAFTERS
No. 1 See Note

ROOF BOARDS
NO. 2.

NO. 1
SHINGLES

CEILING JOIST
NO. 1. See Note

EXTERIOR
TRIM
"B and Better"

FIRESTOPS
NO. 2

STUDS
NO. 2 See Note

STUDS
NO. 2.
See Note

BRIDGING
NO. 2

PLATES
NO. 2

JOIST
No. 1 See Note

WINDOW TRIM
AND FRAME
"B and Better"

SHEATHING
NO. 2

FIRESTOPS
NO. 2

INTERIOR
TRIM
"B and Better"

STUDS NO. 2
See Note

BUILDING
PAPER

FINISH
FLOORING
"B and Better"

SUB-FLOOR
NO. 1 or NO. 2

SIDING
See Species
Grades

BRIDGING
NO. 2

EXTERIOR
TRIM
"B and Better"

BOX SILL

PLATE or MUD SILL
POSTS & GIRDERS NO. 1

JOIST NO. 1
See Note

FOUNDATION

GRADE USE KEY
FOR STANDARD CONSTRUCTION

(Courtesy Douglas Fir Plywood Association)

Fig. 153—Standard construction.

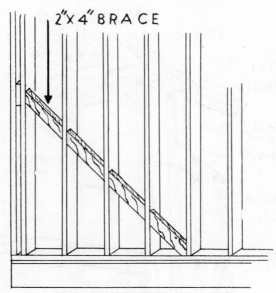

Fig. 154—Cut-in bracing.*

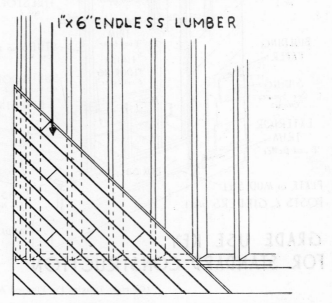

Fig. 155—Diagonal sheathing helps brace the building.

* Figures 154 to 159, inclusive, courtesy Weyerhaeuser Sales Company.

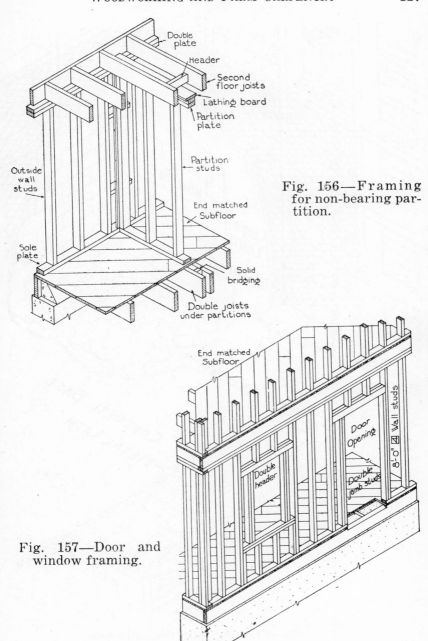

Fig. 156—Framing for non-bearing partition.

Fig. 157—Door and window framing.

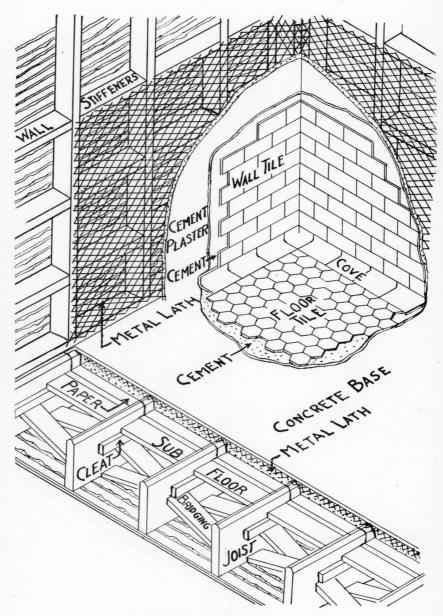

Fig. 158—Framing for a tile bathroom.

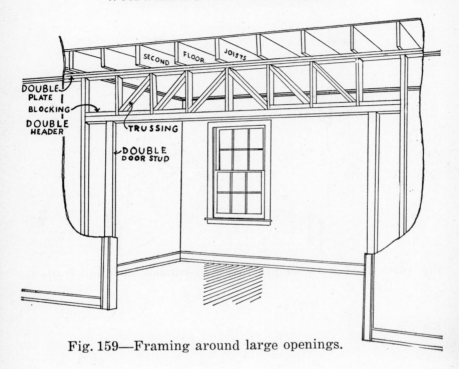

Fig. 159—Framing around large openings.

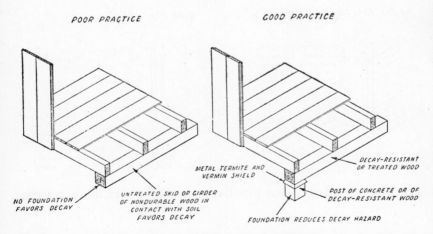

Fig. 160—Good and poor practice for foundations of temporary buildings.*

* Figures 160 to 164 courtesy U. S. D. A.

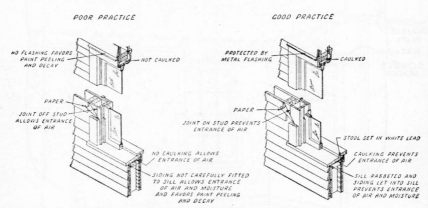

POOR PRACTICE

GOOD PRACTICE

NO FLASHING FAVORS PAINT PEELING AND DECAY

NOT CAULKED

PROTECTED BY METAL FLASHING

CAULKED

PAPER

JOINT OFF STUD ALLOWS ENTRANCE OF AIR

PAPER

JOINT ON STUD PREVENTS ENTRANCE OF AIR

STOOL SET IN WHITE LEAD

NO CAULKING ALLOWS ENTRANCE OF AIR

CAULKING PREVENTS ENTRANCE OF AIR

SIDING NOT CAREFULLY FITTED TO SILL ALLOWS ENTRANCE OF AIR AND MOISTURE AND FAVORS PAINT PEELING AND DECAY

SILL RABBETED AND SIDING LET INTO SILL PREVENTS ENTRANCE OF AIR AND MOISTURE

Fig. 161—Good and poor practice with window sash and frames.

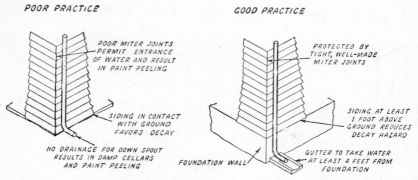

POOR PRACTICE

GOOD PRACTICE

POOR MITER JOINTS PERMIT ENTRANCE OF WATER AND RESULT IN PAINT PEELING

PROTECTED BY TIGHT, WELL-MADE MITER JOINTS

SIDING IN CONTACT WITH GROUND FAVORS DECAY

SIDING AT LEAST 1 FOOT ABOVE GROUND REDUCES DECAY HAZARD

NO DRAINAGE FOR DOWN SPOUT RESULTS IN DAMP CELLARS AND PAINT PEELING

FOUNDATION WALL

GUTTER TO TAKE WATER AT LEAST 4 FEET FROM FOUNDATION

Fig. 162—Good and poor practice with siding and down spouts.

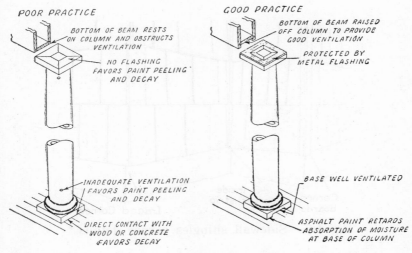

POOR PRACTICE

BOTTOM OF BEAM RESTS
ON COLUMN AND OBSTRUCTS
VENTILATION

NO FLASHING
FAVORS PAINT PEELING
AND DECAY

INADEQUATE VENTILATION
FAVORS PAINT PEELING
AND DECAY

DIRECT CONTACT WITH
WOOD OR CONCRETE
FAVORS DECAY

GOOD PRACTICE

BOTTOM OF BEAM RAISED
OFF COLUMN TO PROVIDE
GOOD VENTILATION

PROTECTED BY
METAL FLASHING

BASE WELL VENTILATED

ASPHALT PAINT RETARDS
ABSORPTION OF MOISTURE
AT BASE OF COLUMN

Fig. 163—Good and poor practice with porch columns.

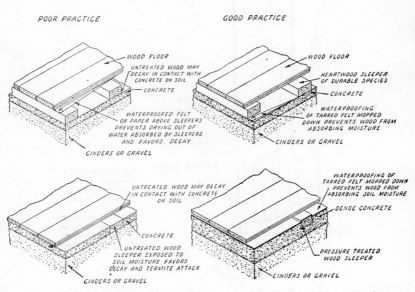

POOR PRACTICE

WOOD FLOOR

UNTREATED WOOD MAY
DECAY IN CONTACT WITH
CONCRETE ON SOIL

CONCRETE

WATERPROOFED FELT
OR PAPER ABOVE SLEEPERS
PREVENTS DRYING OUT OF
WATER ABSORBED BY SLEEPERS
AND FAVORS DECAY

CINDERS OR GRAVEL

UNTREATED WOOD MAY DECAY
IN CONTACT WITH CONCRETE
ON SOIL

CONCRETE

UNTREATED WOOD
SLEEPER EXPOSED TO
SOIL MOISTURE FAVORS
DECAY AND TERMITE ATTACK

CINDERS OR GRAVEL

GOOD PRACTICE

WOOD FLOOR

HEARTWOOD SLEEPER
OF DURABLE SPECIES

CONCRETE

WATERPROOFING
OF TARRED FELT MOPPED
DOWN PREVENTS WOOD FROM
ABSORBING MOISTURE

CINDERS OR GRAVEL

WATERPROOFING OF
TARRED FELT MOPPED DOWN
PREVENTS WOOD FROM
ABSORBING SOIL MOISTURE

DENSE CONCRETE

PRESSURE TREATED
WOOD SLEEPER

CINDERS OR GRAVEL

Fig. 164—Good and poor practice with timber on concrete or
masonry.

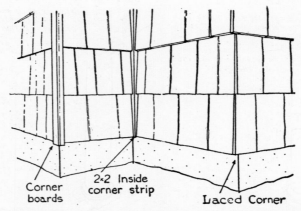

Corner boards

2×2 Inside corner strip

Laced Corner

Fig. 165—Sidewall shingles corner details.*

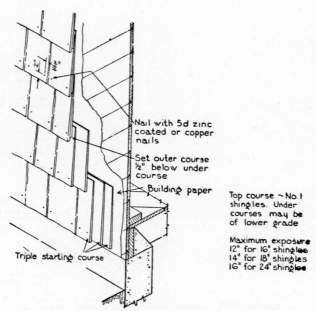

Nail with 5d zinc coated or copper nails

Set outer course ½" below under course

Building paper

Triple starting course

Top course ~ No. 1 shingles. Under courses may be of lower grade

Maximum exposure 12" for 16" shingles 14" for 18" shingles 16" for 24" shingles

Fig. 166—Double coursing of sidewall shingles.

* Figures 165 to 166 courtesy Weyerhaeuser Sales Company.

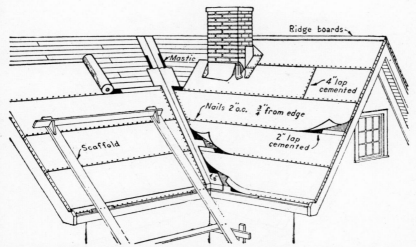

Fig. 167—Roll roofing laid parallel to the eaves; note the scaffold.*

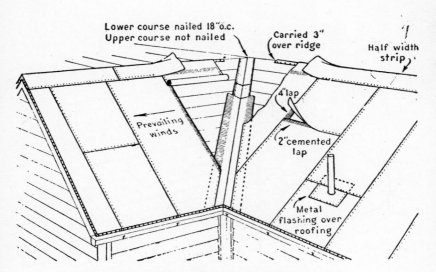

Fig. 168—Roll roofing laid with the slope.

* Figures 167 to 170 courtesy U. S. D. A.

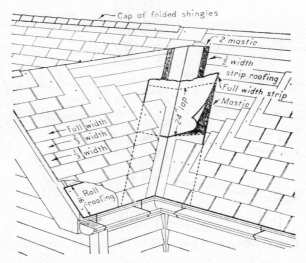

Fig. 169—Method of laying single asphalt shingles.

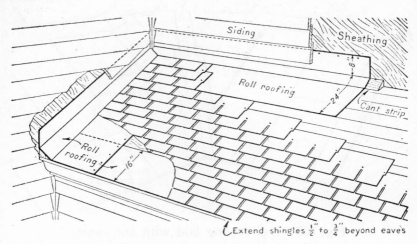

Fig. 170—Method of laying four-shingle strips.

"Nails should be long enough to penetrate about three-fourths the thickness of the sheathing."

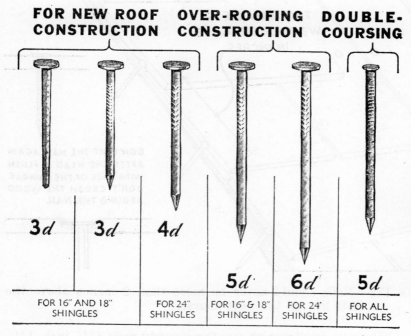

FOR NEW ROOF CONSTRUCTION   **OVER-ROOFING CONSTRUCTION**   **DOUBLE-COURSING**

3d	3d	4d	5d	6d	5d
FOR 16" AND 18" SHINGLES		FOR 24" SHINGLES	FOR 16" & 18" SHINGLES	FOR 24" SHINGLES	FOR ALL SHINGLES

Fig. 171—Use zinc-coated nails.*

* Figures 171 to 172 courtesy Extension Division Oregon State College and Red Cedar Shingle Bureau.

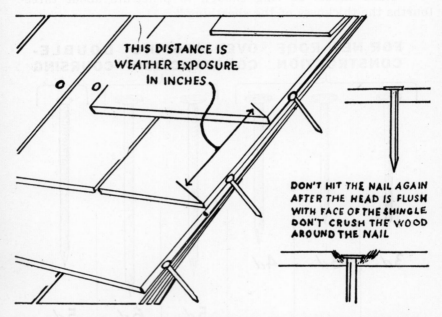

THIS DISTANCE IS WEATHER EXPOSURE IN INCHES

DON'T HIT THE NAIL AGAIN AFTER THE HEAD IS FLUSH WITH FACE OF THE SHINGLE DON'T CRUSH THE WOOD AROUND THE NAIL

Fig. 172—Nails should never be more than 2 inches above the butt line of the next course.

"For new construction, use three-penny nails (1¼-inch, 14½ gauge) for 16″ and 18″ shingles, and four-penny nails (1½-inch, 14 gauge) for 24″ shingles. For over-roofing, use five-penny nails (1¾-inch, 14 gauge) for 16″ and 18″ shingles, and six-penny nails (2-inch, 13 gauge) for 24″shingles. In double-course wall construction, use five-penny nails (1¾-inch, 14 gauge) for all shingles."

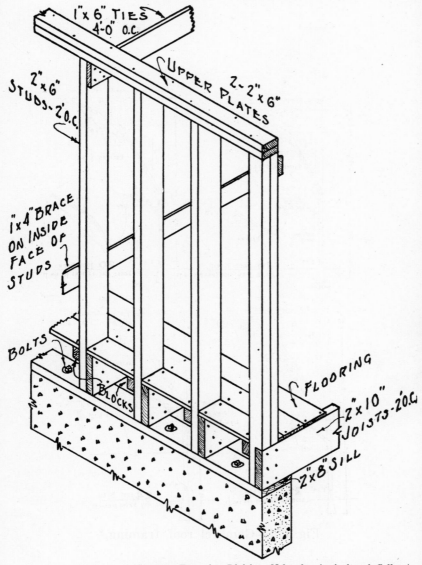

(Courtesy Extension Division, Nebraska Agricultural College)

Fig. 173—Framing detail for new storage structures.

"Equal spacing of studding and joists is essential to sidewall strength. Studs carried down to the sill and side-spiked to the joists assure much greater strength at the floor line than some other framing methods commonly used."

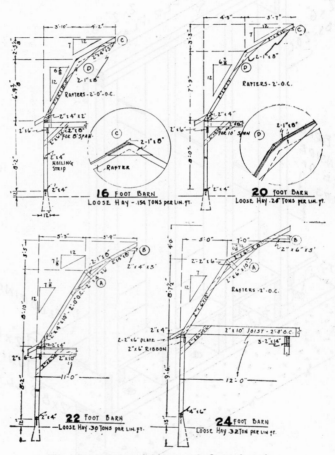

Fig. 174—Gambrel roof framing.*

---

* Figures 174 and 175 courtesy Extension Division, Univ. of Kentucky.

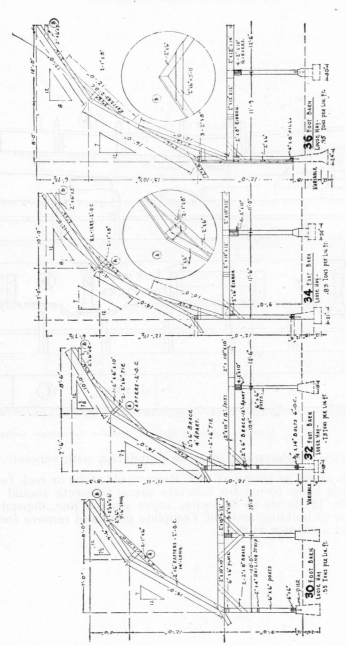

Fig. 175—Gambrel roof framing.

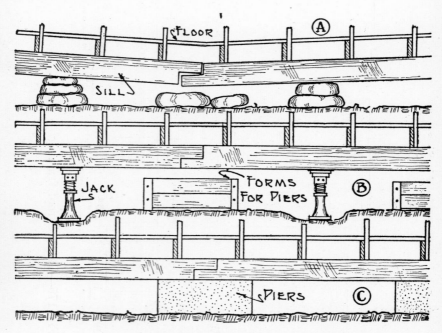

(Courtesy Extension Division, Nebraska Agricultural College)

Fig. 176—Replacement of stone foundation with concrete.

Jack up sill as shown at "B". Remove old stone or rock foundation and place forms for concrete piers. Concrete should extend from 12 inches to 20 inches below ground line, depending upon type of building and soil. Complete piers and remove forms and jacks as shown at "C".

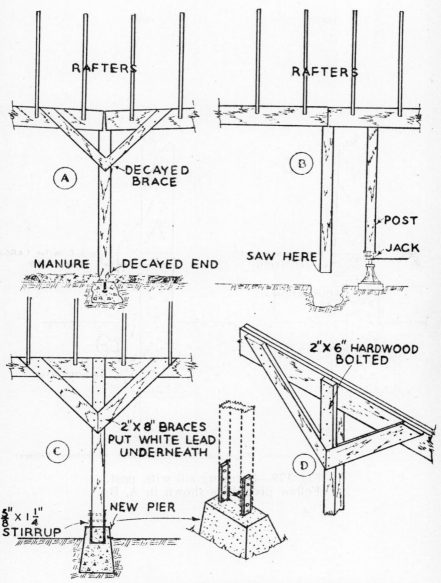

RAFTERS

A

DECAYED
BRACE

MANURE   DECAYED END

RAFTERS

B

SAW HERE

POST

JACK

C

2"X 8" BRACES
PUT WHITE LEAD
UNDERNEATH

2"X 6" HARDWOOD
BOLTED

D

$\frac{5}{8}$"X 1$\frac{1}{4}$"
STIRRUP

NEW PIER

(Courtesy Extension Division, Nebraska Agricultural College)

Fig. 177—Replacing posts on open shed.
(Follow procedure shown in A, B, C, D.)

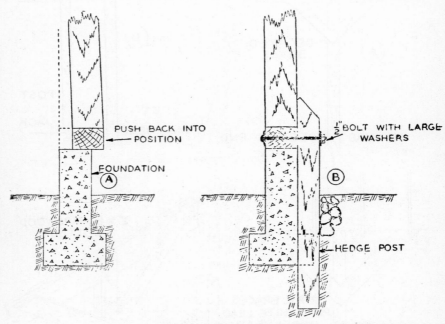

PUSH BACK INTO
POSITION

FOUNDATION
Ⓐ

½"BOLT WITH LARGE
WASHERS

Ⓑ

HEDGE POST

(Courtesy Extension Division, Nebraska Agricultural College)

Fig. 178—Securing sill with post.
(Follow procedure shown in A, B.)

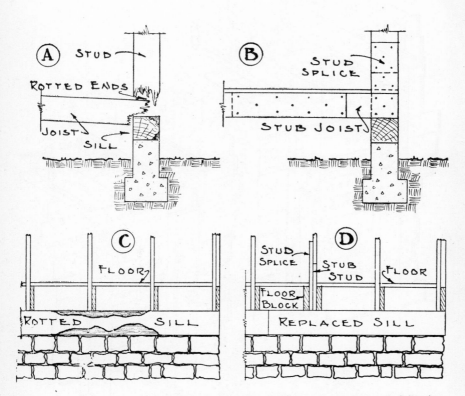

(Courtesy Extension Division, Nebraska Agricultural College)

Fig. 179—Replacement of joists, studding, ends and sills. A, rotted joist; B, repaired joist and stud; C, rotted sill; D, replaced sill.

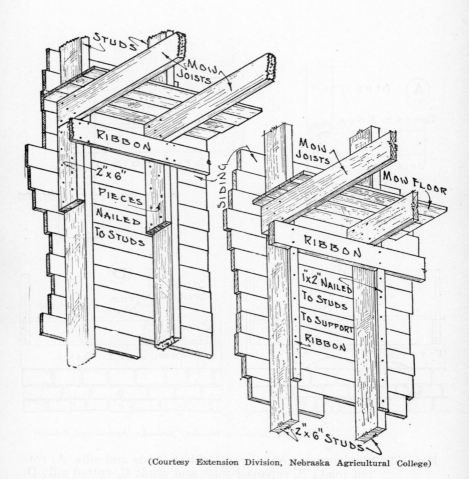

(Courtesy Extension Division, Nebraska Agricultural College)

Fig. 180—Methods of providing additional support for floor joists.

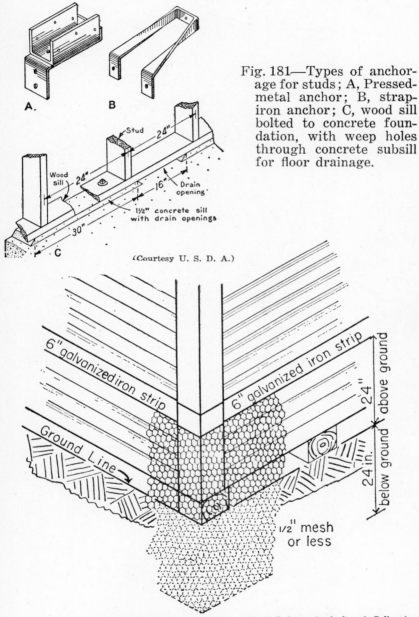

Fig. 181—Types of anchorage for studs; A, Pressed-metal anchor; B, strap-iron anchor; C, wood sill bolted to concrete foundation, with weep holes through concrete subsill for floor drainage.

(Courtesy U. S. D. A.)

(Courtesy Extension Division, North Dakota Agricultural College)

Fig. 182—Rat-proofing old storage.

MISCELLANEOUS EQUIPMENT
for the
Farm and Home

. .

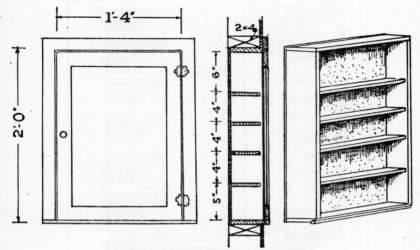

Fig. 183—Medicine cabinet.*

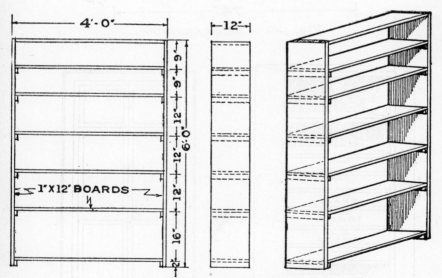

Fig. 184—Shelving for fruit storage.

* Figures 183 to 186 courtesy Arkansas Agricultural College.

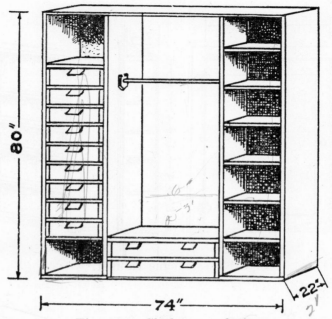

Fig. 185—Clothes wardrobe.

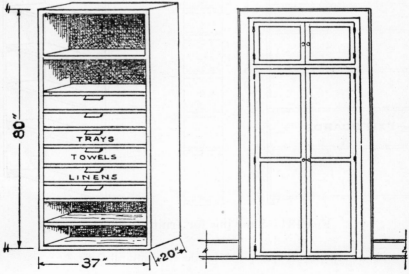

Fig. 186—Linen case.

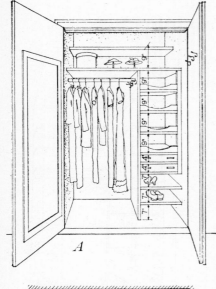

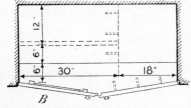

Fig. 187—Bedroom closet designed for one person: A, Perspective; B, plan.

(Courtesy U. S. D. A.)

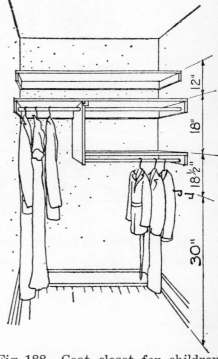

Fig. 188—Coat closet for children and adults.

(Courtesy U. S. D. A.)

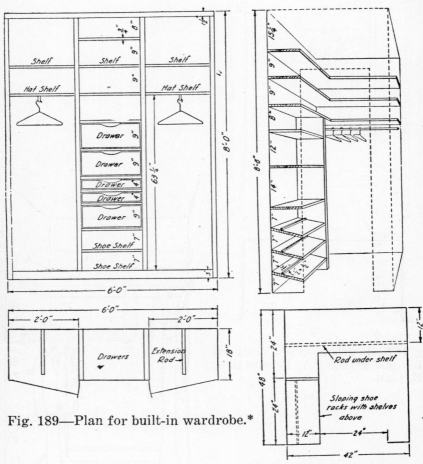

Fig. 189—Plan for built-in wardrobe.*

Fig. 190—Plan for walk-in type closet with rod and shelves.

* Figures 189 and 190 courtesy Extension Division, Michigan State Agricultural College.

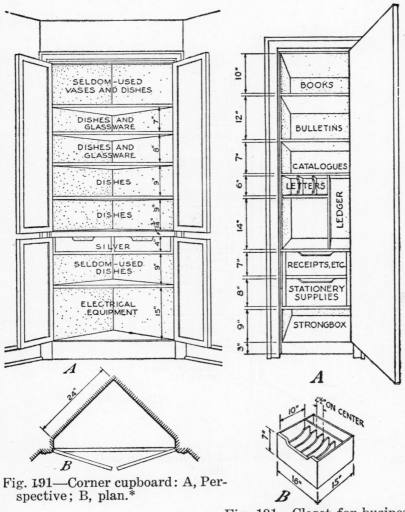

Fig. 191—Corner cupboard: A, Perspective; B, plan.*

Fig. 191—Closet for business materials: A, Perspective; B, detail of drawer for receipts.

* Figures 191 and 192 courtesy U. S. D. A.

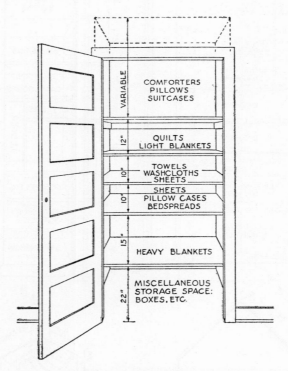

VARIABLE

COMFORTERS
PILLOWS
SUITCASES

12"
QUILTS
LIGHT BLANKETS

10"
TOWELS
WASHCLOTHS
SHEETS

10"
SHEETS
PILLOW CASES
BEDSPREADS

15"
HEAVY BLANKETS

22"
MISCELLANEOUS
STORAGE SPACE:
BOXES, ETC.

Fig. 193—Closet for linen and bed-
ding.*

* Figures 193 and 194 courtesy U. S. D. A.

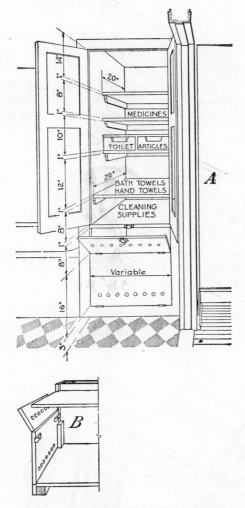

Fig. 194—Bathroom closet suggestions.

A, Perspective;
B, detail of
lower section.

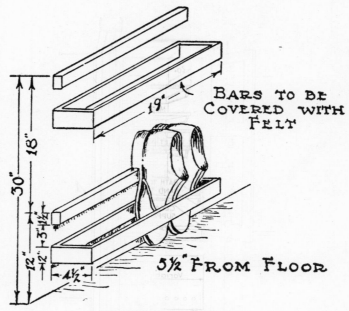

BARS TO BE
COVERED WITH
FELT

5½" FROM FLOOR

Fig. 195—Shoe rack.*

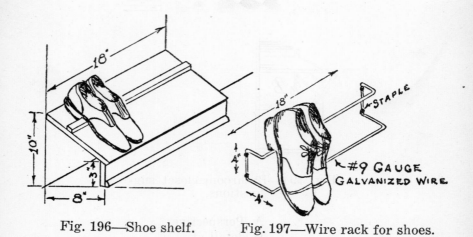

Fig. 196—Shoe shelf.   Fig. 197—Wire rack for shoes.

---

* Figures 195 to 197 courtesy Extension Division, Michigan State Agricultural College. (Adapted from U. S. D. A.)

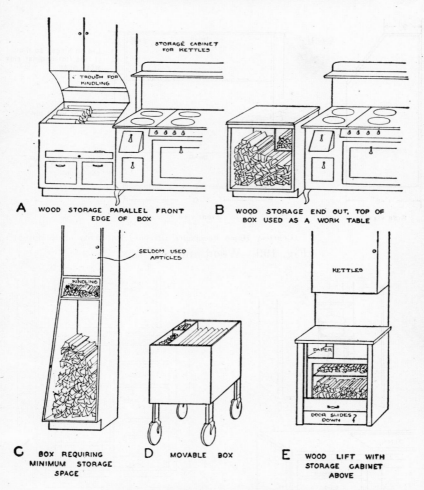

(Courtesy Experiment Station, Oregon State Agricultural College)

Fig. 198—Wood-box designs.

(A) Box with upper cabinet for utensil storage. Space between wood and upper cabinet for kindling. (B) Box under work counter. (C) Wood box or closet. Suitable for use where wall space is limited. (D) Box equipped with rubber-tired wheels for convenience in moving through door for filling. (E) Wood lift. Door drops into basement. Top may be used for work table, and upper cabinet for utensils.

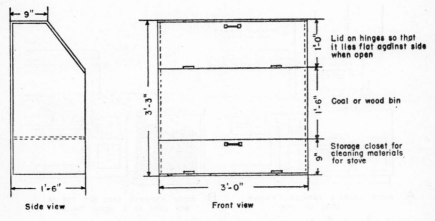

Fig. 199—Wood and coal box.

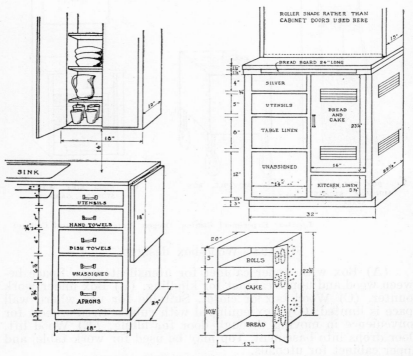

Fig. 200—Two-unit sink and serving installation.

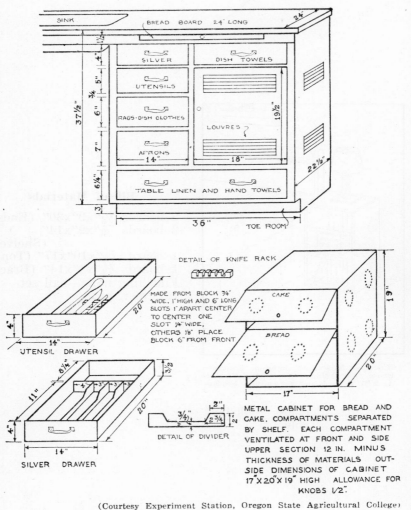

(Courtesy Experiment Station, Oregon State Agricultural College)

Fig. 201—Dimensions of lower sink cabinet with drawers.

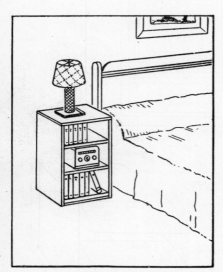

(Courtesy Miss Ruth Jamison, Extension
House Furnishings Specialists, Virginia
A. & M. College, and Agricultural Leaders'
Digest)

Fig. 202—Bedside bookshelf
table.

Bill of Materials

2 boards 7/8"x9"x30" (Ends)
3 boards 7/8"x9"x14"
                    (Shelves)
1 board 7/8"x10"x17" (Top)
1 board 7/8"x3"x14" (Brace)
Finishing nails—nail set
Hammer, putty

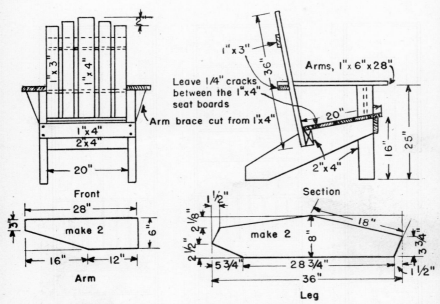

(Courtesy Extension Division, Clemson Agricultural College of South Carolina)

Fig. 203—Lawn chair.

Bill of Materials for Lawn Chair

1 pc. 2″ x 4″ x 6′-0″ legs and brace
1 pc. 1″ x 8″ x 6′-0″ legs
1 pc. 1″ x 6″ x 5′-0″ arms
16 lin. ft. 1″ x 4″ back and seat
16 lin. ft. 1″ x 3″ back
½ lb. 8d common nails
¼ lb. 10d common nails

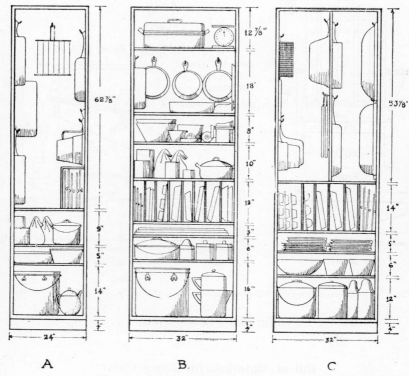

(Courtesy Agricultural Experiment Station, Oregon State College)

Fig. 204—Floor-to-ceiling cabinets used when stove center and mixing center are combined. Small articles are hung on the door of the cabinet.

Fig. 205—Chairs made of seats from a Model A Ford sedan and covered with goods costing 98c a yard. These chairs cost about $3.00 each.*

The following directions for making these chairs are through the courtesy of Miss Laura Connor, home demonstration agent of Williamsburg county:

1. Take one single front seat from a junked car, remove metal attaching it to the car floor for "scrap," and clean and mend upholstery. (Soap, water and sunshine are excellent "cleansers".)

2. From a few odd pieces of rough or

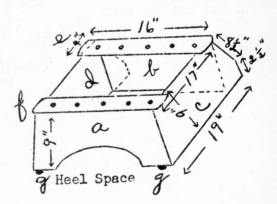

Heel Space

Fig. A—Wood base for old auto seat. Adjust dimensions to fit chair seat. Sides extend slightly beyond back at base.

* Courtesy Harriette B. Layton, Assistant State Home Demonstration Agent, Winthrop College, South Carolina.

smooth lumber, make and attach a wooden foundation to chair according to specifications shown here:

a. & b: Front with heel space. Back without heel space.

c & d: Two sides—same dimensions.

e & f: Cross supports screwed to wooden bottom of seat and to which sides are attached.

g: Put a leg rest at each corner to protect floor.

3. Cover old upholstery with a fitted lining from unbleached muslin, sacks, or any handy strong, clean lining material. (Fig. B.)

4. Over this place the slip cover. This is the final step that changes a junked car seat into a comfortable chair, in good taste for any room.

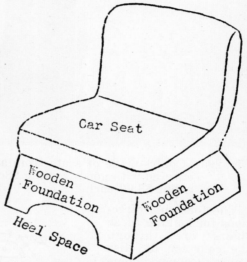

Fig. B—Upholstery covered with a fitted lining.

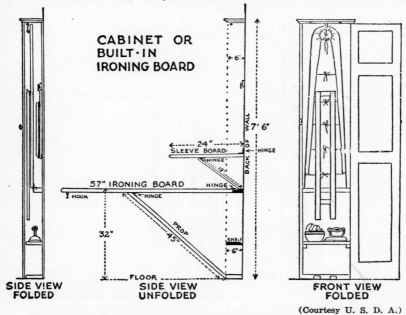

Fig. 206—A folding ironing board and its wall case.

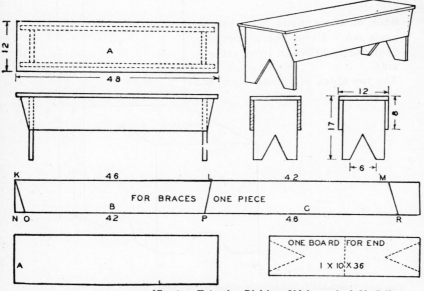

(Courtesy Extension Division, Oklahoma A. & M. College)

Fig. 207—Bench.

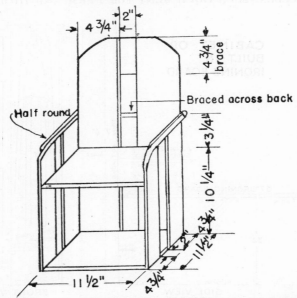

(Courtesy Extension Division, Iowa Agricultural College)

Fig. 208—Child's chair made from orange crate.

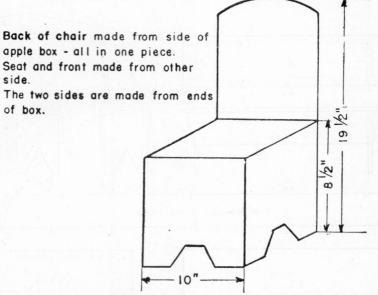

Back of chair made from side of apple box - all in one piece.
Seat and front made from other side.
The **two sides** are made from ends of box.

(Courtesy Vocational Division, Home Economics, North Dakota Agricultural College)

Fig. 209—Child's chair made from apple box.

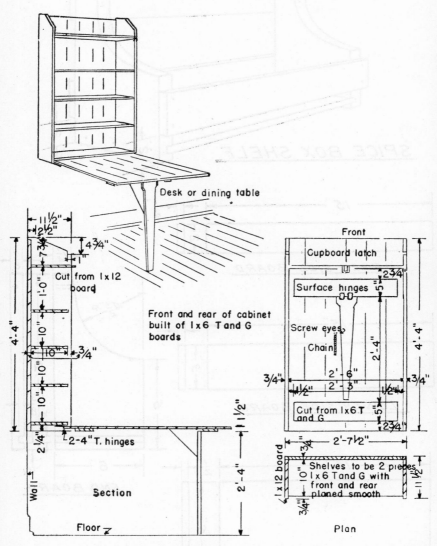

Desk or dining table

11½"
2½"
4¾"
7¾"
1"
Cut from 1 x 12 board
1'-0"
4'-4"
10"
10"
¾"
10"
10"
2¼"
2-4" T. hinges
Wall
Floor
Section

Front and rear of cabinet built of 1 x 6 T and G boards

1½"
2'-4"

Front
Cupboard latch
2¾"
Surface hinges
5"
Screw eyes
Chain
2'-4"
2'-6"
3/4"
1½"
2'-3"
1½"
5"
3/4"
Cut from 1 x 6 T and G
2¾"
4'-4"
2'-7½"
1 x 12 board
10"
3/4"
Shelves to be 2 pieces 1 x 6 T and G with front and rear planed smooth
1½"
1"
Plan

(Courtesy U. S. Office of Education, Education and Training of N. Y. A. Project Workers)

Fig. 210—Foldaway table or desk cabinet.

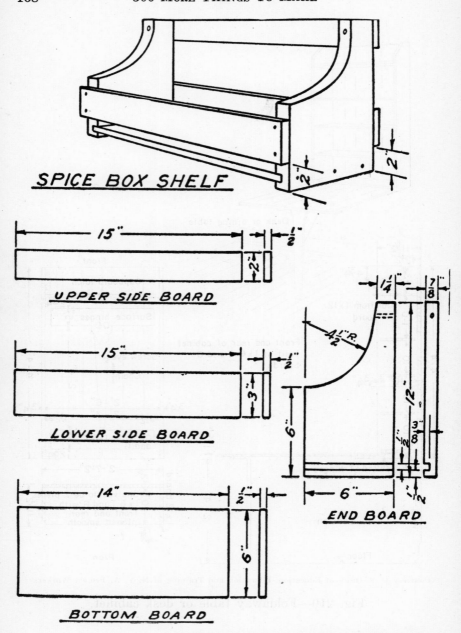

SPICE BOX SHELF

UPPER SIDE BOARD

15"
½"
2"

LOWER SIDE BOARD

15"
½"
3"

BOTTOM BOARD

14"
½"
6"

END BOARD

1¼"
7/8"
4½"R.
12"
6"
3/8"
½"
6"
½"

(Courtesy Extension Division, Michigan State College)

Fig. 211—Shelf for spices.

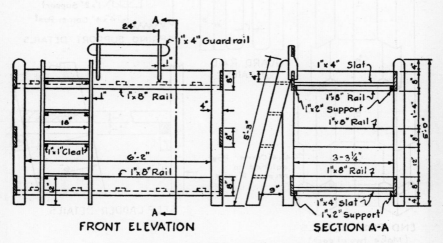

(Courtesy Extension Division, North Dakota Agricultural College)

Fig. 212—Double deck bunk bed. (Completed bunk requires a
space about 7 feet long, 4 feet wide and approximately
7 feet high.)

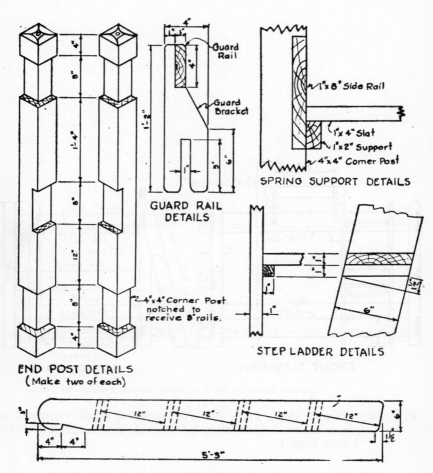

Fig. 213—Detail of double deck bunk beds in Fig. 212.

Bill of Materials

Bunks	Ladder and Guard Rail
4 pcs. corner posts, 4″ x 4″ x 5′0″	2 pcs. ladder rails, 1″ x 6″ x 5′3″
4 pcs. front rails, 1″ x 8″ x 6′8″	4 pcs. ladder steps, 1″ x 6″ x 1′6″
6 pcs. end rails, 1″ x 8″ x 3′11¼″	8 pcs. ladder step cleats, 1″ x 1″ x 6″
10 pcs. slats, 1″ x 4″ x 3′3¼″	1 pc. guard rail, 1″ x 4″ x 2′2″
4 pcs. slat supports, 1″ x 2″ x 6′8″	2 pcs. guard brackets, 1 ″x 4″ x 1′2″

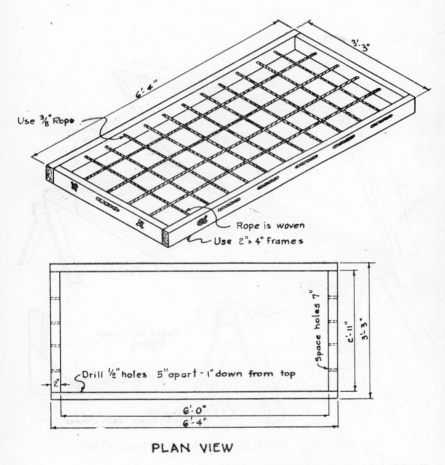

Use ⅜" Rope

Rope is woven

Use 2"x 4" Frames

3'-3"

6'-4"

Space holes 7"

2'-11"

3'-3"

Drill ½" holes 5" apart - 1" down from top

2"

6'-0"

6'-4"

PLAN VIEW

(Courtesy Extension Division, North Dakota Agricultural College)

Fig. 214—Homemade rope spring for double deck bunk bed in Fig. 212.

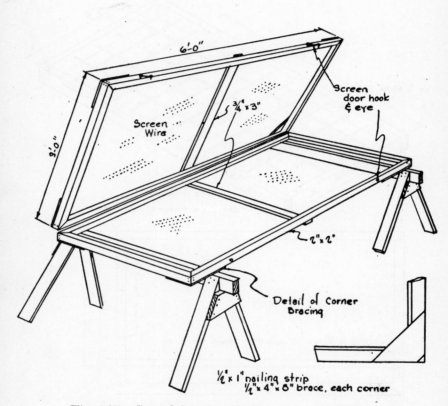

Fig. 215—Sun drier for fruits and vegetables.*

---

* Figures 215 to 217 courtesy Extension Division, Clemson Agricultural College.

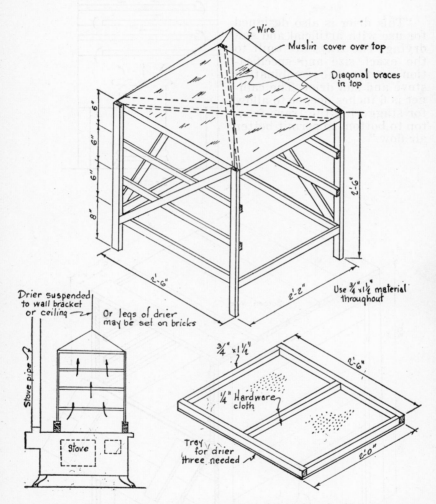

Fig. 216—Combination sun and stove drier for fruits and vegetables.

Economical drying is obtained by removing trays and placing in sun during favorable weather. Sun drying requires use of
thin muslin or mosquito netting to keep out insects.

"This drier is also designed for use with artificial and sun drying. The trays are built to the exact size and specification as for the combination stove and sun drier. The cabinet is 6 inches deeper to allow for staggering the trays from top to bottom to permit better air flow."

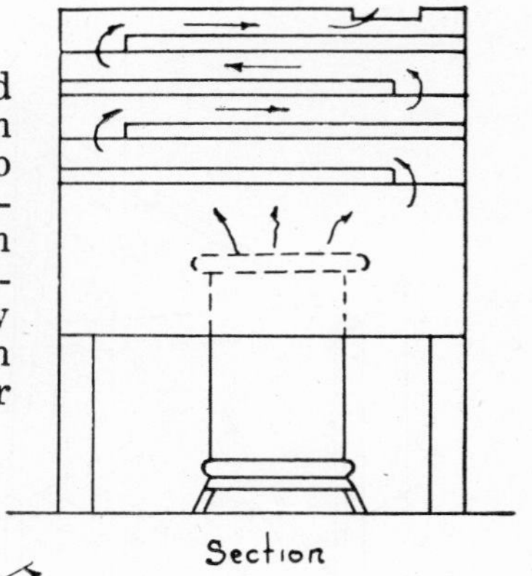

Section

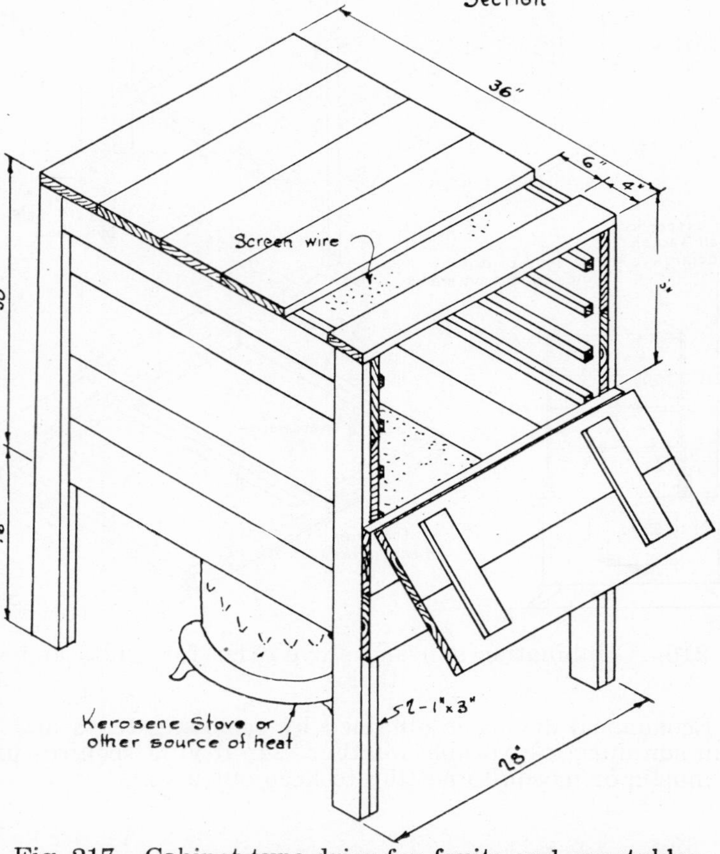

Fig. 217—Cabinet type drier for fruits and vegetables.

Bill of Materials for Fruit and Vegetable Driers

1. Sun Drier: (Fig. 215)

4 pcs. 2″ x 2″ x 6′-0″—sides of top and bottom
4 pcs. 2″ x 2″ x 3′-0″—ends of top and bottom
2 pcs. ¾″ x 2″ x 3′-0″—cross braces
8 pcs. ½″ x 4″ x 0′-8″—corner braces
12 feet 36″ galv. screen wire—top and bottom; 2-3″ butt hinges
36 lin. feet ½″ x 1″ nailing strip material; tacks and nails; 2
    screen door hooks and eye

2. Combination Sun and Stove Drier: (Fig. 216):

18 ¾″ x 1½″ x 2′-6″ legs and side pieces and sides of trays
 4 ¾″ x 1½″ x 2′-0½″ bottom and top and braces
 1 ¾″ x 1½″ x 14′-0″ diagonal braces (cut as needed)
 9 ¾″ x 1½″ ends and braces for trays
30 lin. feet ¼″ x 1″ stripping for bottom of trays
 3 ¼″ mesh hardware cloth 2′-0″ x 2′-6″ trays
2 lb. 6d finishing nails; 1 lb. 3d common nails; staples

3. Cabinet Type Drier: (Type 217)

Approximately 40 sq. ft. of tongue and groove material for en-
    closing cabinet
30 lin. feet 1″ x 3″—legs and frame work
24 lin. feet 1″ x 1″—tray runners
44 lin. feet 1″ x 1½″—material for trays
10 feet 24″ x ¼″ mesh hardware cloth—trays
36″ x 36″ screening—tacks, nails, etc.

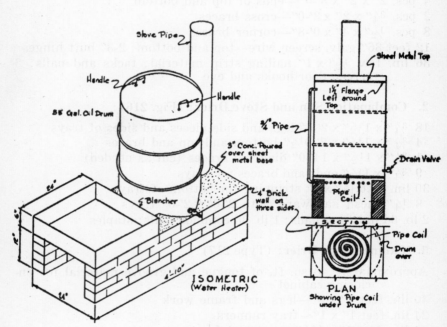

Stove Pipe

Handle

Handle

Sheet Metal Top

55 Gal. Oil Drum

1½" Flange
Left around
Top

¾" Pipe

3" Conc. Poured
over sheet
metal base

Drain Valve

Blancher

4" Brick
wall on
three sides

Pipe
Coil

SECTION

Pipe Coil

Drum
over

24"

6"

8"

4'-10"

ISOMETRIC
(Water Heater)

14"

PLAN
Showing Pipe Coil
under Drum

(Courtesy H. O. West, Mississippi State College)

Fig. 218—Water heater and blancher.

Suggestions for Water Heater and Blancher Illustrated in Fig. 218*

"In canning a considerable amount of hot water is required and in many instances suitable heating facilities are not available. In addition to hot water needed a scalding vat or blancher should be provided. The following illustration shows the water heater and blancher or scalding vat.

Material Needed:

> 1 55 gallon oil drum
> 1 piece of sheet metal 3' square
> ¾" pipe
> Stove pipe
> Brick and concrete

"The following steps should be followed in constructing this type of heater.

"1. Cut the head from a 55-gallon oil drum, leaving a 1½" flange inside the drum. The flange will provide space to hold a cover over the top of the drum as shown in Figure 218. Construct a sheet metal box 24" square and 6" deep as illustrated.

"2. Construct brick furnace 1' high, 2' wide, and 2'-10" long. Place the 24" square sheet metal blancher on the front end of the furnace. Secure a piece of pipe coil as illustrated, placing one end of the coil through the center of the drum at the bottom, allowing the other end of the coil to come out through the side of the furnace and up to within 6" or 8" of the top of the drum. When the fire is applied water will circulate through the coil, thereby heating the water much faster.

"3. A drain valve should be placed at the bottom of the drum to be used in drawing hot water from the heater. Place the drum and stove pipe at the back end of the furnace and pour a concrete slab around the drum and stove pipe.

"4. Cut the cover for the drum from sheet metal and attach handles. This type of heater can be constructed mostly from scrap material."

---

* Courtesy H. O. West, Mississippi State College.

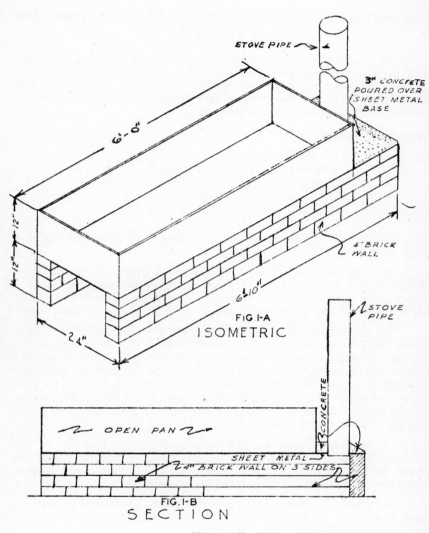

STOVE PIPE

3" CONCRETE
POURED OVER
SHEET METAL
BASE

6'-0"

12"

12"

4" BRICK
WALL

6'-10"

FIG I-A
ISOMETRIC

24"

STOVE
PIPE

CONCRETE

OPEN PAN

SHEET METAL
4" BRICK WALL ON 3 SIDES

FIG. I-B
SECTION

(Courtesy H. O. West, Mississippi State College,

Fig. 219—Open vat type canner. Such a canner is easily constructed and may be used when pressure is not desired.

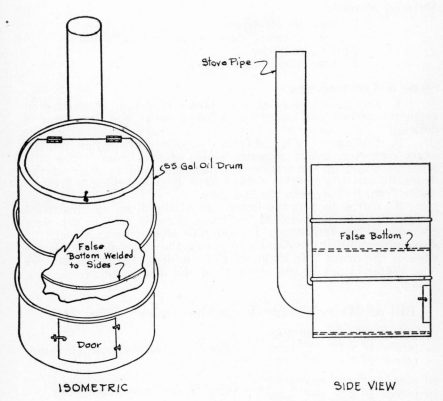

Stove Pipe

55 Gal. Oil Drum

False Bottom Welded to Sides

Door

False Bottom

ISOMETRIC

SIDE VIEW

(Courtesy H. O. West, Mississippi State College)

Fig. 220—Open type oil drum cooker.

Suggestions for Open Type Oil Drum Cooker as Illustrated in Figure 220*

"This type of cooker may be used where a small number of cans are to be canned.

Material Needed:

    1 55-gallon oil drum
    1 piece of boiler plate or flat iron 24″ square
    Stove pipe elbow
    2 stove pipe joints

Steps in Constructing:

"1. Cut the head from a 55-gallon oil drum, as illustrated in figure at left and construct a hinge cover for the drum if desired.

"2. Cut a piece of metal from the boiler plate or flat iron the exact diameter, inside measurements, of the drum. Place this piece of metal in the center of drum and weld to sides of the drum. Be sure the metal is welded securely to the sides to prevent water from leaking into the fire box.

"3. Cut a door at the lower end of the drum as illustrated in figure at left and hinge to the drum. Directly back of this door cut an opening and attach a stove pipe elbow joint. Attach the stove pipe joint to the elbow and fasten the stove pipe to the top edge of the drum. The lower part of the drum serves as the fire box. Water is put in the top part of the drum and serves as a cooker."

Bill of Materials for Vegetable Drier* (Fig. 221)

4 pieces 1″ x 1″, 18″ long
4 pieces 1″ x 1″, 22″ long } For sides, top and bottom frame
4 pieces 1″ x 1″, 14″ long

10 pieces 1″ x 2″, 19″ long
10 pieces 1″ x 2″, 10″ long } For drying trays and drying
10 pieces 1½″ x ½″ x 22″ long tray rests

2 pieces 1″ x 1″, 12″ long } For door frame
2 pieces 1″ x 1″, 20″ long

2 pieces screen wire or cloth for sides 20″ x 22″
1 piece screen wire or cloth for one end 14″ x 20″ For drier
1 piece screen wire or cloth for top 14″ x 22″   covering
1 piece screen wire or cloth for door 14″ x 22″

1 piece galvanized iron for bottom or base of drier, 26″ x 34″

* Courtesy H. O. West, Mississippi State College.

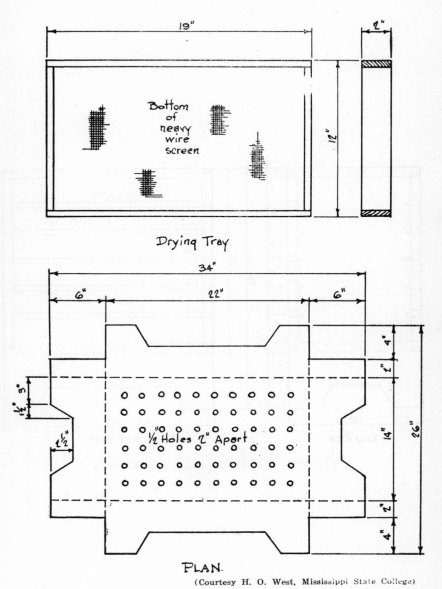

Drying Tray

PLAN.

(Courtesy H. O. West, Mississippi State College)

Fig. 221—Vegetable drier.

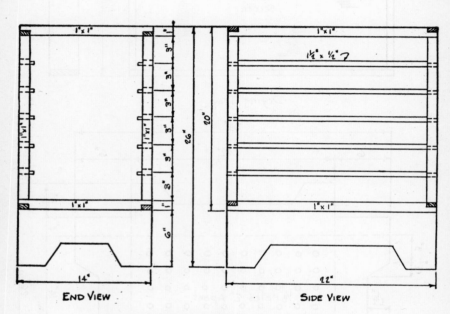

Fig. 222—Vegetable drier (continued).

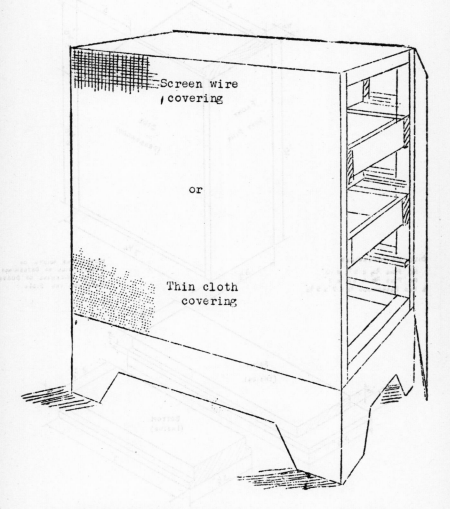

Fig. 223—Completed vegetable drier from Fig. 221.

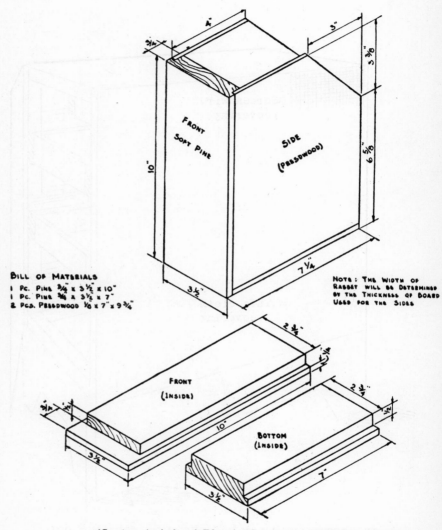

BILL OF MATERIALS
1 PC. PINE 3/4" x 3 1/2 x 10"
1 PC. PINE 3/4 x 3 1/2 x 7"
2 PCS. PEESDWOOD 1/8 x 7" x 9 3/4"

NOTE: THE WIDTH OF
RABBET WILL BE DETERMINED
BY THE THICKNESS OF BOARD
USED FOR THE SIDES

(Courtesy Agricultural Education Department, University of Kentucky)

Fig. 224—Bulletin file box.

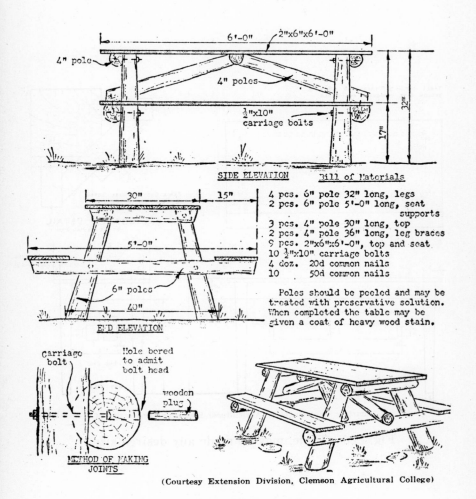

SIDE ELEVATION

END ELEVATION

METHOD OF MAKING JOINTS

Bill of Materials

4 pcs. 6" pole 32" long, legs
2 pcs. 6" pole 5'-0" long, seat supports
3 pcs. 4" pole 30" long, top
2 pcs. 4" pole 36" long, leg braces
9 pcs. 2"x6"x6'-0", top and seat
10 ½"x10" carriage bolts
4 doz. 20d common nails
10   50d common nails

Poles should be peeled and may be treated with preservative solution. When completed the table may be given a coat of heavy wood stain.

(Courtesy Extension Division, Clemson Agricultural College)

Fig. 225—Picnic table.

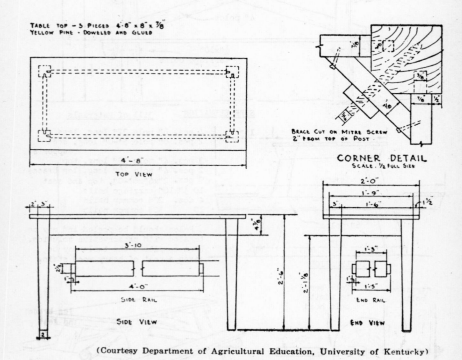

TABLE TOP - 5 PIECES 4'-8" x 8" x 7/8"
YELLOW PINE - DOWELED AND GLUED

4'-8"

TOP VIEW

BRACE CUT ON MITRE SCREW
2" FROM TOP OF POST

CORNER DETAIL
SCALE. 1/2 FULL SIZE

3'-10

4'-0"

SIDE RAIL

SIDE VIEW

2'-0"

1'-9"

1'-6"

END RAIL

END VIEW

(Courtesy Department of Agricultural Education, University of Kentucky)

Fig. 226—Table, may be made any desired size.

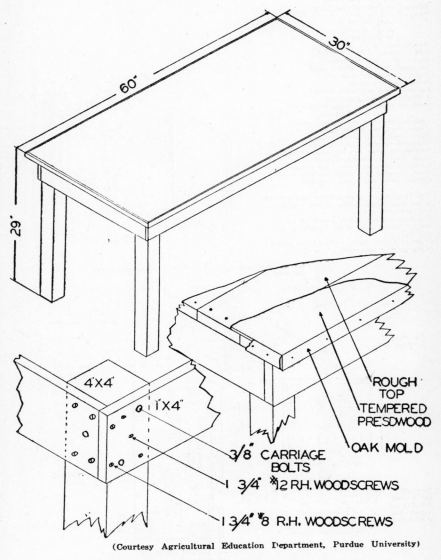

60"

30"

29"

4"X4"

1"X4"

ROUGH
TOP

TEMPERED
PRESDWOOD

OAK MOLD

3/8" CARRIAGE
BOLTS

1 3/4" #12 R.H. WOODSCREWS

1 3/4" #8 R.H. WOODSCREWS

(Courtesy Agricultural Education Department, Purdue University)

Fig. 227—Table, may be made any desired size.

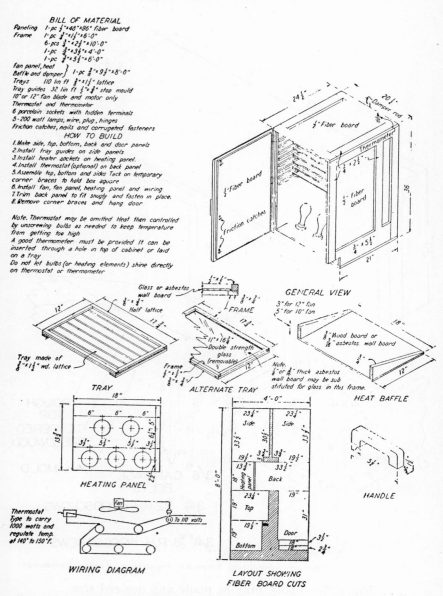

BILL OF MATERIAL

Paneling   1-pc ⅛"×48"×96" fiber board
Frame   1-pc ¾"×1¼"×6'-0"
6-pcs ¾"×2½"×10'-0"
1-pc ¾"×3½"×4'-0"
1-pc ¾"×5½"×6'-0"

fan panel, heat
Baffle and damper } 1-pc ⅜"×9¼"×8'-0"
Trays   110 lin ft ⅜"×1¼" lattice
Tray guides 32 lin ft ¼"×¾" stop mould
10" or 12" fan blade and motor only
Thermostat and thermometer
6 porcelain sockets with hidden terminals
5-200 watt lamps, wire, plug, hinges
Friction catches, nails and corrugated fasteners

HOW TO BUILD

1. Make side, top, bottom, back and door panels
2. Install tray guides on side panels
3. Install heater sockets on heating panel.
4. Install thermostat (optional) on back panel
5. Assemble top, bottom and sides Tack on temporary corner braces to hold box square
6. Install fan, fan panel, heating panel and wiring.
7. Trim back panel to fit snugly and fasten in place.
8. Remove corner braces and hang door.

Note. Thermostat may be omitted Heat then controlled by unscrewing bulbs as needed to keep temperature from getting too high
A good thermometer must be provided It can be inserted through a hole in top of cabinet or laid on a tray
Do not let bulbs (or heating elements) shine directly on thermostat or thermometer

GENERAL VIEW
3" for 12" fan
5" for 10" fan

TRAY
Tray made of ⅜"×1¼" wd. lattice
12"

ALTERNATE TRAY

HEAT BAFFLE

HEATING PANEL

HANDLE

WIRING DIAGRAM
Thermostat Type to carry 1000 watts and regulate temp. at 140° to 150°F.
Fan   To 110 volts

LAYOUT SHOWING FIBER BOARD CUTS

Fig. 227a—Detailed plans for building a cabinet-type fruit and vegetable dehydrator for home use (revised).

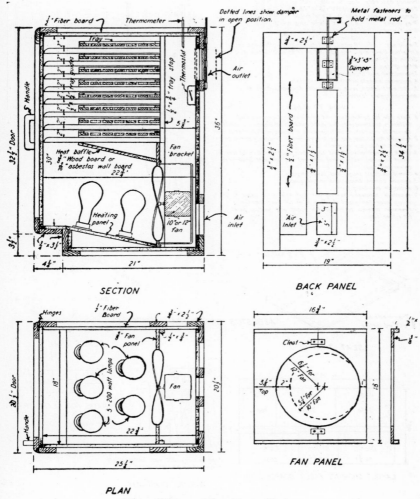

Fig. 227a—(Continued).*

---

* Figures 227a and 227b courtesy G. A. Shuey, University of Tennessee Agricultural Experiment Station, and the Tennessee Valley Authority, Commerce Department.

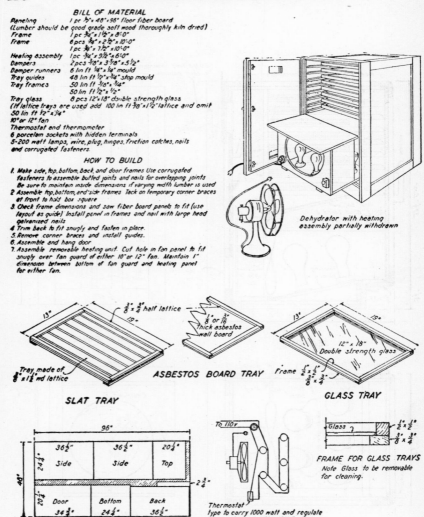

BILL OF MATERIAL

Paneling	1 pc 1/2" x 48" x 96" floor fiber board
(Lumber should be good grade soft wood thoroughly kiln dried)	
Frame	1 pc 3/4" x 1 1/2" x 8'-0"
Frame	6 pcs 3/4" x 2 1/2" x 10'-0"
	1 pc 3/4" x 7 1/2" x 10'-0"
Heating assembly	1 pc 3/4" x 9 1/2" x 6'-0"
Dampers	2 pcs 3/8" x 3 5/8" x 5 1/2"
Damper runners	6 lin ft 1/4" x 1/4" mould
Tray guides	48 lin ft 1/2" x 3/4" stop mould
Tray frames	50 lin ft 3/8" x 3/4"
	50 lin ft 1/2" x 1/2"
Tray glass	8 pcs 12" x 18" double strength glass

(If lattice trays are used add 100 lin ft 3/8" x 1 1/2" lattice and omit 50 lin ft 1/2" x 1/4"
10" or 12" fan
Thermostat and thermometer
6 porcelain sockets with hidden terminals
5-200 watt lamps, wire, plug, hinges, friction catches, nails and corrugated fasteners.

HOW TO BUILD

1. Make side, top, bottom, back, and door frames Use corrugated fasteners to assemble butted joints and nails for overlapping joints Be sure to maintain inside dimensions if varying width lumber is used
2. Assemble top, bottom, and side frames Tack on temporary corner braces at front to hold box square
3. Check frame dimensions and saw fiber board panels to fit (use layout as guide) Install panel in frames and nail with large head galvanized nails
4. Trim back to fit snugly and fasten in place.
5. Remove corner braces and install guides.
6. Assemble and hang door
7. Assemble removable heating unit. Cut hole in fan panel to fit snugly over fan guard of either 10" or 12" fan. Maintain 1" dimension between bottom of fan guard and heating panel for either fan.

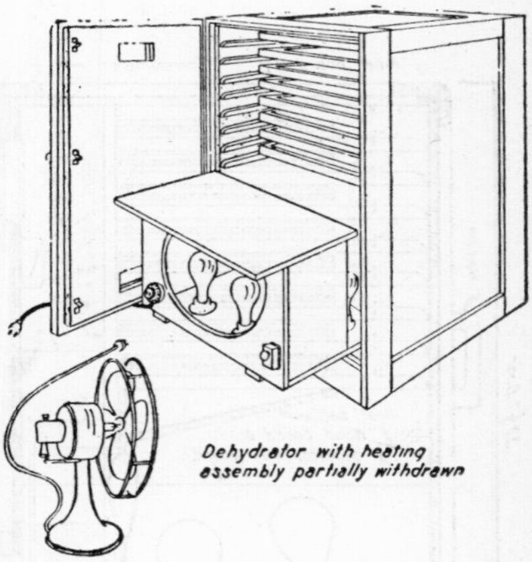

Dehydrator with heating assembly partially withdrawn

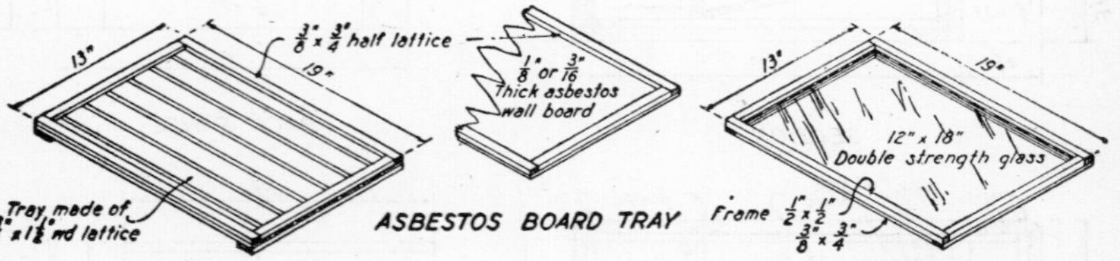
3/8 x 3/4 half lattice
13"
19"
Tray made of 3/8 x 1 1/2 nd lattice
1/8" or 3/16" Thick asbestos wall board
13"
19"
12" x 18" Double strength glass
Frame 1/2 x 1/2
3/8 x 3/4

SLAT TRAY ASBESTOS BOARD TRAY GLASS TRAY

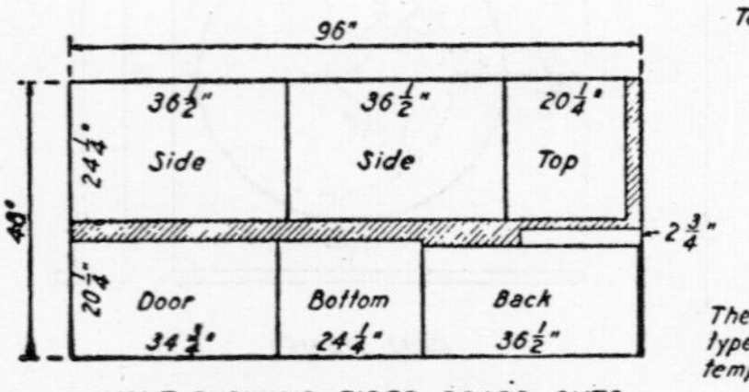
96"
48"
36 1/2"
Side
36 1/2"
Side
20 1/4"
Top
24 1/4"
2 3/4"
20 1/4"
Door
34 3/4"
Bottom
24 1/4"
Back
36 1/2"

LAYOUT SHOWING FIBER BOARD CUTS

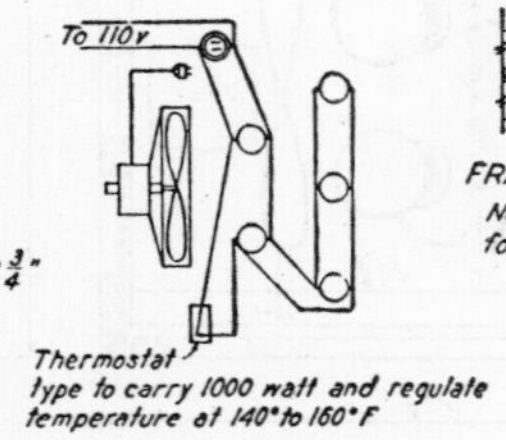
To 110v
Thermostat
type to carry 1000 watt and regulate temperature at 140°to 160°F

WIRING DIAGRAM

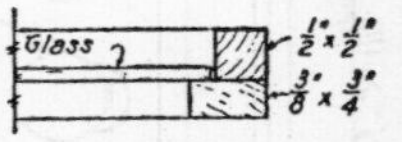
Glass
1/2 x 1/2
3/8 x 3/4

FRAME FOR GLASS TRAYS
Note Glass to be removable for cleaning.

Do not let bulbs (for heating elements) shine directly on thermostat or thermometer.
Thermostat may be omitted Heat then controlled by unscrewing bulbs as needed to keep temperature from getting too high.
A good thermometer with a range in excess of 180°F must be provided.
It can be inserted through a hole in the top of cabinet or laid on a tray.
If box is used for sulphuring, be sure to remove heating assembly and fan during treatment
A bracket fan may be used in place of pedestal fan.

Fig. 227b—Alternative plans for building a cabinet-type dehydrater with removable heating assembly. A bracket or pedestal-type fan may be used.

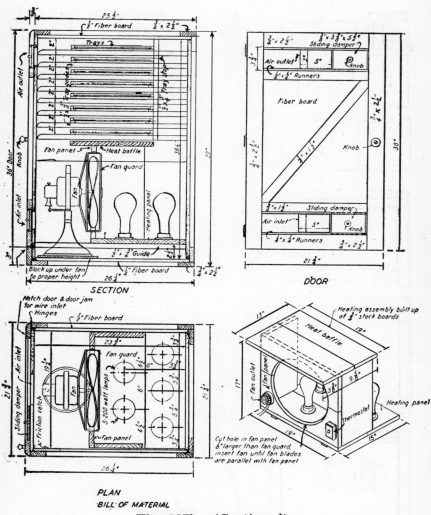

Fig. 227b—(Continued).

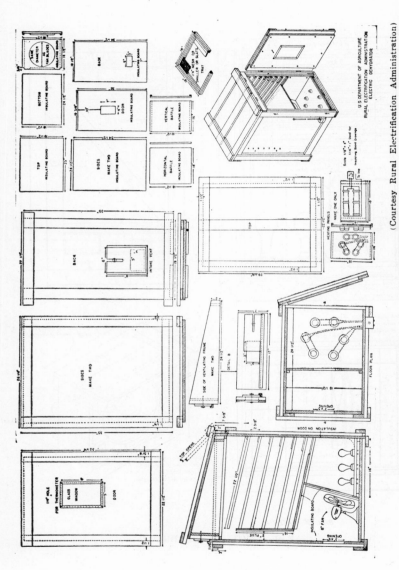

(Courtesy Rural Electrification Administration)

Fig. 227c—Electric dehydrater.

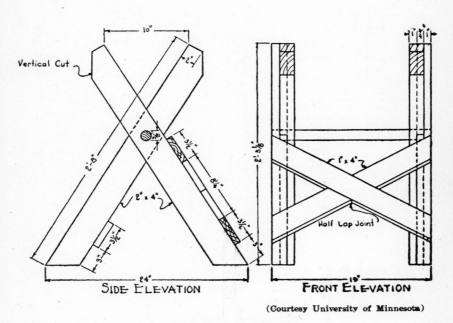

SIDE ELEVATION   FRONT ELEVATION

(Courtesy University of Minnesota)

Fig. 228—Sawbuck.

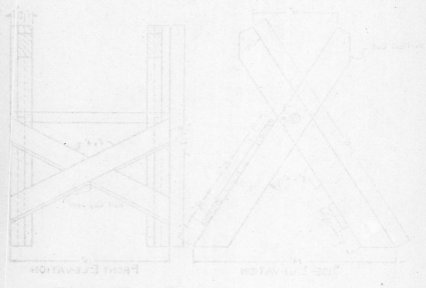

Vertical Cut

Half Lap Joint

FRONT ELEVATION   SIDE ELEVATION

(Courtesy University of Minnesota)

FIG. 225.—Sawbuck.

Equipment for Crops

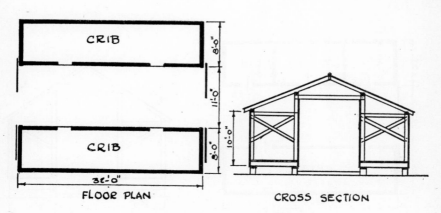

CRIB

8'-0"

11'-0"

CRIB

8'-0"

10'-0"

36'-0"

FLOOR PLAN

CROSS SECTION

Fig. 229—Double corn crib.*

* Figures 229 and 230 courtesy Continental Steel Corporation.

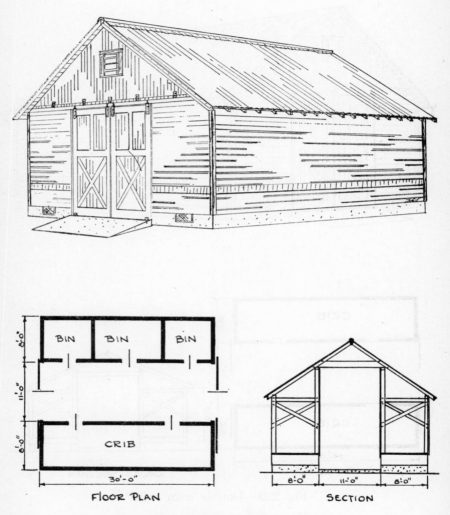

Fig. 230—Corn crib and granary.

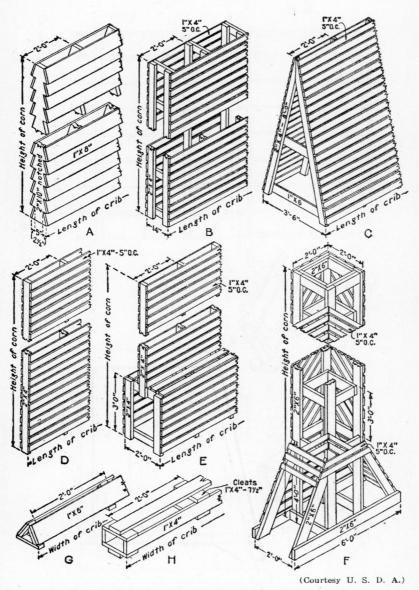

(Courtesy U. S. D. A.)

Fig. 231—Suggested forms of ventilating shafts.

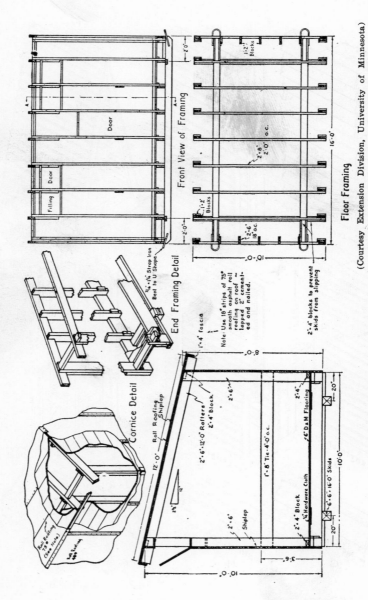

Front View of Framing

Floor Framing

End Framing Detail

Cornice Detail

(Courtesy Extension Division, University of Minnesota)

Fig. 232—Movable grain bin, 1000-bushel capacity.

Bill of Materials for 1000-Bushel Movable Bin

Lumber

	Pieces	Size
Skids	2	6″ x 6″—16′
Joists	9	2″ x 8″—10′
Studding	16	2″ x 6″—18′
Door framing	2	2″ x 6″—10′
Rafters	9	2″ x 6″—12′
Headers and blocks	6	2″ x 4″—14′
Floor and doors (D&M)	26	1″ x 6″—16′
Side sheathing and roof boards (shiplap)	52	1″ x 8″—16′
End sheathing (shiplap)	31	1″ x 8″—10′
Floor blocks	2	1″ x 2″—10′
Fascia	2	1″ x 4″—16′
Corner flashing	4	1″ x 4″—18′
Battens	288 linear feet	
Total lumber	1743 F.B.M.	
Roll roofing (75-pound)	2¼ rolls	
Roll roofing (45-pound)	5 rolls	

Hardware

	Amount	Kind
Hardware cloth	32 square feet	¼-inch mesh
T Hinges	3 pair	6-inch
Hinge hasps	3	3-inch
Nails		16 d., 10 d., 8 d.
Nails		Gal. roofing
Casein glue	½ pound	
Clevis	$\frac{3}{16}$″ x 1¼″—12′	Strap iron
Bolts	8—½″ x 6½″	Machine

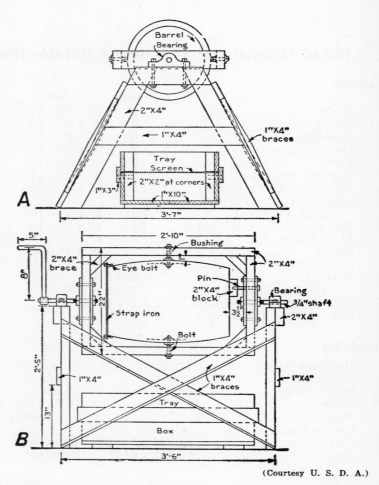

(Courtesy U. S. D. A.)

Fig. 233—Barrel scarifier, using 15-gallon barrel mounted in a rotating frame so it can be tilted for filling and empty-ing; A, end elevation; B, side elevation, showing barrel in horizontal position; C, side elevation, showing barrel tilted for emptying or filling.

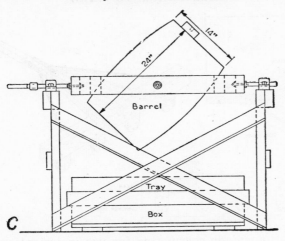

Fig. 233 (continued).

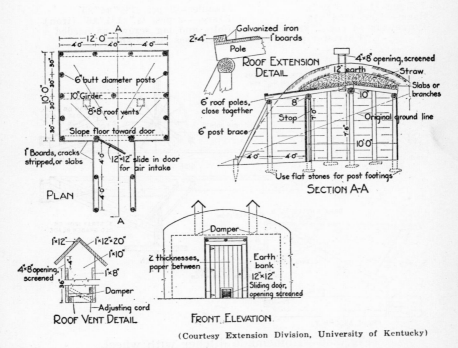

(Courtesy Extension Division, University of Kentucky)

Fig. 234—10′ x 12′ pole and board fruit and vegetable storage cellar.

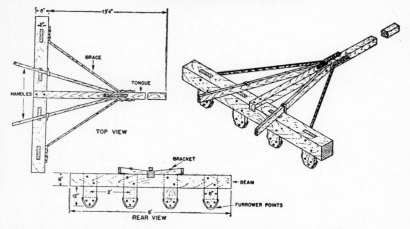

Fig. 235—Homemade corrugator for use in irrigation.*

Bill of Materials for Corrugator

Tongue—1 pc. 8"x8"x8'
Beam—1 pc. 4"x4"x14'
Furrowers—4 pcs. 2"x8"x20"
Furrower points—4 old steel discs cut to shape

Handles—2 pcs. 1½"x4"x5'
Braces—2 pcs. ¼"x1¼"x6' (iron)
Bolts and lag screws as needed

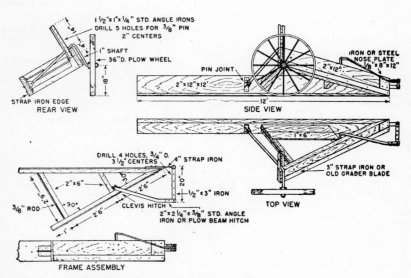

Fig. 236—Homemade ditcher with wheel.

* Figures 235 and 236 courtesy Extension Division, Montana State College.

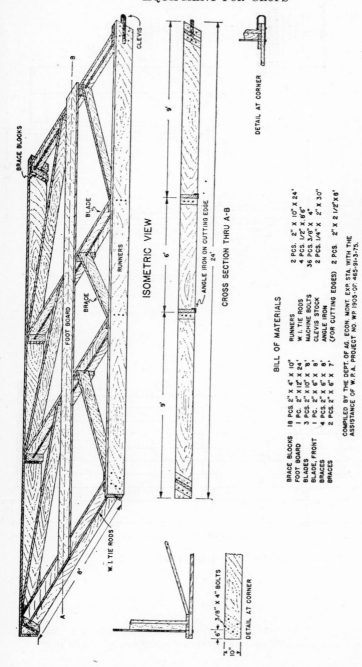

ISOMETRIC VIEW

CLEVIS

BRACE BLOCKS

FOOT BOARD

BRACE

BLADE

RUNNERS

W. I. TIE RODS

B

A

8'

9'

6'

9'

24'

ANGLE IRON ON CUTTING EDGE

CROSS SECTION THRU A-B

DETAIL AT CORNER

DETAIL AT CORNER

3/8" X 4" BOLTS

6"

4"

10"

BILL OF MATERIALS

BRACE BLOCKS	18 PCS. 2" X 4" X 10"	RUNNERS	2 PCS. 2" X 10" X 24'
FOOT BOARD	1 PC. 2" X 12" X 24'	W. I. TIE RODS	4 PCS. 1/2" X 8'6"
BLADES	3 PCS. 2" X 10" X 8'	MACHINE BOLTS	36 PCS. 3/8" X 4"
BLADE, FRONT	1 PC. 2" X 6" X 8'	CLEVIS STOCK	2 PCS. 1/4" X 2" X 30"
BRACES	4 PCS. 2" X 6" X 8'	ANGLE IRON	
BRACES	2 PCS. 2" X 6" X 7'	(FOR CUTTING EDGES)	2 PCS. 2" X 2 1/2" X 8'

COMPILED BY THE DEPT. OF AG. ECON. MONT. EXP. STA. WITH THE
ASSISTANCE OF W.P.A. PROJECT NO. WP 1905-OF 465-91-3-75.

(Courtesy Extension Division, Montana State College)

Fig. 237—Homemade leveler or box float for use in irrigation farming.

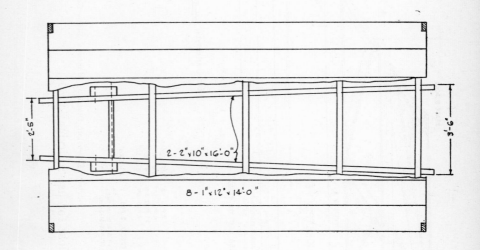

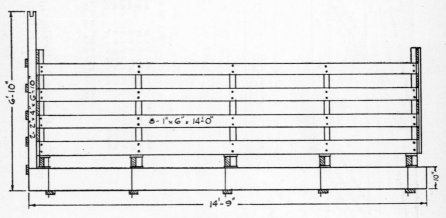

Fig. 238—Hay rack.*

---

* Figures 238 and 239 courtesy Nebraska College of Agriculture.

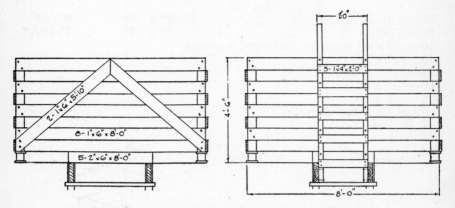

Fig. 239—End views of hay rack shown in Fig. 238.

Bill of Materials for Hay Rack in Figure 238

Lumber:

Bolts:
110—³⁄₈″ x 4½″
40—³⁄₈″ x 2½″
30—³⁄₈″ x 3″
8—³⁄₈″ x 4″
2—½″ x 3′ 5″
4—½″ x 7″
Washers

2—2″ x 10″—16′-0″   2—2″ x 6″—16′-0″
8—6″ x 12″—14′-0″   1—2″ x 6″—12′-0″
8—1″ x 6″—14′-0″   4—2″ x 4″—10′-0″
4—1″ x 6″—16′-0″   2—2″ x 4″—12′-0″
1—1″ x 6″—12′-0″   1—2″ x 4″—14′-0″
1—1″ x 4″—10′-0″   1—4″ x 6″—2′-0″
10 hay rack clamps length 18″
20 socket clamps

Bill of Materials for Hay Rack in Figure 240

Item	Pieces	Size	Exact Length
Stringers	2	4″ x 4″	14′- 0″
Sills	2	4″ x 6″	14′- 0″
Floor beam	2	4″ x 4″	7′- 6¼″
Side stakes	10	2″ x 4″	2′- 6″
End stakes	2	2″ x 4″	3′- 2″
Ladder uprights	2	2″ x 4″	6′- 0″
Floor	22	1″ x 8″	7′- 6¼″
Side rails	6	1″ x 4″	14′- 0″
End rails	6	1″ x 4″	7′- 9½″
Ladder rails	1	1″ x 4″	1′- 3½″
Ladder rails	1	1″ x 4″	1′- 7″
Wheel box top	2	1″ x 12″	3′- 2″
Wheel box sides	4	2″ x 4″	3′- 2″
Wheel box ends	4	2″ x 4″	0′- 8¼″

Wheel box framing	2	2″ x 4″	3′- 2″
Wheel box "	4	2″ x 4″	1′-10$\frac{7}{16}$″

40—$\frac{5}{16}$″ x 3″ machine bolts and washers
40—$\frac{5}{16}$″ x 5″ " " " "
24—½″ x 6″ " " " "
10—½″ x 8″ " " " "
4—½″ x 10″ " " " "
4 lbs. 8d common nails
1 lb. 16d " "

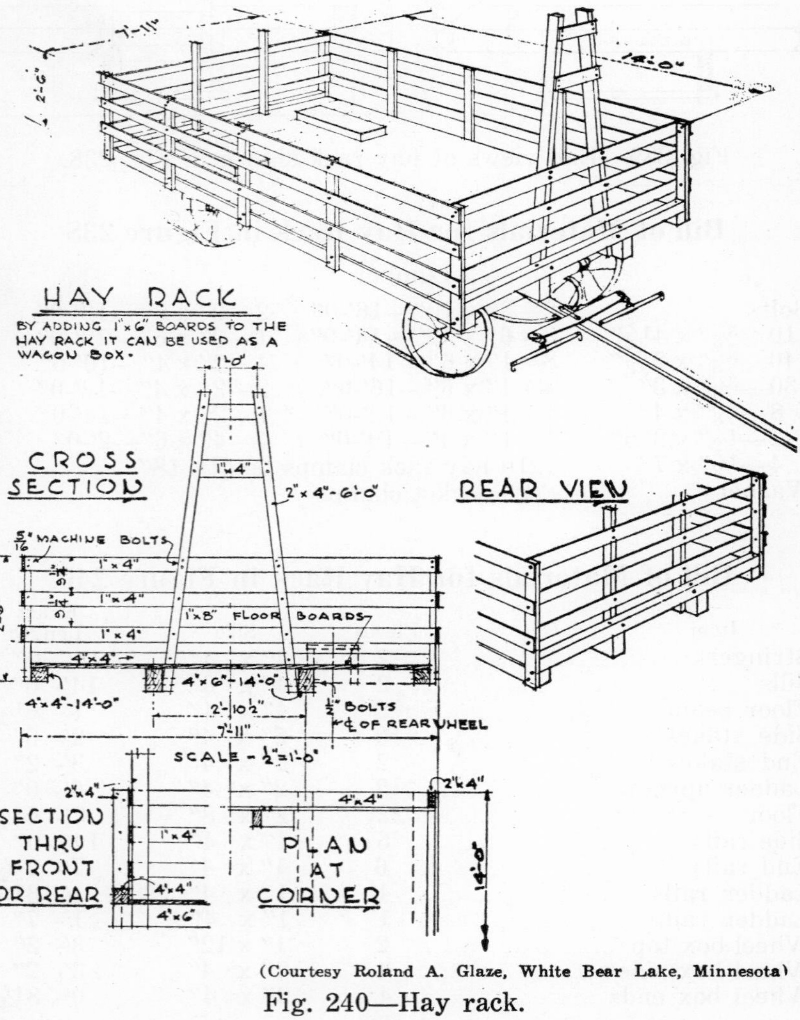
7'-11"
2'-6"
14'-0"
HAY RACK
BY ADDING 1"x6" BOARDS TO THE HAY RACK IT CAN BE USED AS A WAGON BOX.
CROSS SECTION
1'-0"
1"x4"
2"x4"-6'-0"
REAR VIEW
5/16" MACHINE BOLTS
1"x4"
1"x4"
1"x4"
2'-6"
1"x8" FLOOR BOARDS
4"x4"
4"x6"-14'-0"
4"x4"-14'-0"
2'-10½"
½" BOLTS
℄ OF REAR WHEEL
7'-11"
SCALE - ½"=1'-0"
2"x4"
SECTION THRU FRONT OR REAR
1"x4"
4"x4"
4"x6"
PLAN AT CORNER
4"x4"
2"x4"
14'-0"

(Courtesy Roland A. Glaze, White Bear Lake, Minnesota)

Fig. 240—Hay rack.

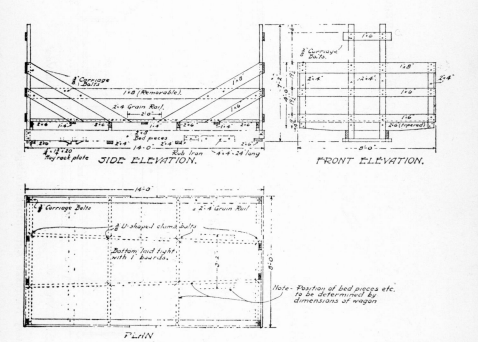

Fig. 241—Hay and bundle rack.

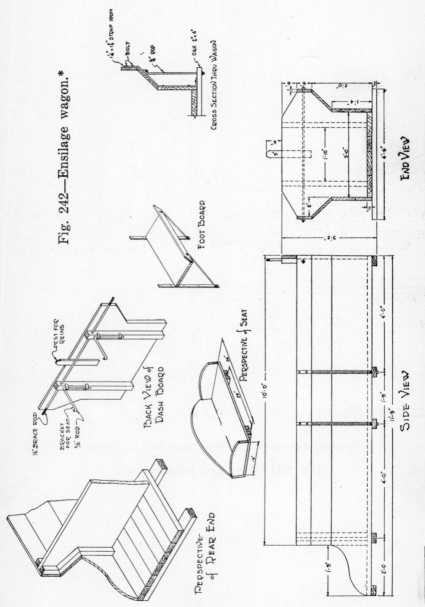

Fig. 242—Ensilage wagon.*

CROSS SECTION THRU WAGON

FOOT BOARD

BACK VIEW of DASH BOARD

PERSPECTIVE of SEAT

PERSPECTIVE of REAR END

END VIEW

SIDE VIEW

* Figures 242 and 243 courtesy Nebraska Agricultural College.

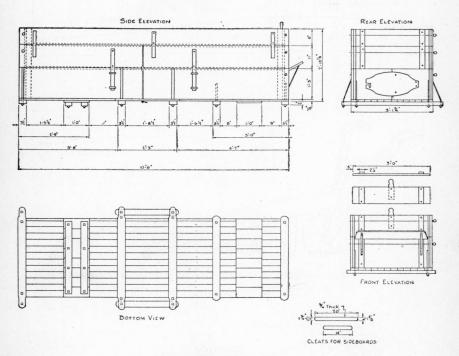

Fig. 243—Wagon box.

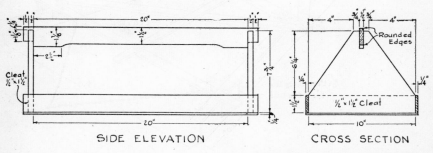

(Courtesy University of Minnesota)

Fig. 244—Berry box carrier.

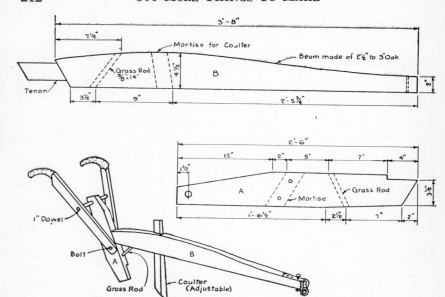

(Courtesy Justin R. Tucker, Arkansas Division of Vocational Education)

Fig. 245—Homemade plow stock.

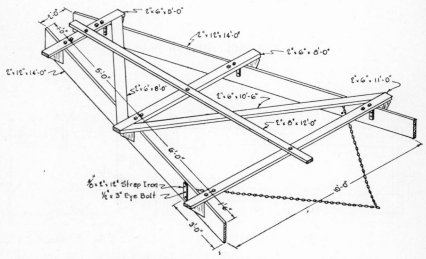

Fig. 246—Border Drag.*

---

* Figures 246 and 247 courtesy Extension Division, North Dakota Agricultural College.

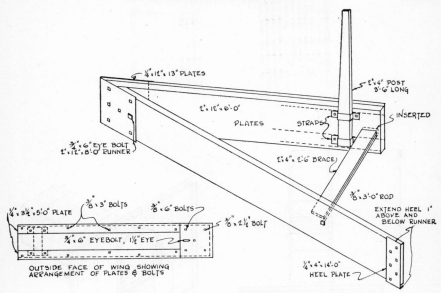

Fig. 247—Homemade ditcher.

Bill of Materials for Border Drag

2—2″	x 12″ x 14′- 0″	Runners	
1—2″	x 6″ x 11′- 0″	Cross brace	
1—2″	x 6″ x 8′- 0″	"	"
1—2″	x 6″ x 5′- 0″	"	"
1—2″	x 6″ x 10′- 6″	Diagonal brace	
1—2″	x 6″ x 8′- 0″	"	"
1—2″	x 8″ x 12′- 0″	Tie brace	
6—2″	x 10″ x 0′-10″	Braces	
6—3⁄8″	x 2″ x 1′- 4″	L-shaped strap irons	
2—3⁄8″	x 2″ x 1′- 0″	Strap irons	
2—1⁄2″	x 3″	Eye bolts	
24—3⁄8″	x 3″	Carriage bolts	
5—3⁄8″	x 4½″	"	"
2 lbs. 20d		Nails	

Bill of Materials for Homemade Ditcher

1— 2″ x 4″ x 2′-6″	1—1⁄8″ x 2″ x 8½″ strap
1— 2″ x 4″ x 3′-6″	20—3⁄8″ x 3″ Machine Bolts
1— 2″ x 12 x 6′-0″	3—3⁄8″ x 2½″ Machine Bolts
1— 2″ x 12″ x 8′-0″	1—3⁄8″ x 4″ Machine Bolts
Total FBM—32	2—3⁄8″ x 6″ Machine Bolts
2—1⁄4″ x 3½″ x 5′-0″ Plates	1—3⁄4″ x 6″ Eyebolt
2—1⁄4″ x 12″ x 13″ Plates	1—3⁄8″ x 3′-0″ Rod
1—1⁄4″ x 4″ x 14″ Plate	

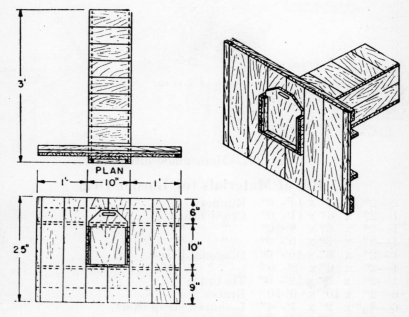

PLAN

(Courtesy Extension Division, Montana State College)

Fig. 248—Wooden turnout for use in irrigation.

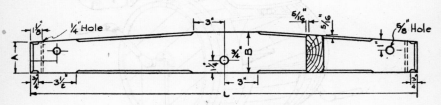

Fig. 249—Evener.*

L	A	B
36″	1⅝″ x 3″	1⅝″ x 4″
38″	1¾″ x 3¼″	1¾″ x 4¼″
46″	1⅞″ x 3½″	1⅞″ x 4¾″
48″	2 ″ x 3¾″	2 ″ x 5 ″

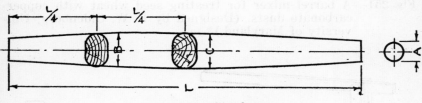

Fig. 250—Singletree.

L	A	B	C
26″	1⅜″	1 9/16″ x 1 15/16″	1⅝″ x 2⅜″
28″	1½″	1 11/16″ x 2¼″	1¾″ x 2½″
32″	1⅝″	1 13/16″ x 2½″	1⅞″ x 2¾″
34″	1¾″	1 15/16″ x 2 11/16″	2 ″ x 3 ″

---

* Figures 249 and 250 courtesy Shop Practice Department, Kansas State Agricultural College.

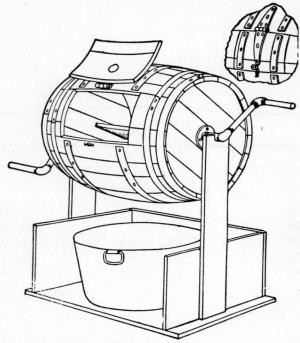

Fig. 251—A barrel mixer for treating seed wheat with copper·
carbonate dusts. (Designed by F. W. Oldenberg, University of Maryland.)*

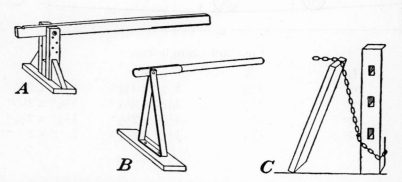

Fig. 252—Suggestions for pulling fence posts; A, a homemade
wood-frame post puller; B, a steel form of puller; C, a
form for pulling a post with a team or tractor.

* Figures 251 and 252 courtesy U. S. D. A.

Equipment for Poultry

Equipment for Poultry

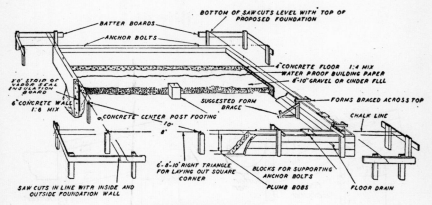

PERSPECTIVE VIEW

(Courtesy Extension Division, Michigan State College of Agriculture)

Fig. 253—Laying out poultry house floor **and foundation.**

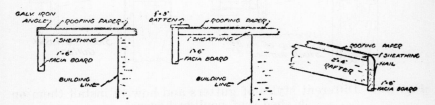

Fig. 254—Methods of fastening roofing paper at the edges of the roof.*

* Figures 254 and 255 courtesy Extension Division. Univ. of California.

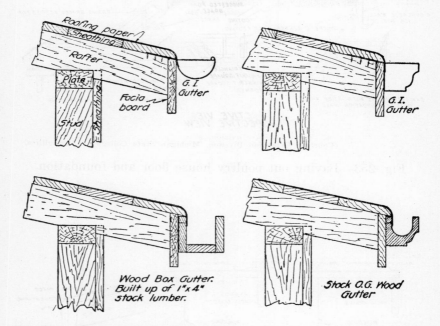

Fig. 255—Different styles of gutters and how to install them on a shed-roof poultry house.

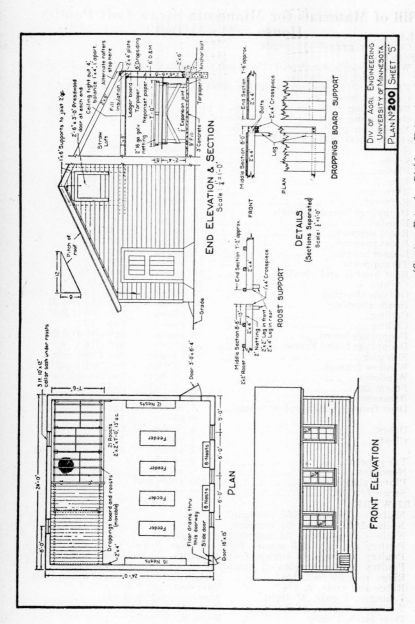

DIV OF AGRI. ENGINEERING
UNIVERSITY OF MINNESOTA
PLAN Nº 200 SHEET 'S'

END ELEVATION & SECTION
Scale: ¼=1'-0"

DETAILS
(Sections Separated)
Scale: ½"=1'-0"

DROPPINGS BOARD SUPPORT

ROOST SUPPORT

PLAN

FRONT ELEVATION

(Courtesy Extension Division, University of Minnesota)

Fig. 256—Straw-loft poultry house.

Bill of Materials for Minnesota Straw Loft Poultry House — 24 x 24 feet

FILL:
Cinder or gravel—16 yards

MASONRY:
Wall—5 yards concrete, 1:2½:5 mix; cement, 26 sacks; sand, 2¼ yards; gravel, 4½ yards
Floor—1:2:4; cement, 36 sacks; sand, 3 yards; gravel, 6 yards
Carriage bolts—25, ½"x12"
Reinforcing steel for foundation, 8 pieces, ⅜"x24'
Reinforcing steel for floor, 22 pieces, ⅜"x22'
Expansion joint, ½"x4", 96 feet.

LUMBER AND MILLWORK:

Sills	6 pieces	2x6—16
Studs	35 pieces	2x6—14
Plates	3 pieces	2x4—16
Ties	13 pieces	2x6—24
Rafters	14 pieces	2x6—16
Rafters	12 pieces	2x6—14
Droppings board support	7 pieces	2x4—16
Roosts	12 pieces	2x2—14
Roost support	3 pieces	2x4—16
Roost support	6 pieces	1x4—16
Ledger boards	3 pieces	1x4—16
Tie supports	11 pieces	1x6—12
Roof boards and cornice	50 pieces	1x12—16
Cornice	16 pieces	1x4—16
Outside sheeting	126 pieces	1x6—16 drop siding
Inside sheeting	60 pieces	1x6—16 D & M
Ceiling	20 pieces	1x6—16 D & M
Ceiling	64 pieces	1x4—16
Droppings board	30 pieces	1x6—16 D & M
Droppings board braces	2 pieces	1x6—16
Shingles	30 bundles	No. 1 red cedar
Window frames	3 8 light	9x12 with pulleys
Windows	3 8 light	9x12 check rail
Storm sash	2 8 light	9x12
Basement sash	4 3 light	10x14
Door frames, rear window frame	4 pieces	1x8—12
	4 pieces	1x4—16
Doors	4 pieces	1x6—16 D & M
Cleats	1 piece	1x10—14
	2 pieces	2'6"x3 presdwood
Tar paper	4 rolls	
Neponset	2 rolls	
Planer shavings	360 cubic feet	
Straw for loft	2 tons	

HARDWARE:
Nails— 10 pounds 16d common
Nails—100 pounds 8d common
Nails— 20 pounds 3d galvanized shingle
Poultry netting—225 square feet, 16-gauge, 2-inch mesh, 60"
Poultry netting—18 square feet, 16-gauge, ¾-inch mesh, 36"
Poultry netting staples—1 pound, 1"

Ridge roll, 30 feet, 1½"   Sash weights and cord, 3 windows
Ridge roll ends, 2, 1½"   Turn buttons, 2 dozen
T-hinges, 1 pair, 4" light   Awning pulleys, 4 only
T-hinges, 1 pair, 6" heavy   Rope, 40 feet, ¼"
Door latch, 1 only   Bolts, 8, ⅜"x6"

PAINT: **INCIDENTALS:**
Linseed oil, 1 gallon   Screen door
Turpentine, 1 gallon   Inside storm door
Paint, 4 gallons   Nests, feeders, and water stands

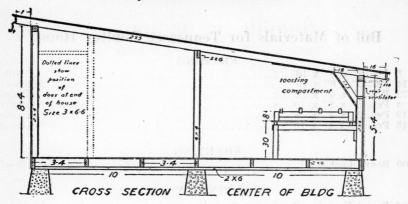

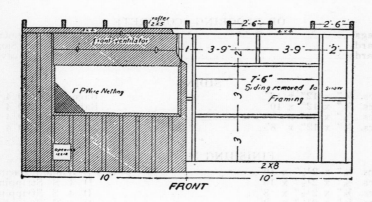

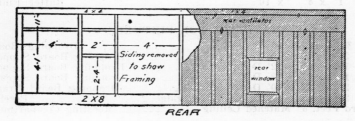

(Courtesy Extension Division, University of Tennessee)

Fig. 257—Poultry house for 100 hens.

"Common barn boards fitted well together, running perpendicular, and the joints stripped will give a good wall. The T. & G. siding, shiplap, and other similar materials may be used but are more expensive. The door should be placed at the end of the building and is 3' x 6'-6" in dimension."

Bill of Materials for Tennessee Poultry House

FRAMING

```
 8 Pcs. 2" x 8" x 10'_____Sills
14 Pcs. 2" x 6" x 10'_____ Sleepers
22 Pcs. 2" x 4" x 12'_____Rafters
 4 Pcs. 2" x 2" x 10'_____Sleeper Support
19 Pcs. 2" x 4" x  8'_____ Framing
15 Pcs. 2" x 4" x 10'_____ Framing
```

SHEETING

```
500 Board Feet—⅞"_____Roof
```

FLOORING—WOOD

```
500 Board Feet No. 2 Common T. & G._____Flooring
```

OR FLOORING—CONCRETE

```
45 Bags _____Cement
 4 Yards _____Sand
6½ Yards _____Gravel
```

SIDING

```
20 Pcs. ⅞" x 12" x 16'_____Barn Board D 4 S
17 Pcs. ⅞" x 12" x 10'_____Barn Board D 4 S
11 Pcs. ⅞" x 12" x  8'_____Barn Board D 4 S
 4 Pcs. ⅞" x 12" x  8'_____Barn Board D 4 S
```

FINISHING MATERIALS

```
11 Pcs. ⅝" x 2½" x 10'_____D 4 S Window Facing
16 Pcs. ⅜" x 2½" x 10'_____D 4 S  Stripping
56 Pcs. ⅜" x 2½" x  8'_____D 4 S  Stripping
 3 Pcs. ⅜" x 2½" x  8'_____D 4 S  Stripping
 8 Pcs. 1" x 4"   x 10'_____Rafter  Finish
```

MATERIAL FOR FIXTURES

```
 10 Pcs. ⅞" x 12" x 10' D 4 S_____Dropping  Board
  5 Pcs. 2" x  4" x 10' D 4 S_____Dropping Board Support
  3 Pcs. 1" x  3" x 12' D 4 S_____Dropping Board Support
  1 Pc.  1" x  2" x 12' D 4 S_____Dropping Board Support
  6 Pcs. 2" x  2" x 10' D 4 S_____Dropping Board Frame
  8 Pcs. 2" x  4" x 10' D 4 S Nosed Edge_____Perches
160 Board Feet, 5" Matched Ceiling_____Roosting Compartment
```

HARDWARE

```
 5 Pair 4" Strap Hinges_____Ventilators and Doors
16 Feet 1" Mesh—36" Poultry wire or ¾" mesh 36" Hardware (Cloth)
20 Lbs.  8d Nails    5 Lbs. 16d Nails
 4 Lbs.  6d Nails    5 Rolls 3-Ply Asphalt Roofing (gravel surface)
 8 Lbs. 10d Nails    2 4-light 8" x 10" Basement Sash.
```

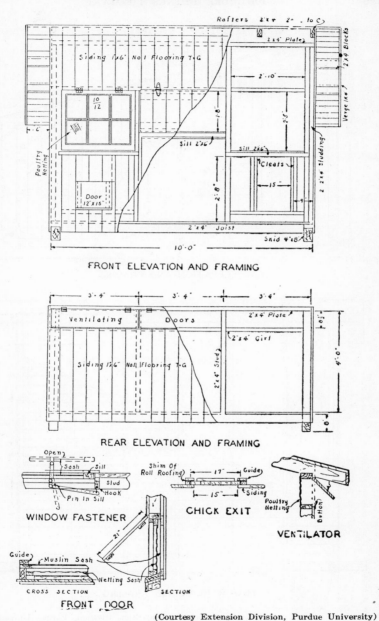

FRONT ELEVATION AND FRAMING

REAR ELEVATION AND FRAMING

WINDOW FASTENER

CHICK EXIT

VENTILATOR

FRONT DOOR

(Courtesy Extension Division, Purdue University)

Fig. 258—Purdue portable brooder house. (See Fig. 259 also.)

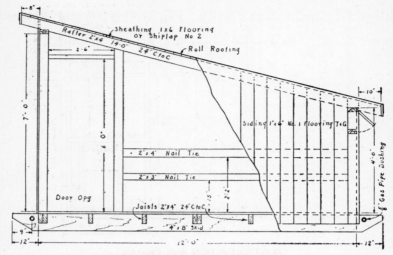

SIDE ELEVATION AND FRAMING

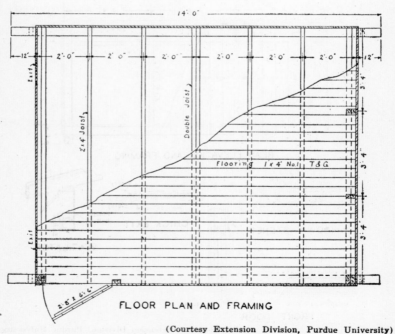

FLOOR PLAN AND FRAMING

(Courtesy Extension Division, Purdue University)

Fig. 259—Purdue portable brooder house.

Bill of Materials for Purdue Portable Brooder House

Lumber

  2 pieces 4″ x 8″—14 feet, oak
  1 piece 2″ x 6″—10 feet, No. 1 common yellow pine
  6 pieces 2″ x 4″—14 feet, No. 1 common yellow pine
  8 pieces 2″ x 4″—12 feet, No. 1 common yellow pine
22 pieces 2″ x 4″—10 feet, No. 1 common yellow pine
  2 pieces 2″ x 3″—12 feet, No. 1 common yellow pine
  1 piece 1″ x 10″—10 feet, No. 1 common yellow pine
  1 piece 1″ x 6″—12 feet, No. 1 common yellow pine
  2 pieces 1″ x 4″—14 feet, No. 1 common yellow pine
  2 pieces 1″ x 4″—12 feet, No. 1 common yellow pine
  1 piece 1″ x 4″— 8 feet, No. 1 common yellow pine
  2 pieces 1″ x 3″— 8 feet, No. 1 common yellow pine
  1 piece 1″ x 2″—12 feet, No. 1 common yellow pine
  1 piece 1″ x 2″—10 feet, No. 1 common yellow pine
  2 pieces 1″ x 2″— 8 feet, No. 1 common yellow pine
38 pieces 1″ x 4″—12 feet, B & B tongued and grooved
        flooring
50 pieces 1″ x 6″—12 feet, B & B tongued and grooved
        flooring
35 pieces 1″ x 6″—12 feet, No. 2 tongued and grooved
        flooring
  2 six-light 10″ x 12″ barn sash
  2 rolls 3-ply black prepared roofing with nails

Hardware and Miscellaneous

  5 pairs 3-inch loose-pin butt hinges, ¾-inch No. 8 screws
  1 pair 6-inch strap hinges, ¾-inch No. 8 screws
  1 pair 8-inch strap hinges, 1-inch No. 9 screws
12 pairs 1½-inch turn buttons, ¾-inch screws
        (For windows, shutters and rear ventilators)
  1 lb. ¾-inch galvanized staples
12 lb. 16d nails
20 lb. 7d nails
  2 lb. 6d nails
  6 ft. 1″ mesh poultry netting 3 ft. wide
  4 ft. 1″ mesh poultry netting 2 ft. wide
10 ft. 1″ mesh poultry netting 1 ft. wide
  1 four-inch hasp with ¾-inch screws
        (One which folds back to cover screws is preferable)
  6 four-inch hook and eye latches
  4 pieces ⅝-inch iron pipe 4 inches long
  1 gallon outside paint
  1 quart turpentine

Cutting Plan of Lumber for Purdue Poultry Brooder House

RUNNERS
>   2 pieces 4″ x 8″—14 feet—oak

FLOOR JOISTS
>   10 pieces 2″ x 4″—10 feet

STUDDING
>   6 pieces 2″ x 4″—12 feet
>   (Cut one front and one rear stud from each piece—the blocks may be used under the overhanging roof on the sides)

DOOR FRAMING
>   1 piece 2″ x 4″—10 feet

FRONT AND REAR GIRTS
>   2 pieces 2″ x 4″—10 feet

NAIL TIES
>   2 pieces 2″ x 4″—12 feet (upper ties)
>   2 pieces 2″ x 3″—12 feet (lower ties)
>   1 piece 2″ x 4″—10 feet (under window and shutter sills)

WINDOW AND SHUTTER SILLS
>   1 piece 2″ x 6″—10 feet

PLATES
>   2 pieces 2″ x 4″—10 feet

RAFTERS
>   6 pieces 2″ x 4″—14 feet

PERCHES
>   6 pieces 2″ x 4″—10 feet

VERGE BOARDS
>   2 pieces 1″ x 4″—14 feet (ends)
>   2 pieces 1″ x 4″—12 feet (front and rear)

FLOOR
>   38 pieces 1″ x 4″—12 feet—tongued and grooved flooring

SIDE WALLS
>   50 pieces 1″ x 4″—12 feet tongued and grooved flooring

ROOF BOARDS
>   35 pieces 1″ x 6″—12 feet—tongued and grooved
>   (No. 2 lumber may be used for the roof)

REAR VENTILATOR DOORS
>   1 piece 1″ x 10″—10 feet

BRACES
>   1 piece 1″ x 6″—12 feet (large door)
>   1 piece 1″ x 4″— 8 feet (wooden shutter)

MUSLIN FRAME
>   1 piece 1″ x 2″—12 feet

NETTING SASH FRAME
>   1 piece 1″ x 2″—12 feet

GUIDE CLEATS
>   1 piece 1″ x 3″— 8 feet (front exit doors)
>   1 piece 1″ x 2″— 8 feet (front exit doors)
>   1 piece 1″ x 3″— 8 feet (muslin frame)
>   1 piece 1″ x 2″— 8 feet (muslin frame)

WINDOW AND SHUTTER STOPS
>   1 piece 1″ x 2″—10 feet

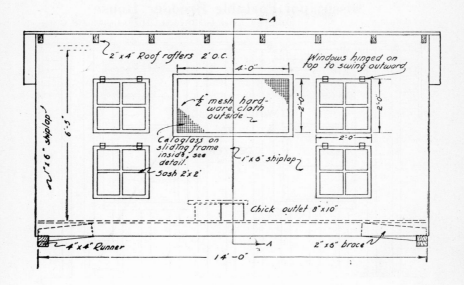

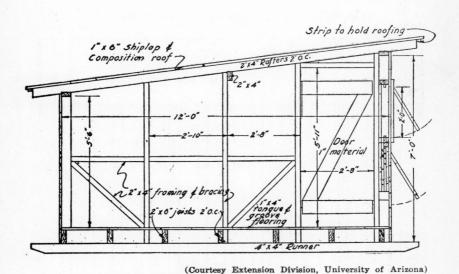

(Courtesy Extension Division, University of Arizona)

Fig. 260—Brooder house.

Mississippi Portable Brooder House

(Courtesy Extension Division, Mississippi State College)

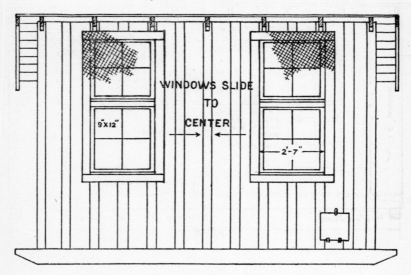

Fig. 261—Front elevation (brooder house).

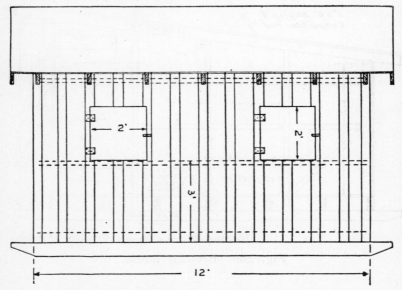

Fig. 262—Rear elevation (brooder house).

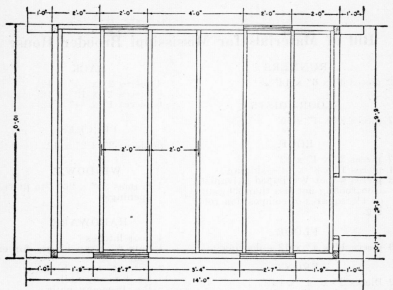

(Fig. 263—Floor plan (Mississippi brooder house).

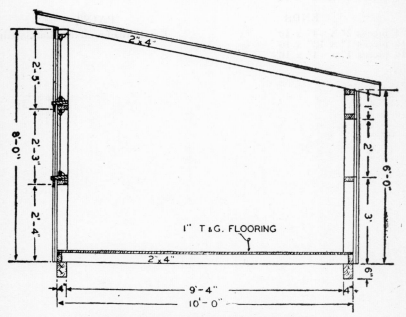

Fig. 264—Cross section (brooder house).

Bill of Materials for Mississippi Brooder House

RUNNERS

2 pieces 4" x 6" x 14'

FLOOR JOISTS

7 pieces 2" x 4" x 10'

ROOF

7 pieces 2" x 4" x 12'
21 pieces 1" x 8" x 14'—shiplap
13 pieces 6-foot V-crimped galvanized iron roofing not less than 29-gauge or 1½ squares of composition roofing.

FLOOR

40 pieces 1" x 4" x 12'—flooring

FRONT

2 Pieces 2" x 4" x 12'
2 pieces 2" x 4" x 8'
5 pieces 1" x 12" x 16'
6 pieces 1" x 4" x 16'

ENDS

4 pieces 2" x 4" x 10'
10 pieces 1" x 12" x 16'
10 pieces 1" x 4" x 16'

BACK

4 pieces 2" x 4" x 12'
6 pieces 1" x 12" x 12'
6 pieces 1" x 4" x 12'

PERCHES

6 pieces 2" x 2" x 12'

WINDOWS

4 frames 24" x 26"—to fit front openings

HARDWARE

4 door latches
1 pair 6" strap hinges for east door
3 pairs 4" strap hinges
15 lbs. 8-penny nails
5 lbs. 16-penny nails
10 feet 30" wide 1" mesh poultry wire

PAINT

1 gal. ready mixed house paint

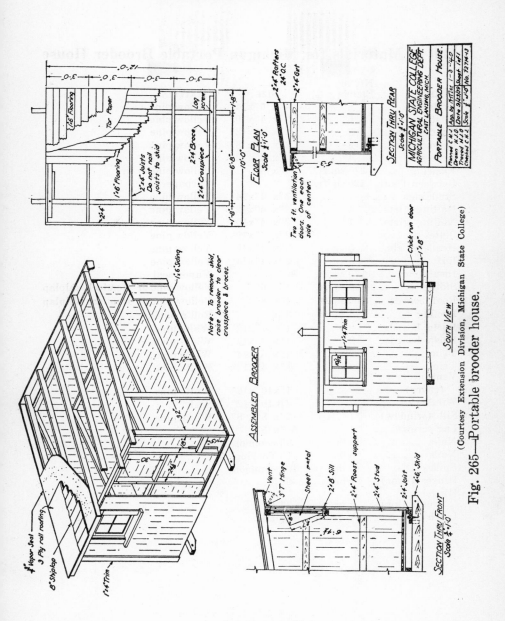

Fig. 265—Portable brooder house.

(Courtesy Extension Division, Michigan State College)

Bill of Materials for Michigan Portable Brooder House

Use	No. of Pieces	Size	Material
Skids	2	4"x 6"x14'	Yellow pine
Joists	5	2"x 4"x10'	Yellow pine
Headers (joist)	2	2"x 4"x12'	Yellow pine
Crosspieces	2	2"x 4"x 8"	Yellow pine
Braces	4	2"x 4"x 2'	Yellow pine
Flooring	270 sq. ft.	1"x 6"	Yellow pine or fir
Between floors	120 sq. ft.		Tarpaper
Studdings	4	2"x 4"x14'	Yellow pine
Nailing girts	4	2"x 4"x12'	Yellow pine
Nailing girts	1	2"x 4"x10'	Yellow pine
Plates	2	2"x 4"x10'	Yellow pine
Headers, etc.	3	2"x 4"x12'	Yellow pine
Rafters	6	2"x 4"x14'	Yellow pine
Insulation	170 sq. ft.	¾"	Vapor-seal
Siding	400 sq. ft.	1"x 6"	Yellow pine or Hemlock shiplap
Roof boards	200 sq. ft.	1"x 8"	Yellow pine or Hemlock shiplap
Roofing	175 sq. ft.	3-ply	Roll roofing
Facia boards	2	1"x 4"x12'	White pine
Facia boards	2	1"x 4"x14'	White pine
Trim	2	1"x 4"x14'	White pine
Trim	4	1"x 4"x12'	White pine
Ventilators (eaves)	2	1"x10"x12'	White pine
Windows	2	4 lt.10"x12"	Sash
Sill (window)	1	2"x 8"x 8"	White pine
Lag screws	4	⅜"x 5"	
Nails	15 lb.	8d common	
Nails	3 lb.	6d flooring	
Spikes	5 lb.	16d common	
Hinges (door)	1 pr.	6" T	
Hinges (ventilator)	4 pr.	3" T	
Latch	1	Small	

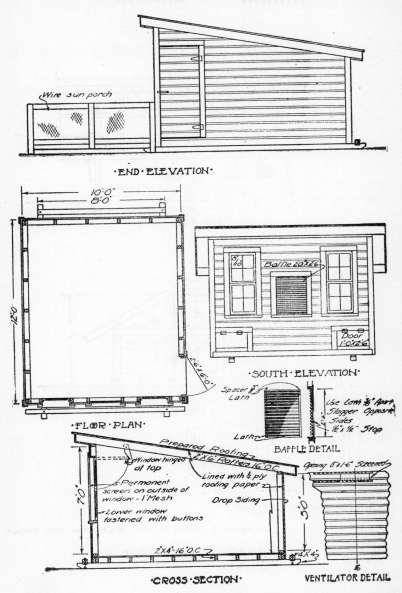

· END · ELEVATION ·

· FLOOR · PLAN ·

· SOUTH · ELEVATION ·

BAFFLE DETAIL

· CROSS · SECTION ·

VENTILATOR DETAIL

(Courtesy Extension Division, University of Wisconsin)

Fig. 266—Plan for an 8 x 12 foot or 10 x 12 foot colony house.

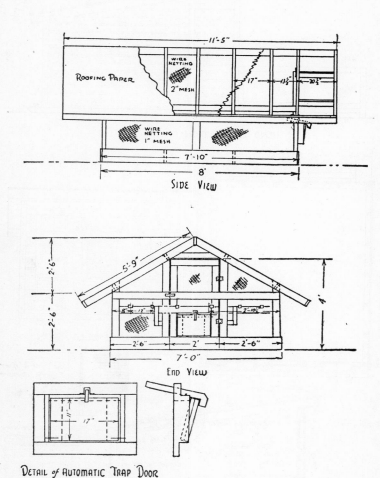

SIDE VIEW

END VIEW

DETAIL of AUTOMATIC TRAP DOOR

(Courtesy Extension Division, Washington State College)

Fig. 267—Range shelter.

Bill of Materials for Range Shelter

Use	No. Pieces	Size	Length
Sills	2	1 x 6	7'-10"
Sills	2	1 x 6	7'-10"
Floor braces	1	1 x 6	7'-10"
Floor braces	2	1 x 6	6'-10"
Studs	6	2 x 3	2'-10"
Studs	4	2 x 3	4'- 3"
Girts	2	1 x 3	7'- 0"
Girts	1	1 x 3	7'- 0"
Girts	2	1 x 3	2'- 6"
Rafters	18	1 x 4	5'- 5"
Ridgeboard	1	1 x 4	11'- 5"
Eavesboards	2	1 x 3	11'- 5"
Brace over door	1	1 x 3	2'- 0"
Roosts	6	2 x 2	7'-10"
Roost supports	4	1 x 3	2'-10½"
Door	2	1 x 3	3'- 6"
Door	4	1 x 3	2'- 0"
Laths	24		
Roofing		1½ rolls 36" 2-ply roofing paper	

Hardware

Wire for sides 36' of 1" mesh; 2' wide poultry netting

Wire for floor 16' of 1½" mesh 4' wide poultry netting No. 16 gauge

Wire for roof, 23' of 2" mesh 6' wide poultry netting

Nails—2 lbs. 8d

Nails—1 lb. 6d

Staples—1 lb.

Hinges—1 pr. 2"

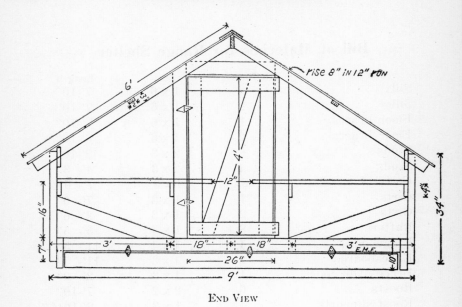

END VIEW

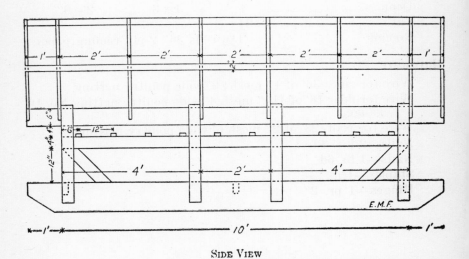

SIDE VIEW

(Courtesy Extension Division, Pennsylvania State College)

Fig. 268—Summer shelter for pullets

Bill of Materials for Pennsylvania Summer Shelter for Pullets

	Detailed Bill	Order Bill
Skids	2—2"x10"x12'	2—2"x10"x12'
Sills	2—2"x 4"x 8' 8"	11—2"x 4"x12'
Floor joists	3—2"x 4"x 9' 8"	
Spacer	2—2"x 4"x 2' 7"	
Spacer	2—2"x 4"x 1' 4"	
Studs	8—2"x 4"x 2'10"	
Studs	4—2"x 4"x 4' 6"	
Braces	4—2"x 4"x 3' 3"	
Braces	4—2"x 4"x 2'	
Rafters	16—1"x 3"x 6'	8—1"x 3"x12'
Rafter spacers	2—1"x 2"x12'	9—1"x 2"x12'
Perches	20—1"x 2"x 4'	
Ridge beam	1—1"x 4"x12'	5—1"x 4"x12'
Ridge cap	2—1"x 4"x12'	
Door	2—1"x 4"x 4'	
Door	2—1"x 4"x 2' 3"	
Door	1—1"x 4"x 4' 9"	
Tie beams	2—1"x 4"x 2'12"	
Perch supports	4—1"x 4"x10'	4—1"x 4"x10'
Plates	2—1"x 6"x12'	2—1"x 6"x12'
Base boards	2—1"x 6"x 8' 8"	2—1"x 6"x10'
Roof (or)	2—6' x12' wall board	2—6' x12' wall board
Roof (or)	2—6' x12' corrugated roofing	2—6' x12' corrugated roofing
Shingles	1½ square	1½ square

HARDWARE

Wire	55 ft.—1" mesh 2' wide
Wire	30 ft.—1" or 1½" mesh 3' wide (16 gauge)
Nails	3 lbs.—20d
Nails	2 lbs.—8d
Nails	2 lbs.—8d finish
Nails	3 lbs.—1½" galvanized roofing
Staples	2 lbs.—wire
Hinges	4 pair—3" strap

PAINT—Asphalt paint, 2 gallons

Fig. 269—A convertible poultry shelter house.

The shelter house illustrated above is so planned that it can be used with open sides and ends for hot weather, or it can be enclosed as is shown, for early pullets. And, by further enclosing the front end, it can be pressed into service as a brooder house. The lower illustration shows one end and two sides closed for early season use on the range. If the house is used for brooding, the front end could also be enclosed.

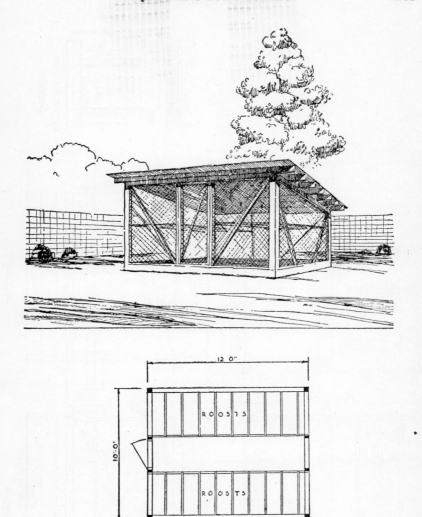

(Courtesy Extension Division, University of Georgia)

Fig. 270—"Knock-down" type range shelter.

"This knock-down type of range shelter has also been used for brooding baby chicks and turkey poults. When used as a brooder house, it is necessary to have a floor and to tack cheap building paper around the sides."

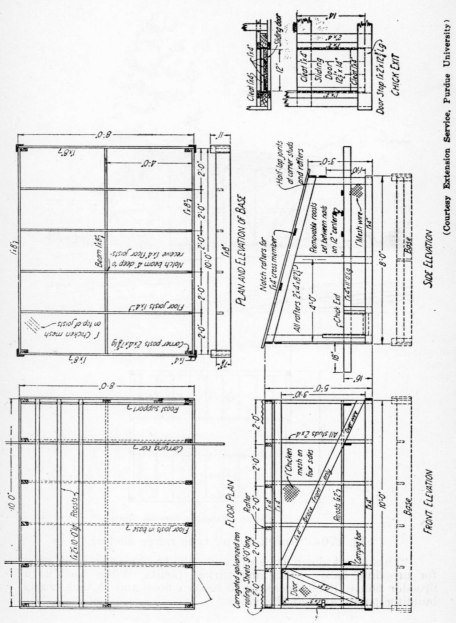

CHICK EXIT

PLAN AND ELEVATION OF BASE

SIDE ELEVATION

FLOOR PLAN

FRONT ELEVATION

(Courtesy Extension Service, Purdue University)

Fig. 271—Summer shelter for pullets.

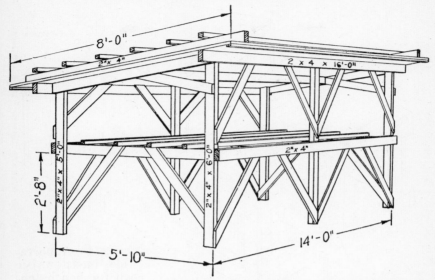

(Courtesy Extension Division, University of Minnesota)

Fig. 272—Plan of turkey range shelter.

"There is a solid roof on this shelter with additional roosts set on 2 x 4's. Birds will take to the roof in good weather so one might as well provide something for them to sit on. Many growers build this shelter on skids for easy moving. In a large flock, these shelters may be set back to back."

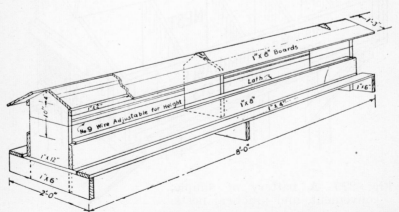

(Courtesy Extension Division, University of Missouri)

Fig. 273—A large range feeder for turkeys.

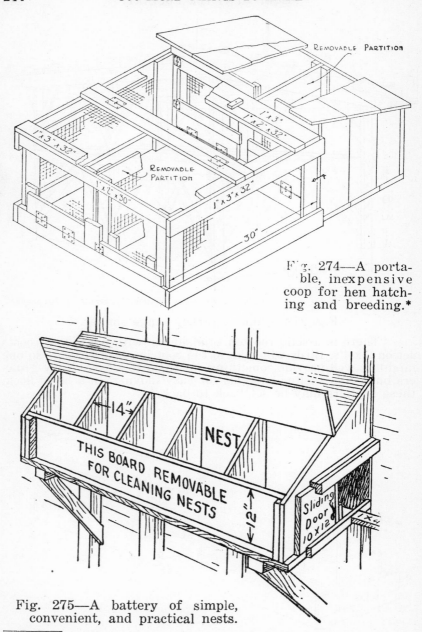

Fig. 274—A porta-
ble, inexpensive
coop for hen hatch-
ing and breeding.*

Fig. 275—A battery of simple,
convenient, and practical nests.

---

* Figures 274 and 275 courtesy Agricultural Experiment Station, Kansas State College.

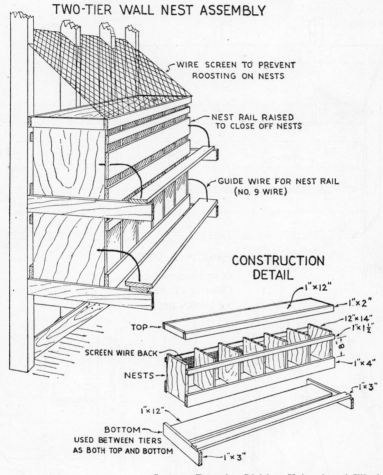

TWO-TIER WALL NEST ASSEMBLY

WIRE SCREEN TO PREVENT ROOSTING ON NESTS

NEST RAIL RAISED TO CLOSE OFF NESTS

GUIDE WIRE FOR NEST RAIL (NO. 9 WIRE)

CONSTRUCTION DETAIL

1"×12"

1"×2"

12"×14"
1"×1½"

TOP

8"

1"×4"

SCREEN WIRE BACK

NESTS

1"×3"

1"×12"

BOTTOM
USED BETWEEN TIERS
AS BOTH TOP AND BOTTOM

1"×3"

(Courtesy Extension Division, University of Illinois)

Fig. 276—Open nests.

"These wire-back open nests built in sections allow for plenty of ventilation and easy cleaning, two important considerations. The size of the nest is governed by the kind of chicken that is to use it. A large bird needs a nest measuring 14 by 14 inches. Smaller birds, such as leghorns, need only 12 x 12-inch nests. For every 100 hens there should be 20 nests."

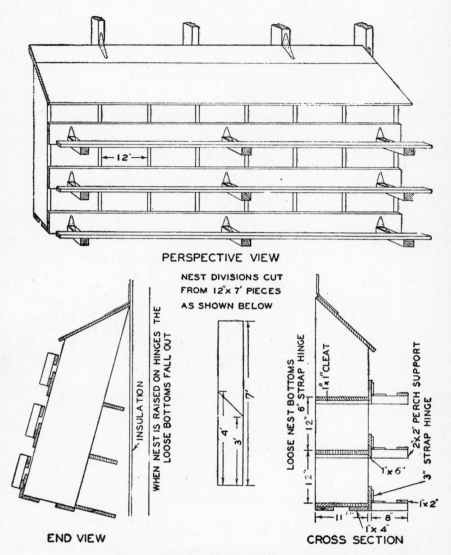

PERSPECTIVE VIEW

NEST DIVISIONS CUT
FROM 12"x 7' PIECES
AS SHOWN BELOW

END VIEW   CROSS SECTION

(Courtesy Extension Division, Michigan State Agricultural College)

Fig. 277—Battery of loose bottom nests.

Bill of Materials for Loose Bottom Nests
(21 Nests)

Nest divisions _____ 2—1″ x 12″ x 14′
Front and top _____ 2—1″ x 6 ″ x 16′
Top and nest bottoms _____ 2—1″ x 12″ x 16′
Bottoms _____ 1—1″ x 4″ x 16′
Perches _____ 3—1″ x 2″ x 8′
Cleats _____ 2—1″ x 1″ x 14′
Perch support _____ 1—2″ x 2″ x 8′
Hinges _____ 9—3″ tee
Hinges _____ 2—6″ strap

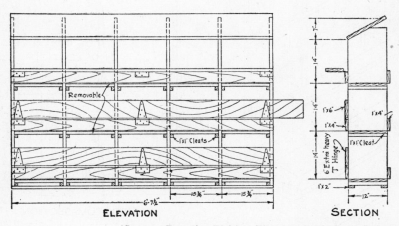

ELEVATION   SECTION

(Courtesy Extension Division, Wisconsin Agricultural College)

Fig. 278—Nests along side wall.

The T-hinges are placed on the running boards backward so as to act like brackets during the day and can be closed at night.

Bill of Materials for Nests Along Wall

3 pieces 1″ x 12″ x 4′-3″ long   6 pieces 1″ x 12″ x 3′-3½″ long
7 pieces 1″ x 4″ x 6′-7½″ long   12 pieces 1″ x 1″ x 12″ long
3 pieces 1″ x 6″ x 6′-8″ long   9 extra heavy T hinges
1 piece 1″ x 6″ x 7′-6″ long   No. 10 screws, ¾″
1 piece 1″ x 8″ x 6′-8″ long   ¾ lbs. 6d box nails

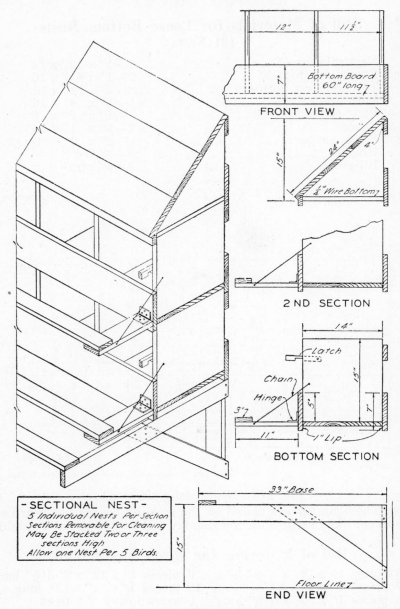

FRONT VIEW

2 ND SECTION

BOTTOM SECTION

- SECTIONAL NEST -
5 Individual Nests Per Section
Sections Removable for Cleaning
May Be Stacked Two or Three
sections High
Allow one Nest Per 5 Birds.

END VIEW

(Courtesy Extension Division, University of Maine)

Fig. 279—Nests.

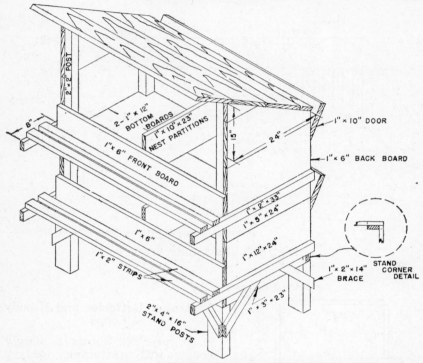

(Courtesy Extension Division, Ohio State University)

Fig. 280—Box nests. They can be made any desired length. Six-inch boards in front and rear hold the litter. A 10-inch board is hinged to remove the eggs.

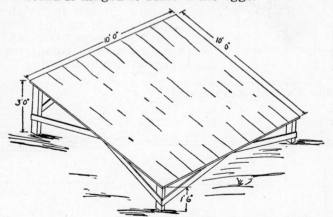

(Courtesy Extension Division, University of Minnesota)

Fig. 281—Shade shelter.

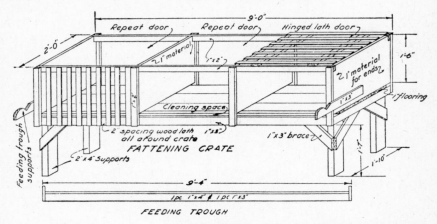

(Courtesy Extension Division, University of Arizona)

Fig. 282—Fattening crate.

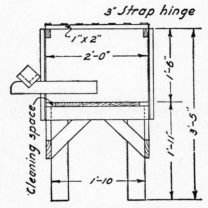

(Courtesy University of Arizona.)

Fig. 283—Fattening crate, end view.

Fattening Batteries and Broody Coops

"Figure 282 shows a simply constructed fattening battery which may well be used as a broody coop. This coop may be constructed almost entirely of ½-inch mesh hardware cloth if waste lumber material is not available. It may be constructed as a single compartment battery or a series of compartments as shown in the drawing."

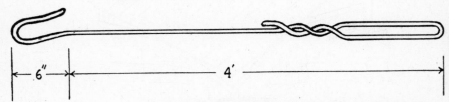

(Courtesy Extension Division, University of Missouri)

Fig. 284—Catching hook (homemade).

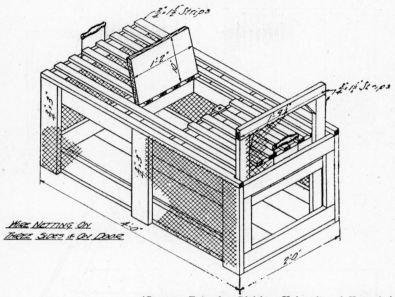

(Courtesy Extension Division, University of Kentucky)

Fig. 285—A catching coop.

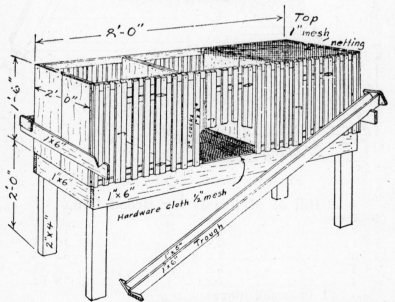

(Courtesy Extension Division, Texas A. and M. College)

Fig. 286—Fattening coop.

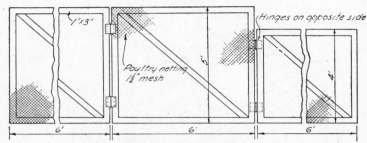

FOLDING CATCHING FRAME
Suitable for 125-150 bird pen
(Courtesy Extension Division, University of Maine)

Fig. 287—Catching crate.

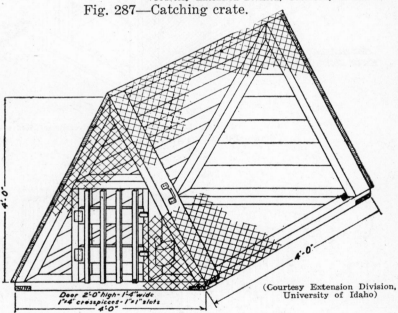

(Courtesy Extension Division,
University of Idaho)

Fig. 288—Brood coop for turkeys.

Bill of Materials for Brood Coop

No. Pieces	Size	Length
2	2 x 4	16 Ft.
1	2 x 4	10 Ft.
5	1 x 6	12 Ft.
1	1 x 4	4 Ft.
1	1 x 1	8 Ft.

1 Pr. small hinges.
7 Ft. of 1-inch mesh netting 4 Ft. wide.
1 strip rolled roofing 14 Ft. long.

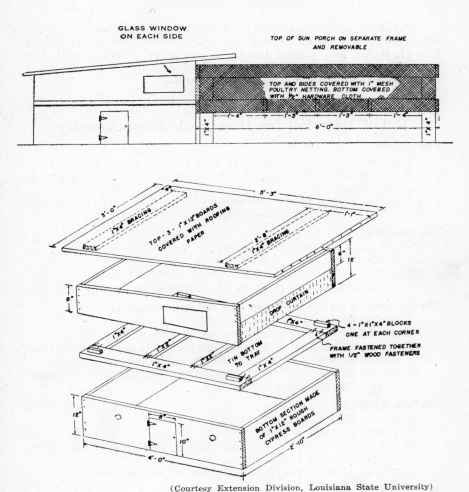

(Courtesy Extension Division, Louisiana State University)

Fig. 289—Homemade lamp brooder for 75 to 100 chicks.

"The brooder is heated with an ordinary low type kitchen lamp. (The type of lamp usually fastened on the wall.) In placing the lamp, care should be taken so as to allow about 1 inch space between the top of the lamp chimney and the floor of the top section. During extreme cold spells it will probably be necessary to use two lamps in heating the brooder. The bottom of the brooder is covered with tin. The tin that is nailed to the frame should come next to the lamp."

"A more uniform distribution of heat in the brooder may be obtained by the use of a one-gallon syrup bucket filled two-thirds full of water and placed inside the brooder directly over the lamp. The bucket should be covered with a lid in which holes have been made to allow escape of steam."

Bill of Materials for Homemade Lamp Brooder

For Roof:

   3 pieces 1″ x 12″ x 5′-3″—To nail roofing paper on.
   2 pieces 1″ x 4″ x 2′-7″—For cleats to hold top planks together.
   1 piece roofing paper 36″ wide, 5′-5″ in length to cover top.
         (Cement outside edge with roof tar.)

Top Section:

   2 pieces 1″ x 12″ x 4′ for sides.
   1 piece 1″ x 8″ x 2′ 8″ for back
   1 piece 1″ x 6″ x 2′-8″ for upper part of opening in front section leaving opening to allow chicks to run on porch.

Tin Bottom to go between top and bottom sections:

   1 piece tin 2′-10″ wide by 4′ long.
   2 pieces 1″ x 4″ by 2′-2″ long for braces to hold tin.
   2 pieces 1″ x 2″ by 2′-2″ long for center braces to hold tin.
   2 pieces 1″ x 4″ x 4′ for side of tin bottom.
   8 pieces 1″ x 1″ x 4″ long to prevent sliding of tin bottom and top section.

Bottom Section:

   2 pieces 1″ x 12″ x 4′ for sides.
   2 pieces 1″ x 12″ x 2′-8″ for ends.
   2 hinges for hanging door cut in one side of brooder (door 8″ wide and 10″ high).
   1 piece 1″ x 2″ x 2′ to reinforce weak section over door.

Sun Porch:

   4 pieces 1″ x 4″ x 6′ for sides of sun porch.
   4 pieces 1″ x 4″ x 2′-10″ for 2 ends of sun porch.
   3 pieces 1″ x 4″ x 2′-8″ for center bracing of sun porch.
   4 pieces 1″ x 4″ x 2′ for post of sun porch.
   1 piece ½″ hardware cloth 36″ wide, 6′-2″ long for bottom.
   1 piece 1″ mesh chick wire 12″ wide and 15′ long for covering two sides and one end of sun porch.

Sun Porch Cover:

   3-pieces 1″ x 4″ x 2′-2″ for ends and center of cover.
   2 pieces 1″ x 4″ x 6′ for sides of cover.
   1 piece 1″ mesh chick wire 36″ wide and 6′ long to cover top.

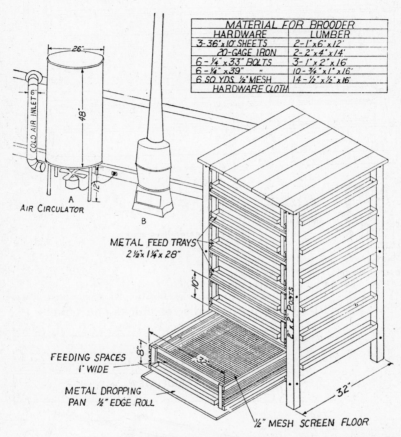

MATERIAL FOR BROODER	
HARDWARE	LUMBER
3 - 36"x 10' SHEETS	2 - 1"x6"x12'
20 - GAGE IRON	2 - 2"x 4"x 14'
6 - ¼"x 33" BOLTS	3 - 1"x 2"x 16'
6 - ¼"x 39" "	10 - ¾"x 1"x 16'
6 SQ. YDS. ½" MESH	14 - ½"x ½"x 16'
HARDWARE CLOTH	

COLD AIR INLET

26"

48"

A
AIR CIRCULATOR

B

METAL FEED TRAYS
2½"x 1¼"x 28"

10"

2 x 2" POSTS

FEEDING SPACES
1" WIDE

8"

32"

METAL DROPPING
PAN ½" EDGE ROLL

32"

½" MESH SCREEN FLOOR

(Courtesy Agricultural Experiment Station, Kansas State College)

Fig. 290—A homemade battery brooder for starting chicks.

"The air circulating tube (A) with electric fan provides an even temperature at all levels in the room. Heat is supplied by a brooder stove (B). The battery brooder (C) has six removable trays. The capacity is 600 chicks one to three weeks of age. The heating units (A) and (B) are sufficient for four to six batteries in one room."

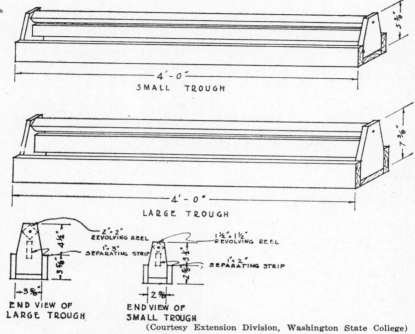

(Courtesy Extension Division, Washington State College)

Fig. 291—Watering troughs for chicks and pullets.

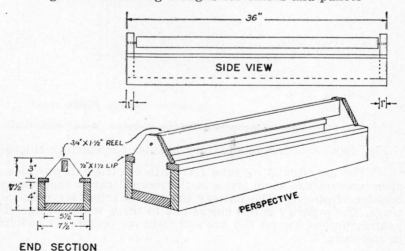

(Courtesy Extension Division, University of Missouri)

Fig. 292—Feed hopper for larger chicks. (Will accommodate 50 chicks 4 to 8 weeks old.)

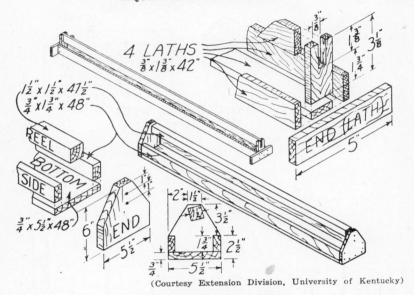

(Courtesy Extension Division, University of Kentucky)

Fig. 293—Chick feed hoppers.

Bill of Materials Needed for Feed Hopper

Lath Feeder
4 laths ⅜″ x ⅜″ x 48″
4 doz. 3d lath nails

Board Feeder
1 pc.   ¾″ x 5½″ x 48″ bottom
2 pcs. ¾″ x 5½″ x 6″ ends
2 pcs. ¾″ x 1¾″ x 48″ sides
1 pc.   1½″ x 1½″ x 47½″ reel
4 doz. 6d finishing nails

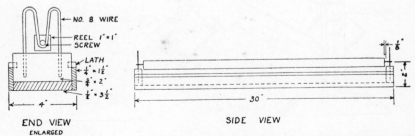

(Courtesy Extension Division, University of Florida)

Fig. 294—Reel-type chick feeder. A similar feeder, only larger, can be used for pullets or layers.

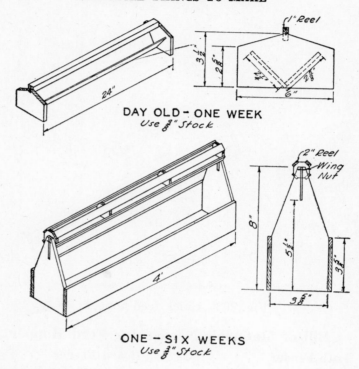

DAY OLD – ONE WEEK
Use ⅜" Stock

ONE – SIX WEEKS
Use ⅜" Stock

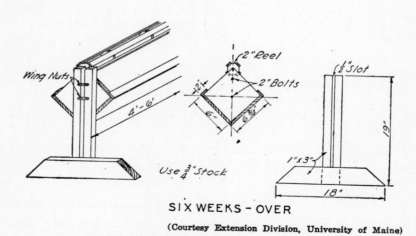

Use ¾" Stock

SIX WEEKS – OVER

(Courtesy Extension Division, University of Maine)

Fig. 295—Feed hopper equipment for chicks.

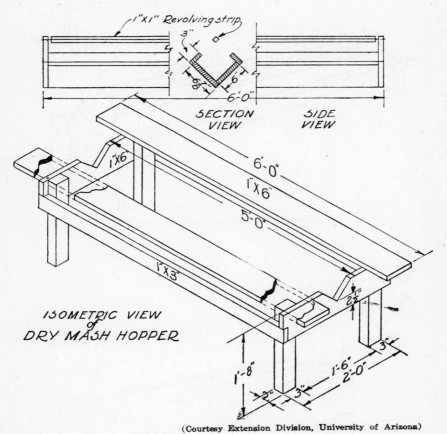

1"x1" Revolving strip

3"

SECTION
VIEW

SIDE
VIEW

6'-0"

1"x6"

6'-0"

1"x6"

5'-0"

1"x3"

ISOMETRIC VIEW
of
DRY MASH HOPPER

2½"

1'-8"

3"

2" 3"

1'-6"
2'-0"

(Courtesy Extension Division, University of Arizona)

Fig. 296—Dry-mash hopper.

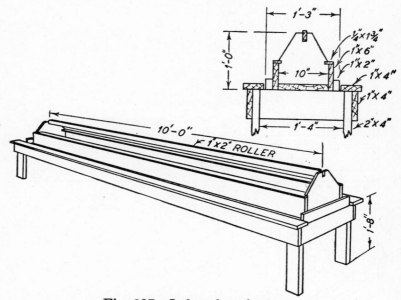

Fig. 297—Indoor hen feeder.*

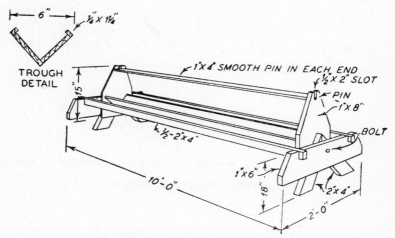

Fig. 298—Indoor hen feeder.

* Figures 297 and 298 courtesy Extension Division, Univ. of Illinois.

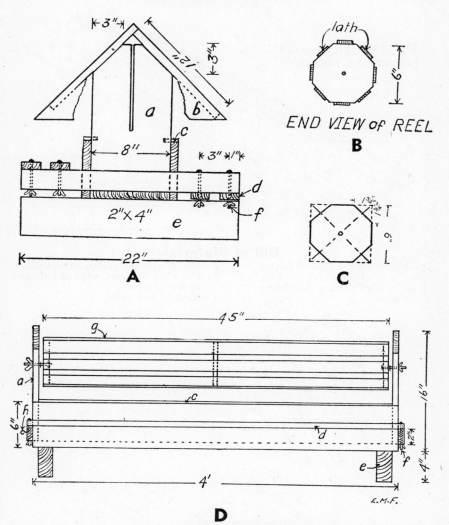

END VIEW of REEL
B

A

C

D

(Courtesy Extension Division, University of Vermont)

Fig. 299—Feeder.

a—end of feeder
b—end of roof
c—lath to prevent waste of food
d—adjustable bird support
e—support, for outdoor use

f—machine bolt with wing nut
g—reel made of lath
h—screw eye for suspending
    feeder

Fig. 300—Dry-mash
hopper and waterer.*

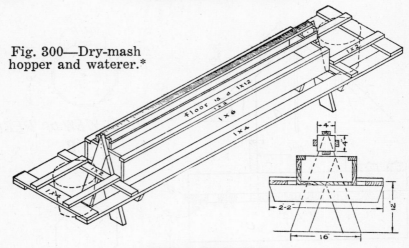

Bill of Materials

1—1"x12"x6' for floor of feeder
2—1"x 6"x7' for sides and ends
2—1"x 4"x6' for legs and cross
    pieces

2—1"x 4"x12' for rails and end ties
8—1"x 2"x6' for reel, edge of box, and
    bucket guides
1 pound 6d box nails

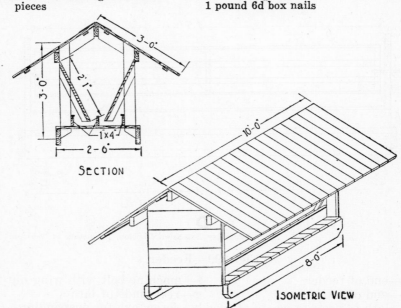

Fig. 301—Outdoor range feeder. Capacity, 20 bushels.

* Figures 300 and 301 courtesy Agricultural Experiment Station, Kansas State College.

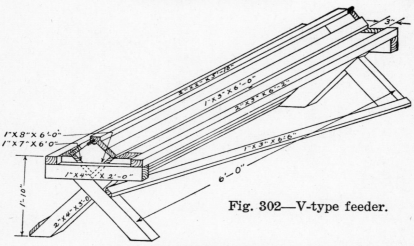

Fig. 302—V-type feeder.

(Courtesy Extension Division, North Carolina Agricultural College)

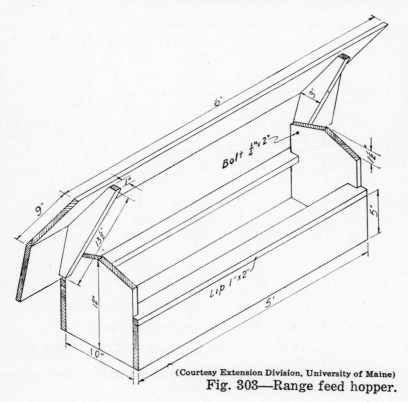

(Courtesy Extension Division, University of Maine)

Fig. 303—Range feed hopper.

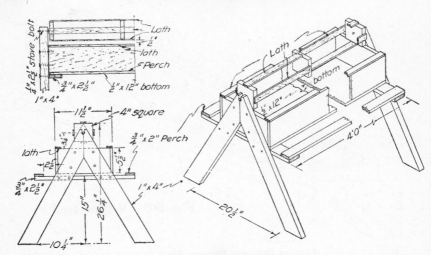

(Courtesy Extension Division, University of California)

Fig. 304—Open type mash hopper.

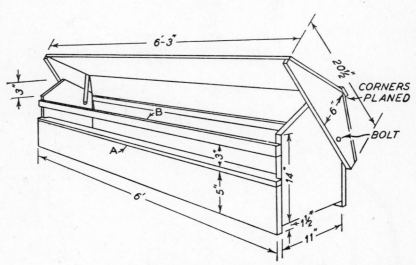

(Courtesy Extension Division, University of Illinois)

Fig. 305—Weatherproof range feeder.

A—Strip of 1½″ x ⅜″ material prevents feed from being picked out of feeder.

B—Strip of 1½″ x 1″ material placed here can be raised or lowered to suit the size of the birds.

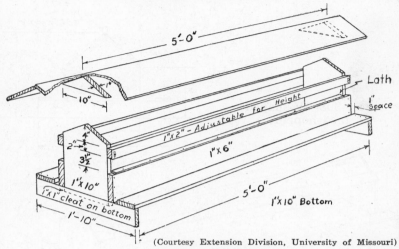

(Courtesy Extension Division, University of Missouri)

Fig. 306—Range feeder.

Bill of Materials

1 pc. 1" x 10"—14'	Bottom, ends and one side of cover
1 pc. 1" x 6"—12'	Sides and blocks under cover
1 pc. 1" x 12"— 6'	One side of cover
1 pc. 1" x 4"—14'	Steps and end braces
1 pc. 1" x 2"—10'	Adjustable side strips
10 feet lath	Top edge of feeder

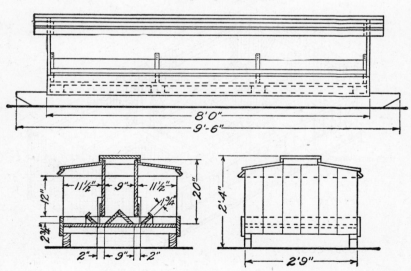

(Courtesy U. S. D. A.)

Fig. 307-—Dry-mash hopper.

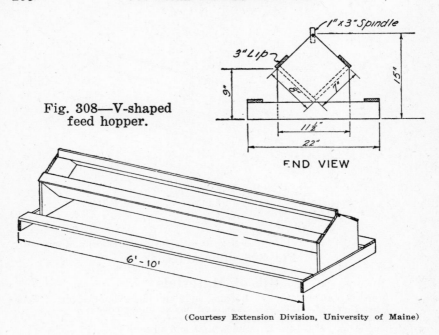

Fig. 308—V-shaped feed hopper.

END VIEW

(Courtesy Extension Division, University of Maine)

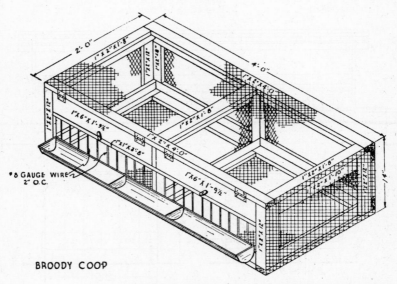

BROODY COOP

(Courtesy Extension Division, Washington State College)

Fig. 309—Broody coop.

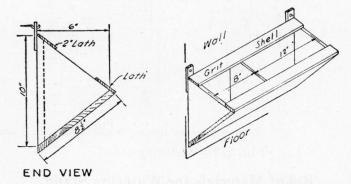

(Courtesy Extension Division, University of Maine)

Fig. 310—Shell and grit hopper.

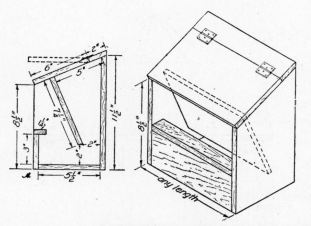

(Courtesy Extension Division, University of California)

Fig. 311—This grit, shell, or whole-grain hopper may be built any length desired and can be divided into compartments for grit, shell, or other materials.

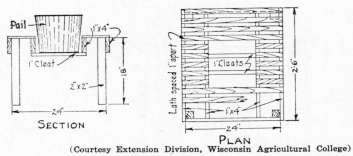

(Courtesy Extension Division, Wisconsin Agricultural College)

Fig. 312—Watering stand.

Bill of Materials for Watering Stand

4 pieces ½″ x 2″ x 18″ or 24″ long
4 pieces 1″ x 4″ x 2′6″ long
2 pieces 1″ x 4″ x 24″ long
2 pieces 1″ x 1″ x 14″ long

6 plastering lath
¼ lb. 6d box nails
¼ lb. 3d lath nails

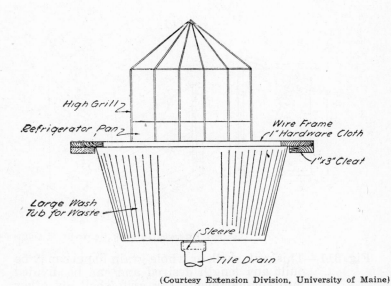

(Courtesy Extension Division, University of Maine)

Fig. 313—No-waste waterer.

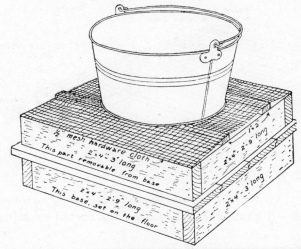

(Courtesy Extension Division, Texas A. and M. College)

Fig. 314—Watering device.

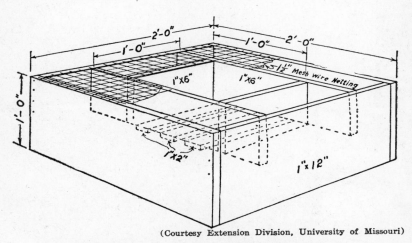

(Courtesy Extension Division, University of Missouri)

Fig. 315—Platform for water bucket or fountain.

Bill of Materials

1 pc. 1″ x 12″—8′   Sides of frame
1 pc. 1″ x 6″—6′   Inside frame
1 pc. 1″ x 2″—3′   Bottom of inside frame
2 feet 24″ width 1½-inch mesh hexagon wire netting

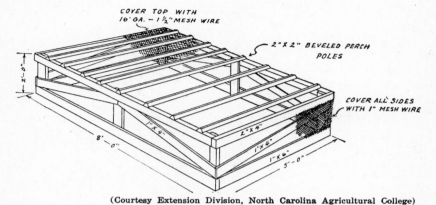

(Courtesy Extension Division, North Carolina Agricultural College)

Fig. 316—A practical and easily constructed roosting rack.

(From Vermont Circular 101. Photograph by Extension Division,
Pennsylvania State College)

Fig. 317—Water-tight bin mounted on truck used in carrying
feed to birds on range.

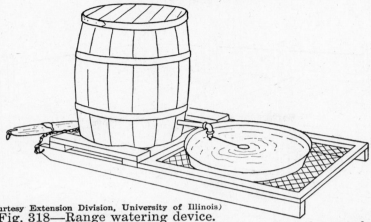

(Courtesy Extension Division, University of Illinois)
Fig. 318—Range watering device.

"The float attachment (*see drawing*) may be purchased from most any concern selling poultry supplies. The wire screen under the drinking trough or dish is a great help in keeping the water clean: ¾-inch mesh is recommended."

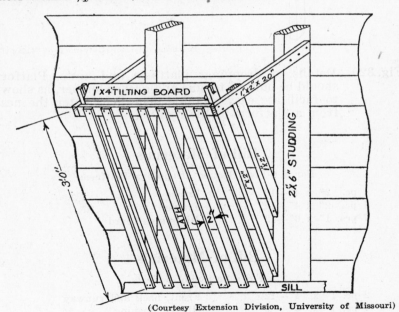

(Courtesy Extension Division, University of Missouri)
Fig. 319—Legume hay feeder

Bill of Materials

1 pc. 1″ x 2″—14′	Frame of rack
1 pc. 1″ x 4″— 2′	Reel
7 lath 3 feet long	Front of rack

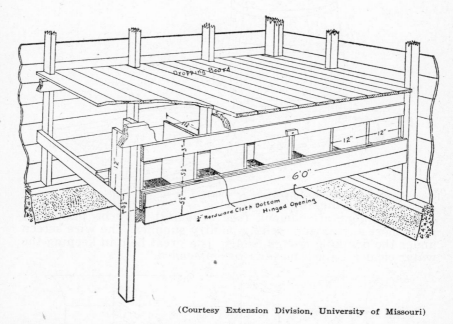

(Courtesy Extension Division, University of Missouri)

Fig. 320—Details of droppings platform and nests. Platform should be built of tongue and groove lumber, as shown, to facilitate easy cleaning. The hens enter the nests from a platform at the rear.

Bill of Materials

For a 6-Foot Section Droppings Platform

1 pc. 2″ x 4″—10′   Frame
1 pc. 2″ x 4″—12′   Frame
7 pcs. 1″ x 6″—12′   Droppings board

Bill of Materials

For a Section of 6 Nests

2 pc. 1″ x 4″—12′   Front, back and runway
1 pc. 1″ x 6″— 6′   Hinged opening
1 pc. 1″ x 12″— 8′   Ends and partitions
1 pc. 12″ width 6′ length ¼″ mesh hardware cloth—Bottom
1 pr. 4″ strap hinges

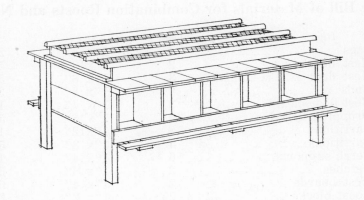

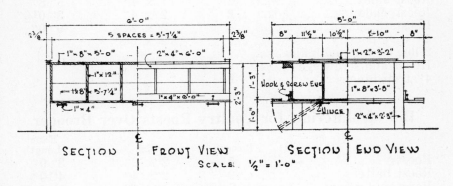

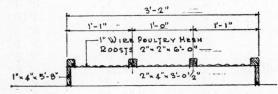

(Courtesy Roland A. Glaze, White Bear Lake, Minnesota)

Fig. 321—Combination roosts and nests.

Bill of Materials for Combination Roosts and Nests

Item	Pieces	Size	Exact Length
Legs	4	2″x 4″	2′ 3″
Nest floor	2	1″x12″	5′ 8¾″
Nest floor	3	1″x 8″	5′ 8¾″
Ends	4	1″x 8″	3′ 8″
Nest floor cleats	3	1″x 4″	1′ 9″
Dropping board	10	1″x 8″	5′ 0″
Partitions	8	1″x12″	1′ 3″
Partitions	4	1″x 8″	5′ 7¼″
Perch supports	6	1″x 4″	1′ 7½″
Perches	2	1″x 4″	6′ 0″
Nest boards	2	1″x 4″	6′ 0″
Roost blocks	2	1″x 2″	3′ 2″
Floor cleat	2	2″x 4″	6′ 0″
Roost sides	2	1″x 4″	5′ 8″
Roost ends	2	2″x 4″	3′ 0½″
Roosts	4	2″x 2″	6′ 0″
1″ wire poultry mesh	1	3′2″x 5′8″	
2 lbs. 6d common nails			
Hooks and screw eyes	6		
4″strap hinges	6		

Bill of Materials for Poultry Roosts Over Brooder

Item	Pieces	Size	Exact Length
Roosts	5	2″x 2″	3′ 9″
Roost battens	2	2″x 4″	4′10″
Roost end pieces	2	1″x 4″	3′ 4″
Stop strips	2	1″x 2″	4′10″
Dropping board	5	1″x10″	5′ 6″
Apron	2	1″x 6″	5′ 0″
Apron	2	1″x 6″	3′ 9″
Side braces (diagonal)	4	1″x 4″	2′ 6″
Legs	4	2″x 4″	2′ 3¼″
End braces	2	1″x 4″	3′ 7½″
Nails	½ lb.	16d	
Nails	1 lb.	8d	
Chicken wire mesh		20 sq. ft.	

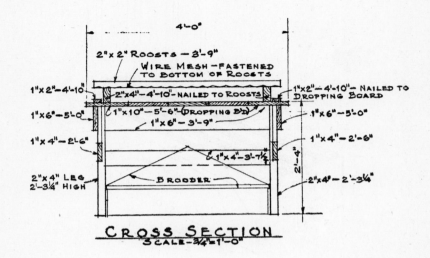

CROSS SECTION
SCALE - 3/4" = 1'-0"

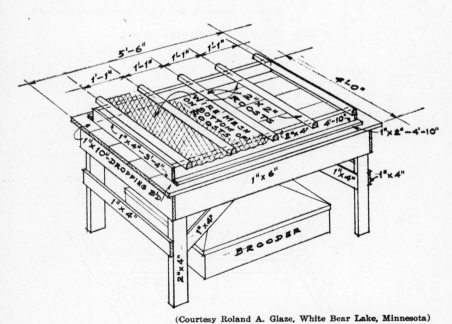

(Courtesy Roland A. Glaze, White Bear Lake, Minnesota)

Fig. 322—Poultry roosts over brooder.

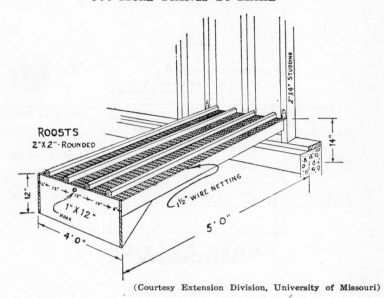

(Courtesy Extension Division, University of Missouri)

Fig. 323—Roosts and dropping pit.

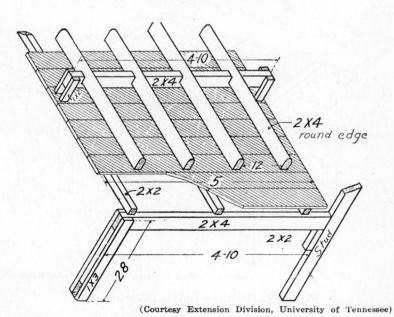

(Courtesy Extension Division, University of Tennessee)

Fig. 324—Roosts

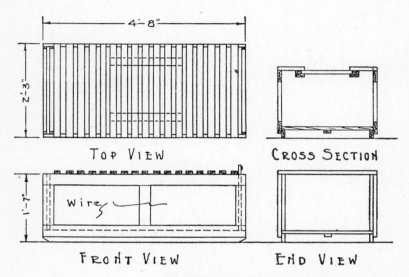

TOP VIEW   CROSS SECTION

FRONT VIEW   END VIEW

(Courtesy Extension Division, University of Illinois)

Fig. 325—Catching crate

Bill of Materials Needed

2 pcs. 1″x3″x5′
6 pcs. 1″x4″x1′6″
4 pcs. 1″x4″x5′ for side rails
14 board feet of flooring

70 linear feet 1″x2″ for slats
2 pcs. 1″x4″x8′ for end gates
14 linear feet of 12″ netting

Equipment for Swine

■ ■ ■

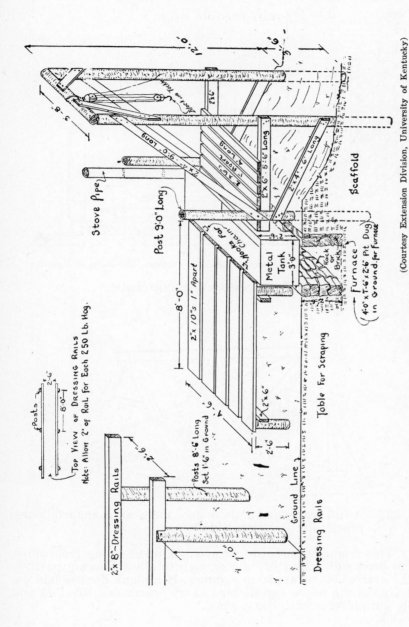

(Courtesy Extension Division, University of Kentucky)

Fig 326—Hog-butchering equipment.

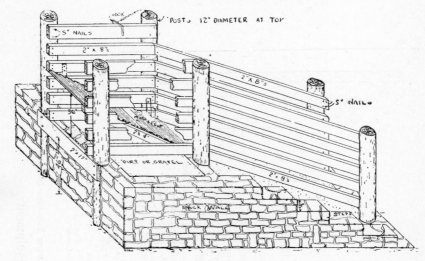

(Courtesy Extension Division, University of Kentucky)

Fig. 327—Livestock loading chute.

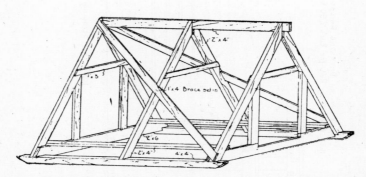

Fig. 328—A full frame and a plank floor make an A-shaped house
practically indestructible.*

"This frame permits the use of any kind of siding from shiplap to drop siding and is rigid enough to allow hinging part of
or the entire side as shade in summer. If a plank floor is laid on
this frame, the house can be made very warm and dry and entirely suitable for early farrowing."

---

* Figures 328 and 329 courtesy Extension Division, Univ. of Illinois.

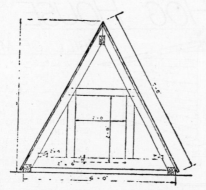

Fig. 329 — Even in A-shaped houses a pig rail will save the lives of young pigs.

"Because of the slope of the roof a pig rail or fender made of 2-by-4's as illustrated affords ample protection for young pigs. Runners made of 4-by-4's, if creosoted, will make the house more durable."

MATERIALS—6'x8' house. Runners, 2 pcs. 4"x4"x9'. A-frame, 6 pcs. 2"x4"x7'. Ties, 2 pcs. 2"x6"x6'. End studding, 4 pcs. 2"x4"x3'6" (one 14' length). Ridge board, 1 pc. 2"x4"x8'. Fenders, 2 pcs. 2"x4"x8'. Braces, 2 pcs. 1"x4"x12'. Drop siding, 175 bd. ft. vertical or horizontal. If vertical add 2 pcs. 2"x4"x8' for girts. Place girts midway between runner and ridge board. Nails, 15 pounds 7d and 16d. Hinges for doors if used. Paint ½ gal.

Materials for Floor—60 surface feet of 1" or 2" flooring. Use 1 pc. 2"x4'x8' batten between runners if 1" flooring is used. Add nails for flooring.

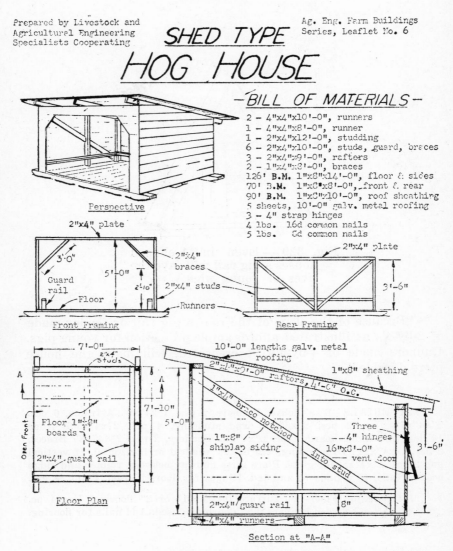

Prepared by Livestock and
Agricultural Engineering
Specialists Cooperating

SHED TYPE
HOG HOUSE

Ag. Eng. Farm Buildings
Series, Leaflet No. 6

—BILL OF MATERIALS—

2 — 4"x4"x10'-0", runners
1 — 4"x4"x8'-0", runner
1 — 2"x4"x12'-0", studding
6 — 2"x4"x10'-0", studs, guard, braces
3 — 2"x4"x9'-0", rafters
2 — 1"x4"x8'-0", braces
126' B.M. 1"x8"x14'-0", floor & sides
70' B.M. 1"x8"x8'-0", front & rear
90' B.M. 1"x8"x10'-0", roof sheathing
5 sheets, 10'-0" galv. metal roofing
3 — 4" strap hinges
4 lbs. 16d common nails
5 lbs. 8d common nails

Perspective

Front Framing

Rear Framing

Floor Plan

Section at "A-A"

(Courtesy Extension Division, Clemson Agricultural College)

Fig. 330—Shed type hog house.

Fig. 331—Shed-roof house.*

"If a frame of studding is used, either vertical or horizontal siding can be applied. The hinged front of this house is dropped from the top rather than raised from the bottom. This allows sunshine to penetrate the interior. Either matched or plain boards may be used on this frame. Projecting eaves afford some protection to the siding."

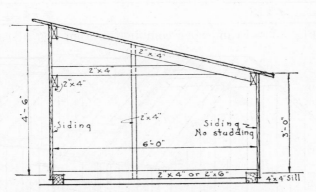

Fig. 332—Cross-section of shed roof house.

MATERIALS—6'x8' house. Runners, 2 pcs. 4"x4"x9'. Ties, 2 pcs. 2"x4"x6'. Plates, 2 pcs. 2"x4"x8'. End plates, 2 pcs. 2"x 4"x6'. Girts, 2 pcs. 2"x4"x5' and 1 pc. 2"x4"x8'. Purlin, 1 pc. 2"x4"x8'. Door trimmer, 1 pc. 2"x4"x4'. Siding, 130 bd. ft. (16' lengths). Roof sheathing, 80 bd. ft. shiplap (14' lengths crosswise; purlin not shown above). Roofing, 1 roll green slate surface. Nails. 10 pounds 7d and 16d. Hinges for doors if used. Paint, ½ gallon.

* Figures 331 and 332 courtesy Extension Division, Univ. of Illinois.

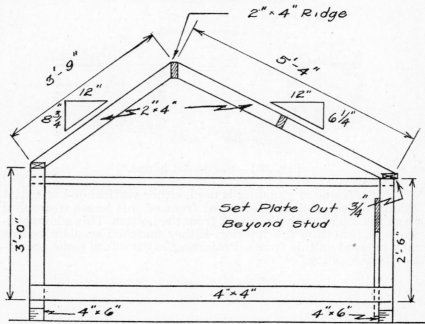

Fig. 333—Framework combination-roof hog house.*

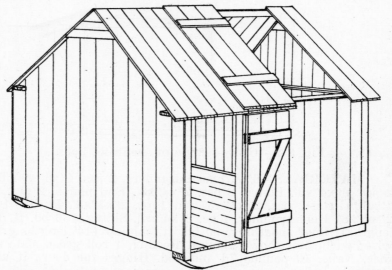

Fig. 334—Combination-roof individual hog house 6′ x 8′ in size.

* Figures 333 and 334 courtesy Extension Division. Univ. of **Missouri**.

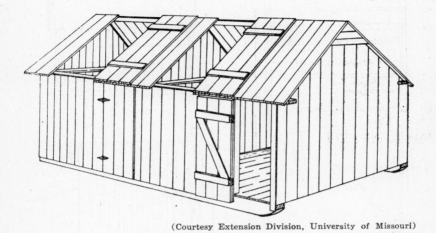

(Courtesy Extension Division, University of Missouri)

Fig. 335—Twin combination-roof house, 12'x8' in size.

Bill of Materials

2—4"x6"x12' No. 1 com. framing
2—4"x4"x 8' No. 1 com. framing
3—2"x5"x 6' No. 2 com. framing
3—2"x4"x 8' No. 2 com. framing
5—2"x4"x12' No. 2 com. framing
3—2"x4"x14' No. 2 com. framing
1—1"x6"x16' surfaced braces
14—1"x6"x 8' shiplap sheathing
14—1"x6"x12' shiplap sheathing
13—1"x6"x12' matched siding
6—1"x6"x 8' matched siding
10—1"x6"x10' matched siding
1—1"x8"x 8' surfaced partition
4—1"x6"x 8' surfaced partition
2—1"x4"x 8' surfaced door cleats
2—1"x4"x10' surfaced door cleats
4—1"x8"x10' surfaced door cleats

5 pr. 8" T hinges
2 pr. 6" T hinges
4 hasps
4—1/4"x9" bolts
4—1/4"x1 1/4"x1'8" flat bars
4 lbs. 16d com. nails
7 lbs. 8d com. nails
1 gal. barn paint
1 gal. carbolenium
     (skids and floor)

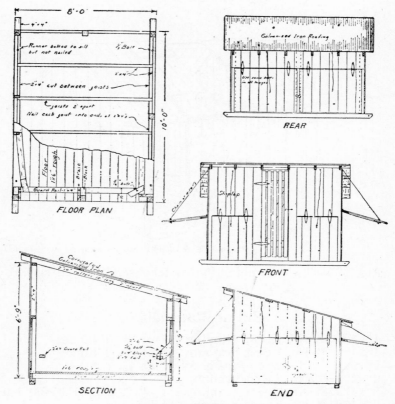

(Courtesy Extension Division, Texas A. and M. College)

Fig. 336—Portable farrowing house.

"The farrowing house plan shown above has given satisfactory results in Texas. Note that this house is so constructed that all sides can be raised to provide good ventilation in warm weather. A large number of openings, of course, increases the cost of the house. This house can be cheapened by closing one or both ends. If only one end is closed it is best to close the west end, because in summer the west doors should be closed each afternoon to prevent the sun from shining in. Therefore, the openings on the west end are not of as much value as the others."

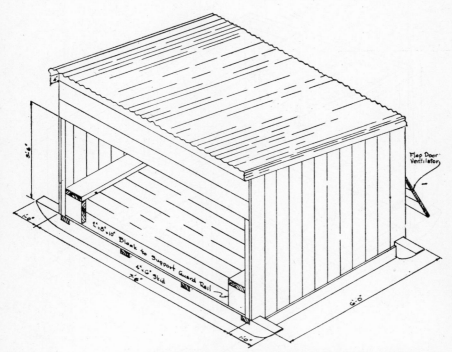

(Courtesy Extension Division, Alabama Polytechnic Institute)

Fig. 337—Portable farrowing house.

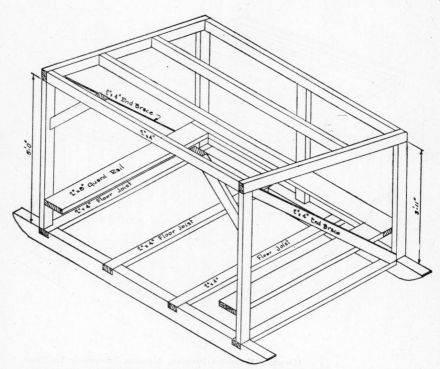

Fig. 338—Framework for farrowing house in Figure 337.

Fig. 339—Illinois sunshine house.*
The above picture is of a house 14 feet long.

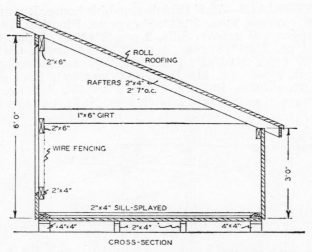

Fig. 340—Cross-section of Illinois sunshine house.

The wire hurdle across the front of the house can be built in permanently or made removable as desired.

* Figures 339 to 341 courtesy Extension Division, University of Illinois.

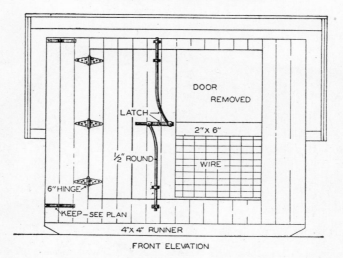

Fig. 341—Front elevation of Illinois sunshine house.

This simple latch does double duty; it keeps the door closed tightly and likewise holds the door firmly when it is open and folded back.

MATERIALS—7'x8' Illinois sunshine house. Runners, 2 pcs. 4"x4"x8' cypress, 2pcs. 2"x4"x8' cypress. Flooring, 18 pcs. 1"x 6"x7' tongue and groove. Sills, 2 pcs. 2"x4"x8', 2 pcs. 2"x4"x7'. Plates, 1 pc. 2"x4"x8' rear, 1 pc. 2"x6"x8' front. Girts, 2 pcs. 1"x6"x7', 1 pc. 2"x4"x8', 1 pc. 2"x6"x8' across doors. Siding, 170 bd. ft. 1"x6" No. 116 D. S. (12' lengths). Roof sheathing, 100 bd. ft. shiplap. Rafters, 4 pcs. 2"x4"x9'. Roofing, 1 square roll. Hinges, 6 pair strap, 2 latch sets. Nails, paint, wire extra.

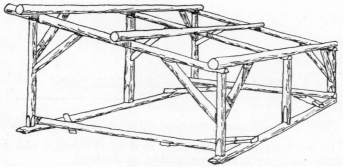

(Courtesy Extension Division, Ohio State University)

Fig. 342—Pole framework may be used for shed roof shelter.

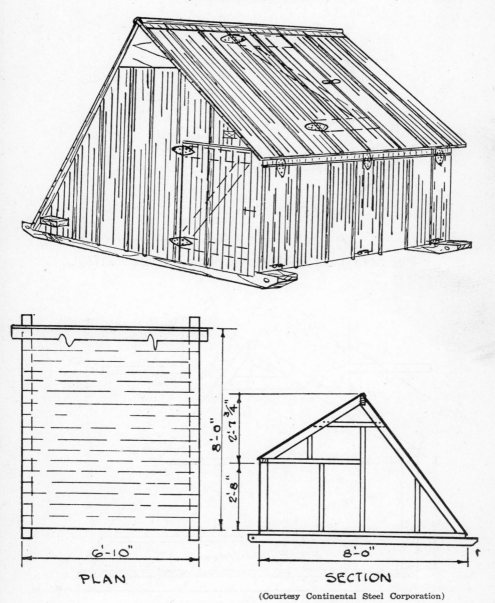

PLAN

SECTION

(Courtesy Continental Steel Corporation)

Fig. 343—Portable hog house.

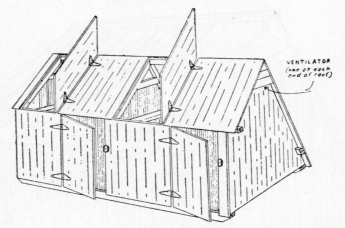

(Courtesy Extension Division, University of Missouri)

Fig. 344—Twin modified A-type house. Size 8'x11½'.

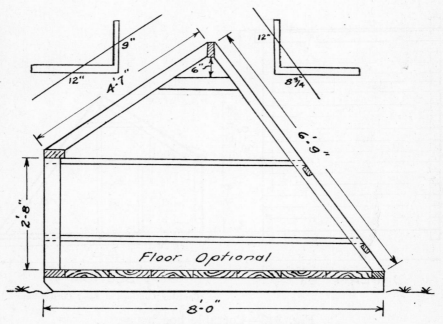

Fig. 345—East-end framework, modified A-type house.

Bill of Materials for Twin Modified A-type Hog House

2—4"x 4"x12' skids

2—2"x 6"x 8' sills

11—2"x12"x 8' floor

1—2"x 4"x12' tie under floor

1—2"x6"x12' plate

3—2"x4"x12' ridge, purlin

2—2"x4"x12' rafters

2—1"x6"x12' door battens

2—1"x6"x10' door battens

140 bd. ft. 4" car siding side ends

13—1"x12"x12' No. 1 Y.P. for roof

4—2"x 4"x 8' No. 1 Y.P. pig guards

4 pairs 8" tee hinges

3 lbs. 16d spikes

1½ lb. 10d common nails

3 lb. 8d common nails

2 lb. 4d common nails

4 doz. 8d cut nails

144 linear ft. metal battens

1 gal. barn paint

1 gal. carbolenium (skids and floor)

Bill of Materials for Modified Gable Roof Hog House

2 pcs. 1"x4"x16' door cleats

3 pcs. 2"x4"x10' guard rails and short rafters

4 pcs. 2"x4"x14' studs and long rafters

3 pcs. 2"x4"x16' framing

8 pcs. 2"x6"x12' floor

1 pc. 2"x8"x10' ridgeboard

2 pcs. 4"x6"x 8' rough lumber skids

19 pcs. 1"x6"x 8' roof (No. 116 siding)

16 pcs. 1"x6"x8' sides (No. 106 siding)

2 pcs. 1"x6"x10' ends (No. 106 siding)

9 pcs. 1"x6"x12' ends (No. 106 siding)

7 ⅜"x4" square head bolts

6 8" strap hinges

1 4" hasp and screws Nails and paint

Fig. 346—Modified gable roof individual hog house.*

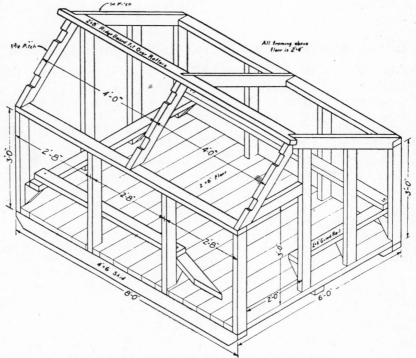

Fig. 347—Isometric view of frame work.

* Figures 346 and 347 courtesy Extension Division, Purdue University.

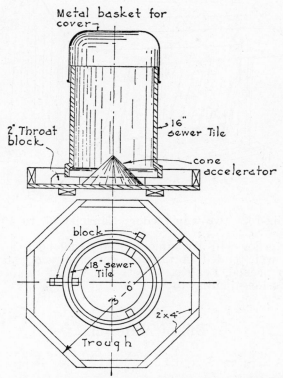

(Courtesy Agricultural Experiment Station, University of Illinois)

Fig. 348—Self feeder.

"This simple construction consists of an inverted sewer tile standing on three blocks in a shallow box which is square, round, or octagonal in shape. A barrel may be used in place of the tile if it is made fast against wind and hogs. A cone-shaped accelerator is set in the center of the box under the tile or barrel. This forces the grain outward into the box around the base of the tile, forming a trough. A large funnel, if inverted, may answer this purpose."

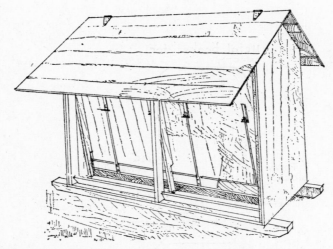

Fig. 349—Six-foot two-way feeder: Capacity 35 to 40 bushels.*

"This feeder will accommodate 50 to 60 head of fattening hogs when well tended. A tankage compartment can be partitioned off if needed. Length, 6 feet. The capacity can be greatly increased by lengthening to 8 or 10 feet."

Bill of Materials

Sills, cypress	2 pcs.	4"x 4"x7'
Floor, T. & G.	14 pcs.	1"x 6"x3'6"
Trough fronts	2 pcs.	2"x 4"x6'
Accelerator	2 pcs.	1"x10"x6'
Corner posts	6 pcs.	2"x 4"x4'
Supports	6 pcs.	2"x 4"x3'
Adjustable throat	2 pcs.	1"x 6"x6'
Top rails	2 pcs.	2"x 6"x6'
Rafters	6 pcs.	2"x 4"x1'8"
Ridge pole	1 pc.	2"x 4"x7'
Ends, T. & G.	20 pcs.	1"x 6"x3'6"
Bin fronts, T. & G.	16 pcs.	1"x 6"x6'
Battens	4 pcs.	1"x 6"x7'
Ridge	2 pcs.	1"x 3"x7'
Roof, shiplap or T. & G.	60 bd. ft.	1"x6"
1 Rod (thread and nut on each end)	⅜"x3'8"	
Strap hinges	3 pairs 6"	
Nails, assorted	10 pounds	
Paint	1 gallon	
Adjusting rods, flattened at one end	8—⅜" round	
Angles, for adjustment rods	8—¼"x1"	

* Figures 349 to 351 courtesy Agricultural Experiment Station. University of Illinois.

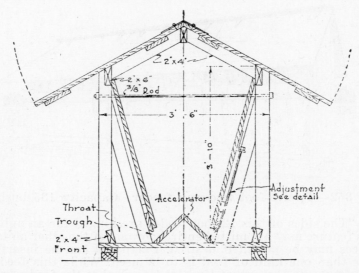

Fig. 350—Cross-section of the six-foot two-way feeder.

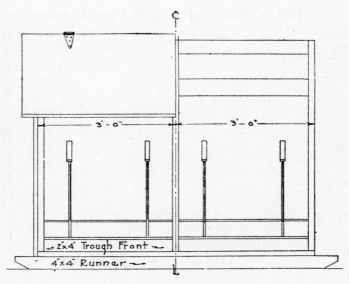

Fig. 351—Front elevation of the six-foot two-way feeder.

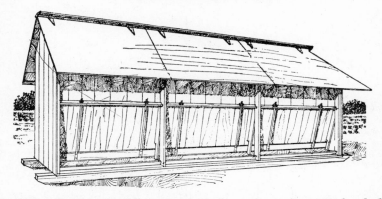

Fig. 352—Twelve-foot two-way feeder: Capacity 135 bushels.*

"The sides of this 12-foot feeder are hinged for an agitator. This feature may be omitted entirely or one of the other agitating devices may be put in if desired. Partitions can be inserted if more than one kind of feed is to be used. While this feeder is large, the center of gravity is kept low, so that the feeder cannot be upset easily. If the length is increased to 16 feet, the capacity will be 180 bushels."

Bill of Materials for 12-Foot Feeder

Large sills	2 pcs.	4"x6"x14'
Sleeper	1 pc.	2"x4"x12'
Floor, T. & G.	20 pcs.	2"x8"x 4'6"
Trough front	2 pcs.	2"x4"x12'
Accelerator, T. & G.	4 pcs.	1"x8"x12'
Studding	8 pcs.	2"x4"x 3'8"
Bin supports	8 pcs.	2"x4"x 2'
Adjustable throat	2 pcs.	1"x6"x12'
Top rails	2 pcs.	2"x6"x12'
Rafters	8 pcs.	2"x4"x 2'3"
Ridge pole	1 pc.	2"x6"x12'
Ridge cover	1 pc.	2"x6"x14'
Adjustment bars	2 pcs.	2"x3"x12'
	or	2"x4"x12'
Battens	4 pcs.	1"x8"x14'
Roof, ends, fronts, T. & G.	350 bd. ft.	1"x6"x16'
Rod (thread each end)	2 pcs.	⅝"x4'8"
Strap hinges (depending upon the number raised)	6 pairs 6"	
Nails, assorted	20 pounds	
Paint	2 gallons	
Adjustment rods, flattened at one end	12—⅝" round	

* Figures 352 to 354 courtesy Agricultural Experiment Station, University of Illinois.

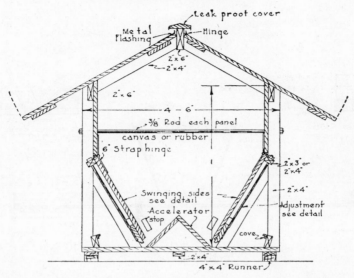

Fig. 353—Cross-section of 12-foot two-way feeder.

Note the swinging-side agitator and the adjustable throat. The size of this feeder calls for sturdy construction.

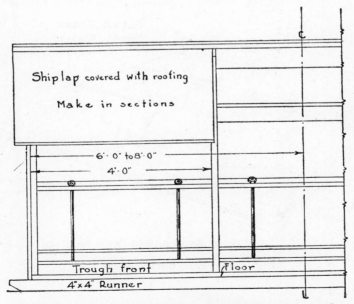

Fig. 354—Front elevation of large two-way feeder.

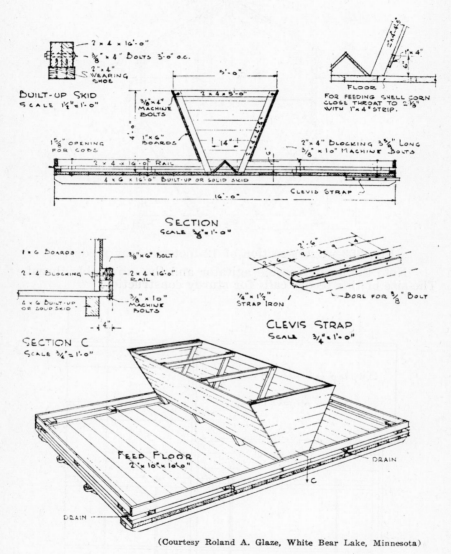

2 x 4 x 16'-0"
3/8" x 4" Bolts 3'-0" o.c.
2" x 4"
WEARING SHOE

BUILT-UP SKID
SCALE 1½" = 1'-0"

5'-0"

2 x 4 x 5'-0"

3/8" x 4"
MACHINE
BOLTS

1" x 6"
BOARDS

14"

2 x 4 x 16'-0"

2" x 4"

FLOOR

FOR FEEDING SHELL CORN
CLOSE THROAT TO 2½"
WITH 1" x 4" STRIP.

1⅝" OPENING
FOR CODS

2 x 4 x 16'-0" RAIL

2 x 4 BLOCKING 3⅝" LONG
3/8" x 10" MACHINE BOLTS

4 x 6 x 16'-0" BUILT-UP OR SOLID SKID

CLEVIS STRAP

16'-0"

SECTION
SCALE 3/8" = 1'-0"

1 x 6 BOARDS

2 x 4 BLOCKING

4 x 6 BUILT-UP
OR SOLID SKID

4"

3/8" x 6" BOLT

2 x 4 x 16'-0"
RAIL

3/8" x 10"
MACHINE
BOLTS

SECTION C
SCALE 3/4" = 1'-0"

2'-6"

2 - 6

9

2" x 6"
9

4

¼" x 1½"
STRAP IRON

BORE FOR 3/8" BOLT

CLEVIS STRAP
SCALE 3/4" = 1'-0"

FEED FLOOR
2" x 10" x 10'-0"

DRAIN

C

DRAIN

(Courtesy Roland A. Glaze, White Bear Lake, Minnesota)

Fig. 355—Ear corn feeder.

Bill of Materials for Ear Corn Feeder

Item	Pieces	Size	Exact Length
Skids	4	4"x 6"	16'0"
Floor	20	2"x10"	10'0"
Side rails	2	2"x 4"	16'0"
Side rails	4	2"x 4"	4'7"
Side rails	2	2"x 4"	6'4"
End rails	2	2"x 4"	9'8¾"
End rails	2	2"x 4"	9'0"
Rail blocking	14	2"x 4"	0'3⅝"
Hopper studs	8	2"x 4"	4'5"
Hopper ties	4	2"x 4"	5'0"
Blocking at end of hopper	4	2"x 4"	2'6"
Hopper bottom	2	1"x10"	9'4½"
Hopper siding		1"x 6"	60 B.F. Random Lengths

14 ⅜"x10" machine bolts   3 lbs. 16d common nails
 8 ⅜"x 6" machine bolts   2 lbs. 8d common nails
 8 ⅜"x 4" machine bolts   2 pcs. strap iron ¼"x1½"x5'0"

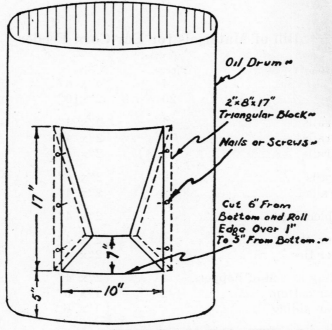

Oil Drum ~

2"x 8"x 17"
Triangular Block ~

Nails or Screws ~

Cut 6" From
Bottom and Roll
Edge Over 1"
To 3" From Bottom. ~

17"

7"

5"

10"

(Courtesy Extension Division, Michigan State College)

Fig. 356—An improvised self-feeder made from an old oil drum.

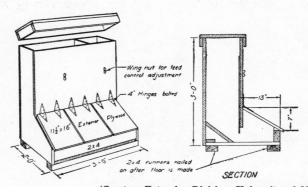

Wing nut for feed
control adjustment

4" Hinges bolted

11½"x16"   Exterior   Plywood

2x4

2'-0"

3'-0"

2x4 runners nailed
on after floor is made

3'-0"

13"

7"

SECTION

(Courtesy Extension Division, University of Minnesota)

Fig. 357—Small self-feeder—In self-feeding, each space in this
feeder will serve four or five pigs. It is easily constructed at home and will serve the needs of the small
producer satisfactorily.

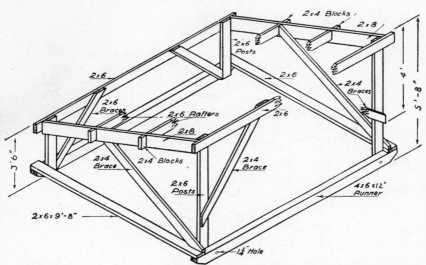

(Courtesy Extension Division, University of Minnesota)

Fig. 358—Hog shade.

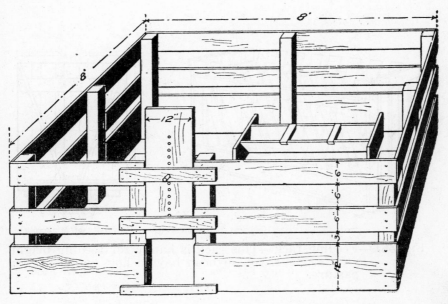

(Courtesy U. S. D. A.)

Fig. 359—Feeding pen for small pigs.

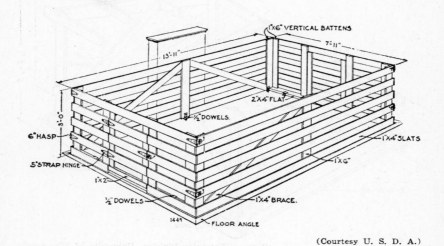

(Courtesy U. S. D. A.)

Fig. 360—Portable scale rack.

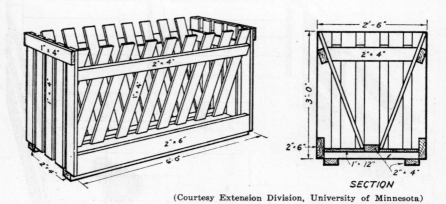

(Courtesy Extension Division, University of Minnesota)

Fig. 361—Feeding rack—This rack is handy for feeding bright
alfalfa, clover, or soybean hay to hogs while not on
pasture.

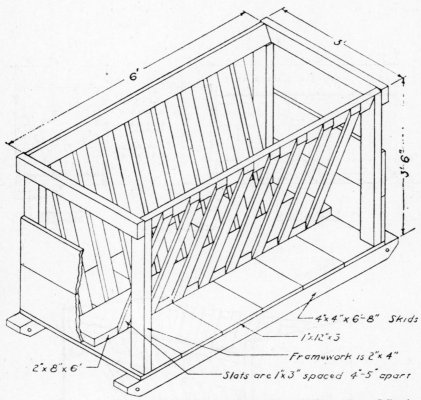

6'

5'

3'-6"

4"x 4"x 6'-8" Skids

1"x 12"x 3'

Framework is 2"x 4"

2"x 8"x 6'

Slats are 1"x 3" spaced 4"-5" apart

(Courtesy Extension Division, Michigan State College)

Fig. 362—Alfalfa rack for swine.

Bill of Materials for Alfalfa Feed Rack

Use	No. Pieces	Size	Material
Skids	2	4"x 4"x6'8"	White pine
Center tie for slats	1	2"x 8"x6'	White pine
Side rail	2	2"x 4"x6'	White pine
End rail	2	2"x 4"x3'	White pine
Vertical frame	4	2"x 4"x3'4½"	White pine
Floor and end boards	10	1"x12"x3'	White pine
Slats	16	1"x 3"x3'6¾"	White pine

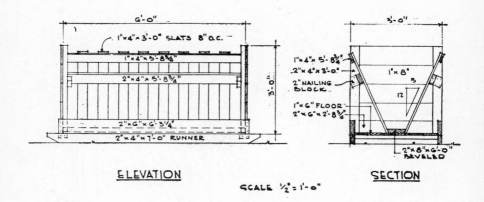

ELEVATION   SECTION

SCALE ½" = 1'-0"

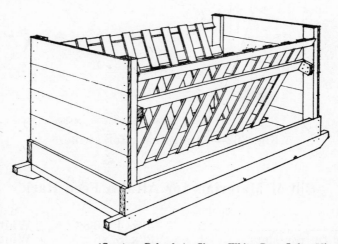

(Courtesy Roland A. Glaze, White Bear Lake, Minnesota)

Fig. 363—Alfalfa feed rack.

Bill of Materials for Alfalfa Rack

Use	Pieces	Size	Length
Runners	2	2″x4″	7′-0″
Joists	2	2″x4″	2′-8¾″
Sides	2	2″x6″	6′-3¼″
Studs	4	2″x4″	3′-0″
End Brace	2	2″x6″	2′-8¾″
Beveled Piece	1	2″x8″	6′-0″
Slat Supports	2	2″x4″	5′-8¾″
Nailing Block	4	2″x4″	0′-3½″
Ends	8	1″x8″	3′-0″
Floor	6	1″x6″	3′-0″
Slats	16	1″x4″	3′-0″
Slats	2	1″x4″	5′-8¾″

½ lb. 6d common nails
2 lbs. 8d   "   "
1 lb. 16d   "   "   .

☆☆☆☆

Bill of Materials for Loading Chute

2 pieces	2″x4″x16′	Studs, braces, etc.	22 bd.ft.
1 piece	2″x4″x14′	Studs and braces	10 bd. ft.
2 pieces	2″x8″x16′	Floor	44 bd. ft.
1 piece	1″x4″x16′	Braces	4 bd. ft.
5 pieces	1″x6″x16′	Sides	80 bd. ft.

1 lb. 16d spikes
1 lb. 8d common nails

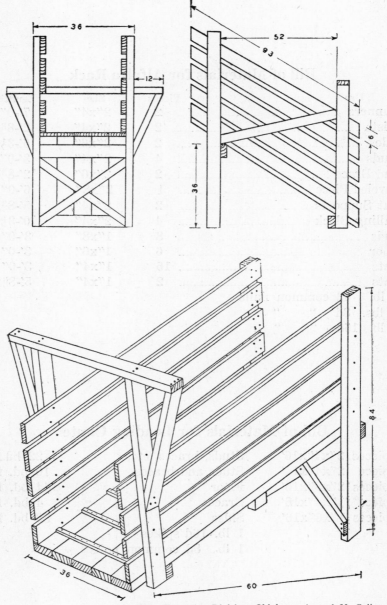

(Courtesy Extension Division, Oklahoma A. and M. College)

Fig. 364—Loading chute.

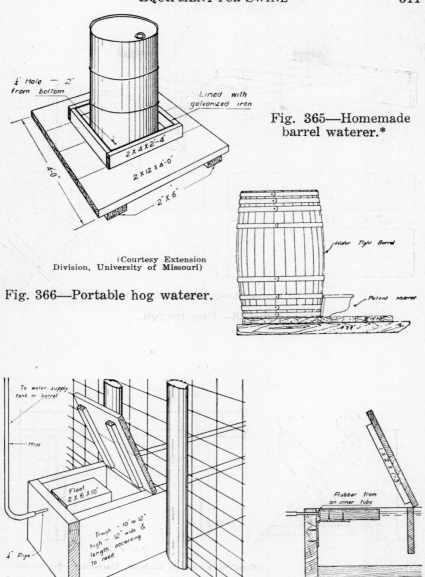

¼" Hole — 2"
from bottom

Lined with
galvanized iron

2 X 4 X 2'-4"

2 X 12 X 4'-0"

4'-0"

2" X 6"

Fig. 365—Homemade
barrel waterer.*

(Courtesy Extension
Division, University of Missouri)

Fig. 366—Portable hog waterer.

Water Tight Barrel

Patent waterer

4 X 4"

To water supply
tank or barrel

Hose

Float
2 X 6 X 10"

Trough — 10" to 12"
high — 12" wide &
length according
to need

½" Pipe

Rubber from
an inner tube

2 X 2 X 3'

SECTION

Fig. 367—Automatic waterer.

* Figures 365 and 367 courtesy Extension Division, Univ. of Minnesota.

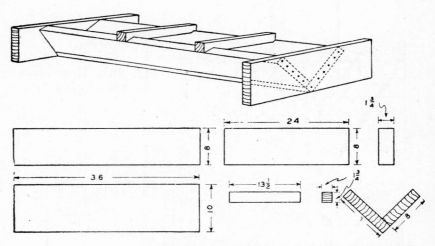

(Courtesy Extension Division, Oklahoma A. and M. College)

Fig. 368—Hog trough.

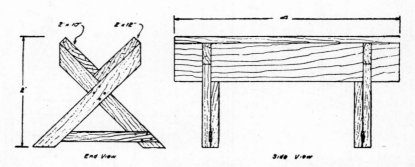

(Courtesy Extension Division, University of Missouri)

Fig. 369—Vaccinating trough or stand.

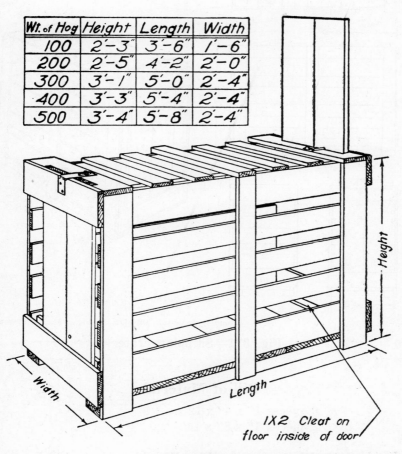

Wt. of Hog	Height	Length	Width
100	2'-3"	3'-6"	1'-6"
200	2'-5"	4'-2"	2'-0"
300	3'-1"	5'-0"	2'-4"
400	3'-3"	5'-4"	2'-4"
500	3'-4"	5'-8"	2'-4"

(Courtesy Extension Division, University of Minnesota)

Fig. 370—Shipping crate. Construct crates according to weight of hogs to be shipped.

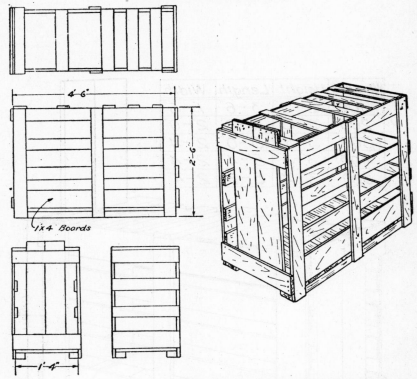

Fig. 371—Shipping crate.

Bill of Materials

6 pieces 1" x 4" x 12'
2 pieces 1" x 8" x 14'

Inside Crate Dimensions for Pigs Weighing Up to 100 Pounds

Width	1'- 0"
Height	2'- 0"
Length	3'-10"

For Pigs from 225 to 550 Pounds

Width	2'- 0"
Height	3'- 4"
Length	6'- 6"

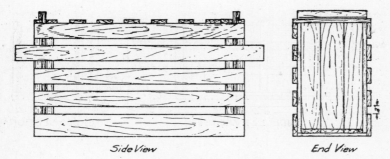

Side View   *End View*

(Courtesy Extension Division, University of Missouri)

Fig. 372—Shipping crate.

Size of Crate to Build

Weight of hog	Length of crate	Width of crate	Height of crate
25 to 75	35	12	23
75 to 150	46	18	28
150 to 250	54	20	34
250 to 350	60	20	38
350 to 500	64	24	40
500 to 800	80	30	48
800 to 1000	84	30	50

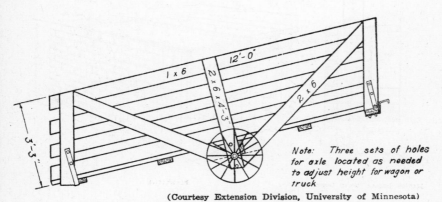

Note: Three sets of holes for axle located as needed to adjust height for wagon or truck

(Courtesy Extension Division, University of Minnesota)

Fig. 373—Portable loading chute.

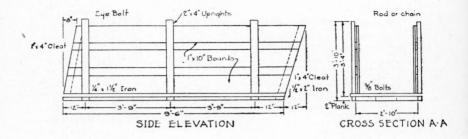

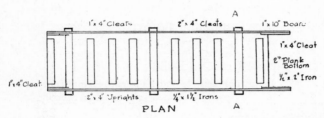

(Courtesy University of Minnesota)

Fig. 374—Takedown loading chute.

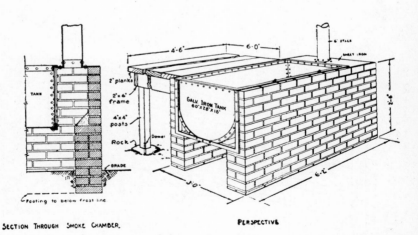

SECTION THROUGH SMOKE CHAMBER.   PERSPECTIVE

(Courtesy U. S. D. A.)

Fig. 375—Combination water heater, scalding vat, and scraping table.

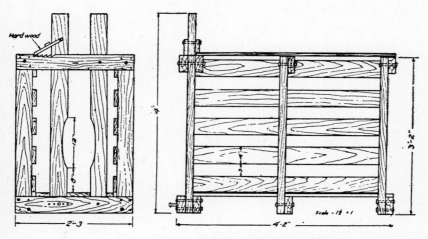

(Courtesy Extension Division, University of Missouri)

Fig. 376—Ringing chute.

Bill of Materials for Ringing Chute

				Estimated cost
2	2"x4"x16'	Studs and stanchions	22 bd. ft.	.99
2	2"x4"x10'	Cross ties	14 bd. ft.	.63
1	1"x6"x14'	Floor	7 bd. ft.	.35
4	1"x4"x14'	Sides	20 bd. ft.	1.00
14	3/8"x5"	Carriage bolts		.70
1	1/4"x4"	Carriage bolt		.05
1 lb. 8d common nails				.10
	Total			$3.82

Equipment for Dairy Cattle

.·.

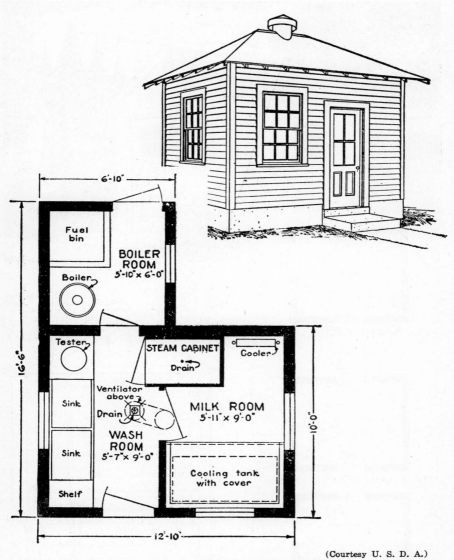

Fuel bin

BOILER ROOM
5'-10" x 6'-0"

Boiler

6'-10"

16'-6"

Tester

STEAM CABINET
Drain

Cooler

Sink

Ventilator above
Drain

MILK ROOM
5'-11" x 9'-0"

WASH ROOM
5'-7" x 9'-0"

Sink

Shelf

Cooling tank with cover

12'-10"

10'-0"

(Courtesy U. S. D. A.)

Fig. 377—A milk house suitable for small dairies of 10 to 20 cows where milk is shipped in cans. This little house consists of two rooms and a shed addition to house the boiler. The floor area of the milk house proper is 9 by 12 feet. Design No. 909.

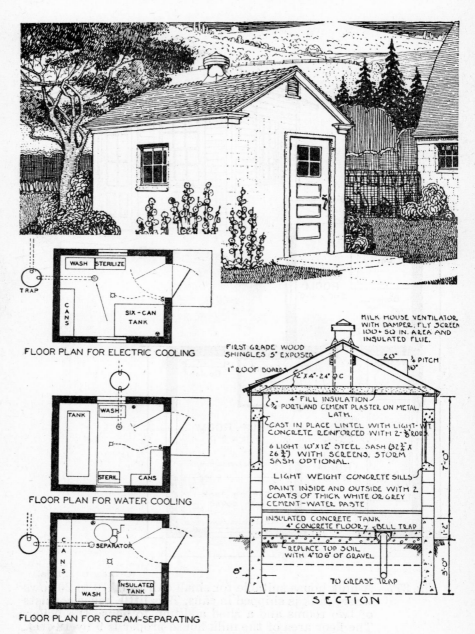

TRAP

WASH STERILIZE

CANS

SIX - CAN
TANK

FLOOR PLAN FOR ELECTRIC COOLING

TANK

WASH

STERIL. CANS

FLOOR PLAN FOR WATER COOLING

CANS

SEPARATOR

INSULATED
TANK

WASH

FLOOR PLAN FOR CREAM-SEPARATING

MILK HOUSE VENTILATOR
WITH DAMPER, FLY SCREEN
100+ SQ IN. AREA AND
INSULATED FLUE.

FIRST GRADE WOOD
SHINGLES 5" EXPOSED

1" ROOF BOARDS

2" X 4" - 24" O C

20"

¼ PITCH

4" FILL INSULATION
¾ PORTLAND CEMENT PLASTER ON METAL
LATH.
CAST IN PLACE LINTEL WITH LIGHT- WT
CONCRETE REINFORCED WITH 2 - ⅝" RODS
6 LIGHT 10"X12" STEEL SASH (32½" X
26½") WITH SCREENS. STORM
SASH OPTIONAL.

LIGHT WEIGHT CONCRETE SILLS

PAINT INSIDE AND OUTSIDE WITH 2
COATS OF THICK WHITE OR GREY
CEMENT-WATER PASTE

INSULATED CONCRETE TANK
4" CONCRETE FLOOR BELL TRAP

REPLACE TOP SOIL
WITH 4" TO 6" OF GRAVEL

TO GREASE TRAP

7'-0"

1'-2"

3'-0"

8"

SECTION

(Courtesy Extension Division, University of Wisconsin)

Fig. 378—A 10'x12' masonry milk house of light weight concrete blocks for marketing milk or cream from a medium-sized herd.

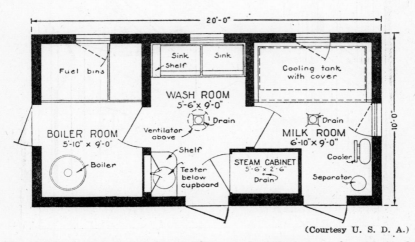

(Courtesy U. S. D. A.)

Fig. 379—Perhaps the best all-around milk house for 20 to 30 cow dairies shipping milk or cream in cans. It is small, conveniently arranged, and relatively inexpensive. The little closet between the milk and wash rooms is to hold sample bottles and glassware for the Babcock test. The cooling tank is sunk below the floor level, to minimize the lifting of cans of milk. Design No. 1336.

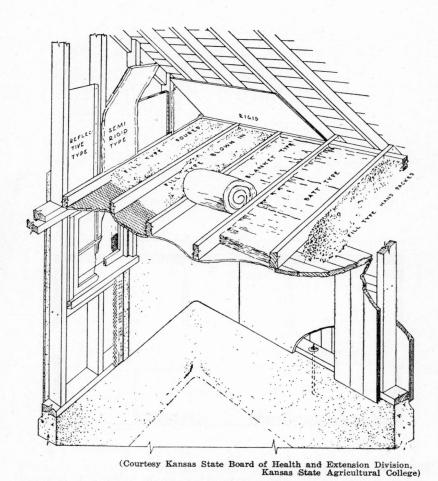

(Courtesy Kansas State Board of Health and Extension Division,
Kansas State Agricultural College)

Fig. 380—Suggestions for ceiling insulation, and wall construction for new and remodeled milk houses.

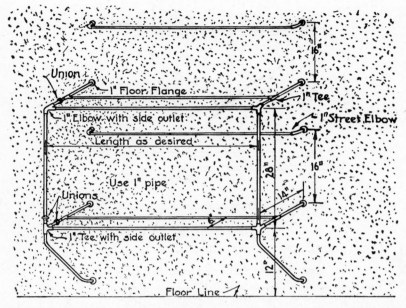

Fig. 381—This can rack, constructed from 1-inch pipe and fittings, may be made any convenient length.*

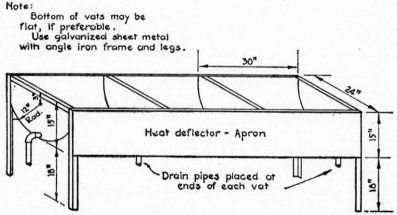

Fig. 382—A three-section wash vat. A vat of this type is very convenient. It may be made with either two or three sections and may have either a round or a flat bottom.

* Figures 381 and 382 courtesy Division of Food and Drugs, Kansas State Board of Health.

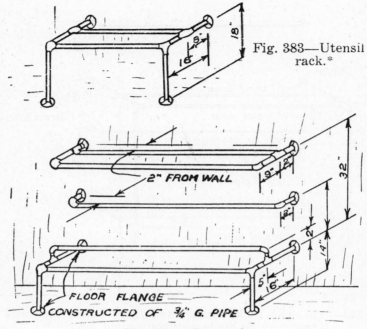

Fig. 383—Utensil rack.*

Fig. 384—Can rack.

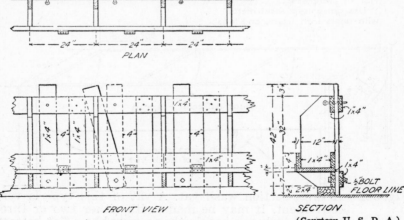

PLAN

FRONT VIEW

SECTION

(Courtesy U. S. D. A.)

Fig. 385—Calf stanchion and manger.

* Figures 383 and 384 courtesy Extension Division, Purdue University.

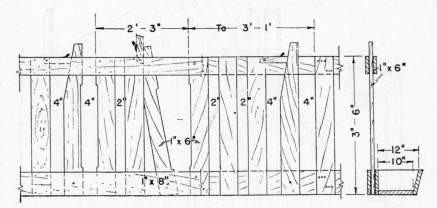

Fig. 386—"Calf ties may well be homemade, for calves are usually tied only while being fed and for a short while afterward. A tie 24 to 28 inches wide and 36 inches high will accommodate calves under 6 months of age."*

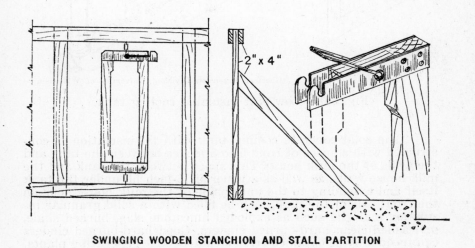

SWINGING WOODEN STANCHION AND STALL PARTITION

Fig. 387—Stanchions like these are comfortable, durable, and easily operated.

* Figures 386 and 387 courtesy Extension Division, Univ. of Illinois.

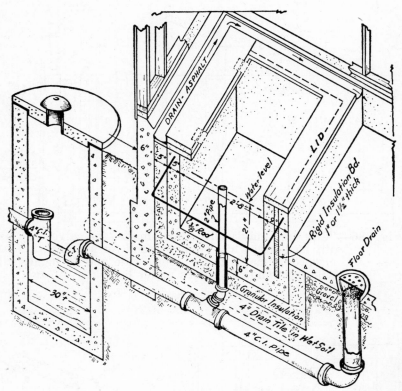

(Courtesy Extension Division, University of Wisconsin)

Fig. 388—Low cost insulated cooling tank.

"The solid concrete cooling tank with fill insulation is constructed with a space of from 5 to 8 inches between the tank and the walls of the milk house. This space between the tank and the milk house walls, as well as a generous 6-inch fill under the tank itself and extending to the under side of the milk house floor on the front side of the tank, may be filled with a solid granular insulation material such as exploded limestone slag, burned shale, or washed clean hard-burned cinders. Good hard-burned cinders can frequently be obtained from steam-electric generating plants, condensaries, paper mills, and at railroad yards. If there is much fine material in the cinders, this should be removed by running over a quarter-inch sand screen. The cinders may also be improved by washing with a hose or in a concrete mixer."

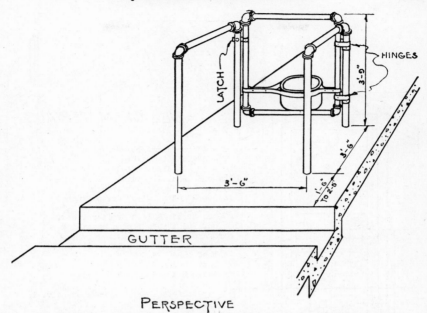

PERSPECTIVE

Adapted from Michigan Agricultural Experiment Station plan.
(Courtesy Agricultural Experiment Station, North Dakota Agricultural College)

Fig. 389—Pipe stall partitions, feed basket and gate for walk-through milking stalls.

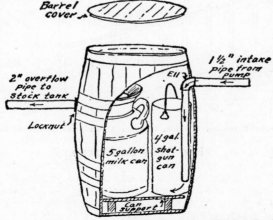

Courtesy Extension Division, Purdue University)

Fig. 390—Milk cooler.

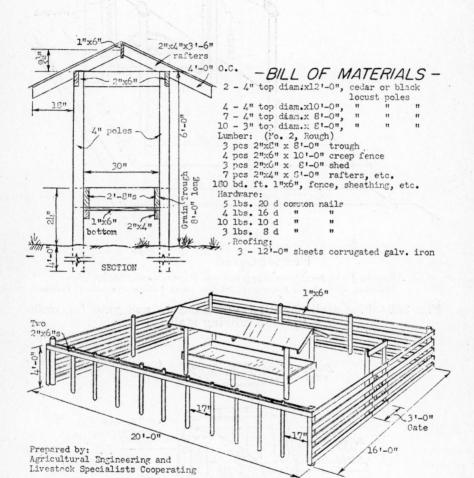

BILL OF MATERIALS

2 - 4" top diam.x12'-0", cedar or black
                                   locust poles
4 - 4" top diam.x10'-0",   "   "   "
7 - 4" top diam.x 8'-0",   "   "   "
10 - 3" top diam.x 8'-0",   "   "   "
Lumber: (No. 2, Rough)
  3 pcs 2"x8" x 8'-0" trough
  4 pcs 2"x6" x 10'-0" creep fence
  3 pcs 2"x6" x 8'-0" shed
  7 pcs 2"x4" x 8'-0" rafters, etc.
180 bd. ft. 1"x6", fence, sheathing, etc.
Hardware:
  5 lbs. 20 d common nails
  4 lbs. 16 d   "   "
 10 lbs. 10 d   "   "
  3 lbs. 8 d   "   "
Roofing:
  3 - 12'-0" sheets corrugated galv. iron

(Courtesy Extension Division, Clemson Agricultural College of South Carolina)

Fig. 391—Calf creep.

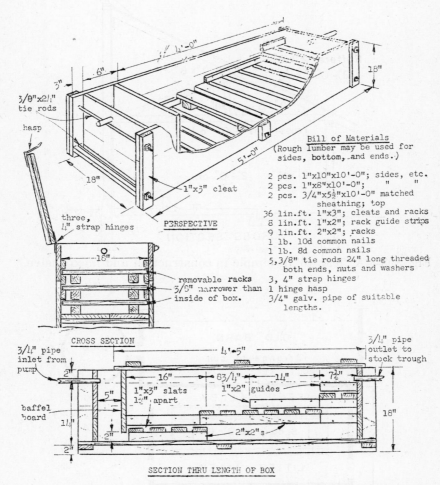

(Courtesy Extension Division, Clemson Agricultural College of South Carolina)

Fig. 392—Milk cooling box.

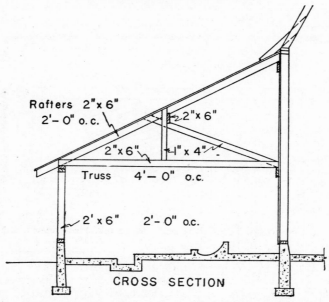

Fig. 393—A "lean-to" is simple in construction and inexpensive.*

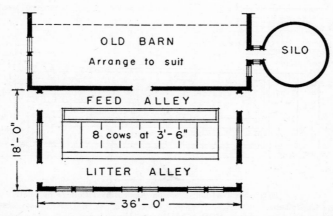

Fig. 393a—In a "lean-to," which usually has but one row of stanchions, both cleaning and feeding are easier if the cows face toward the old barn.

* Figures 393 and 393a courtesy Extension Division, University of Illinois.

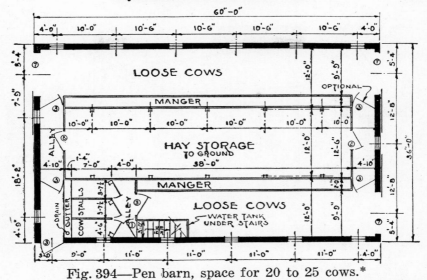

Fig. 394—Pen barn, space for 20 to 25 cows.*

Young stock and bull will need quarters provided in a lean-to or by using removable portions. Drive-through type of milking stalls. Plan No. N. D. 723-2-1, price 15 cents each.

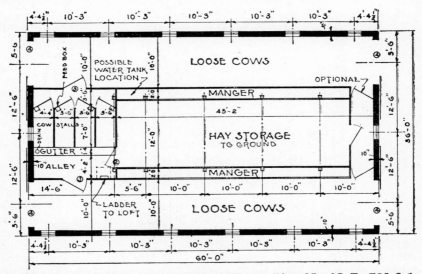

Fig. 395—Pen barn for 15-20 cows. (From Plan No. N. D. 723-3-1, price 15 cents each.)

---

* Figures 394 and 395 courtesy Agricultural Experiment Station, North Dakota Agricultural College.

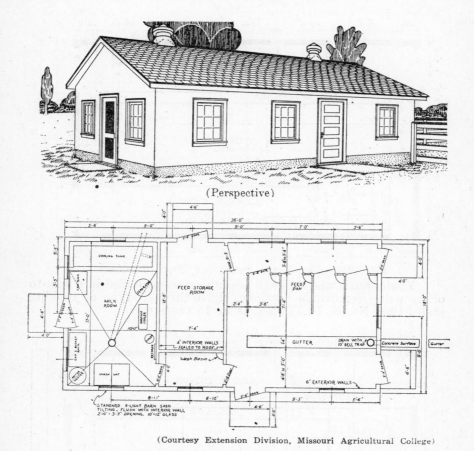

(Perspective)

(Courtesy Extension Division, Missouri Agricultural College)

Fig. 396—Milking room and milk house unit.
(Walk-through type stall.)

"This plan meets the needs of the dairy farmer who wishes to use a loafing barn. This combined milking room and milk house provides a smaller area to be cleaned and a convenient place for handling milk. The walk-through type stall is somewhat more convenient in making changes in that the cows walk forward when leaving the barn. Cows are fed hay and silage in the loafing barn and concentrates in the milking room."

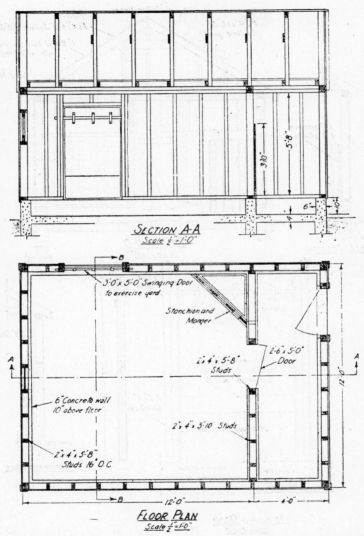

Fig. 397—Floor plan and side section of individual bull barn.*

* Figures 397 and 398 courtesy Extension Division, Michigan State Agricultural College.

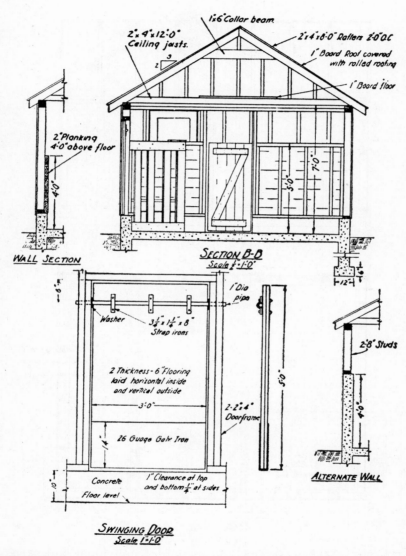

Fig. 398—End section and construction details for individual bull
barn shown in Fig. 397.

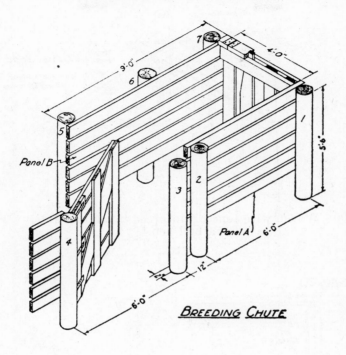

BREEDING CHUTE

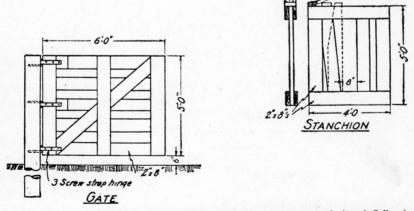

GATE

STANCHION

(Courtesy Extension Division, Michigan State Agricultural College)

Fig. 399—Plans for breeding chute.

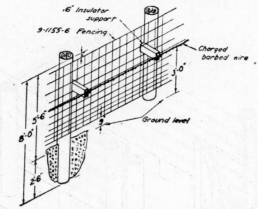

Fig. 400—Woven wire fence, reinforced by an electrified wire for a bull pen.*

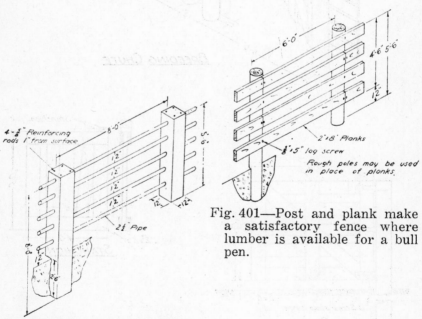

Fig. 401—Post and plank make a satisfactory fence where lumber is available for a bull pen.

Fig. 402—The pipe and concrete post fence recommended for a bull pen.

* Figures 400 to 402 courtesy Extension Division, Michigan State Agricultural College.

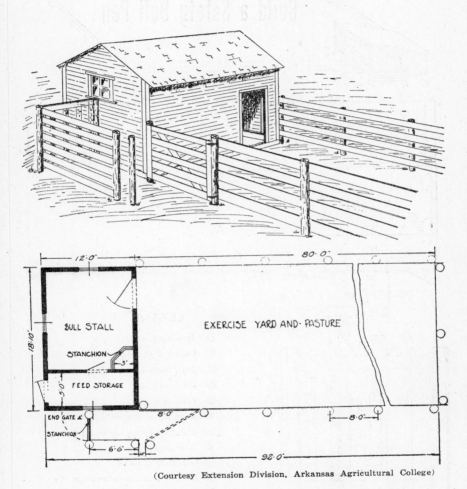

(Courtesy Extension Division, Arkansas Agricultural College)

Fig. 403—The safety bull pen and its construction.

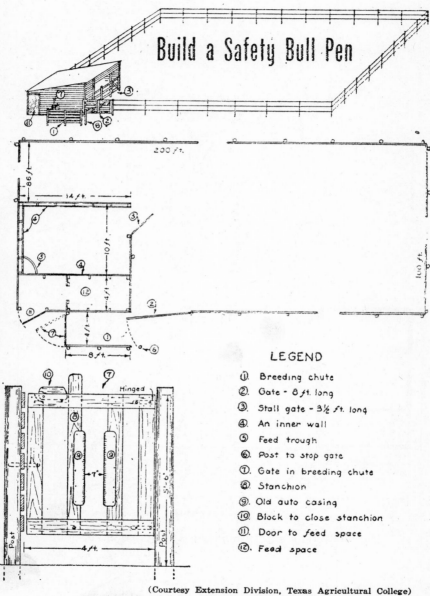

Build a Safety Bull Pen

LEGEND

①. Breeding chute
②. Gate - 8 ft. long
③. Stall gate - 3½ ft. long
④. An inner wall
⑤. Feed trough
⑥. Post to stop gate
⑦. Gate in breeding chute
⑧. Stanchion
⑨. Old auto casing
⑩. Block to close stanchion
⑪. Door to feed space
⑫. Feed space

(Courtesy Extension Division, Texas Agricultural College)

Fig. 404—Safety bull pen.

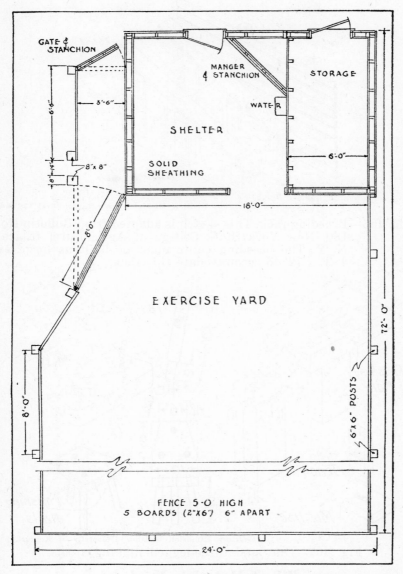

(Courtesy Extension Division, Washington State College)

Fig. 405—Diagram showing plans for safe bull pen, including breeding chute, bull shelter and safety gates.

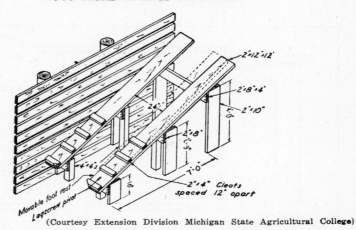

(Courtesy Extension Division Michigan State Agricultural College)

Fig. 406—Breeding rack. This sketch is adapted from Bulletin No. 180, New York State College of Agriculture, Ithaca, N. Y. The breeding chute must be built as large **as** 4'-8" x 12' to accommodate this rack.

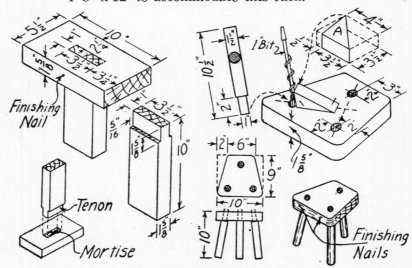

(Courtesy Extension Division, University of Kentucky)

Fig. 407—One- and three-legged milking stools.

Bill of Materials Needed

One-legged stool

1 pc. 1⅝"x5½"x10" for seat
1 pc. 1"x3½"x10" for leg
2 8d finishing nails

Three-legged stool

1 pc. 1⅝"x9"x10" for seat
3 pcs. 1½"x1½"x10½" for legs
3 8d finishing nails

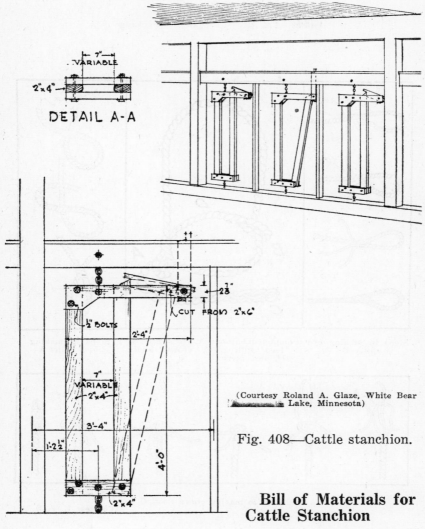

DETAIL A-A

(Courtesy Roland A. Glaze, White Bear Lake, Minnesota)

Fig. 408—Cattle stanchion.

Bill of Materials for Cattle Stanchion

Item	Pieces	Size	Exact Length
Locking member	1	2"x4"	1'-4"
Bottom members	2	2"x4"	1'-2½"
Top members	1	2"x6"	3'-0" cut as
Vertical members	1	2"x4"	4'-0" shown
Vertical members	1	2"x4"	4'-2"
Bolts—Machine	8	½"	5½"
Chain		1½"x¼"	as required

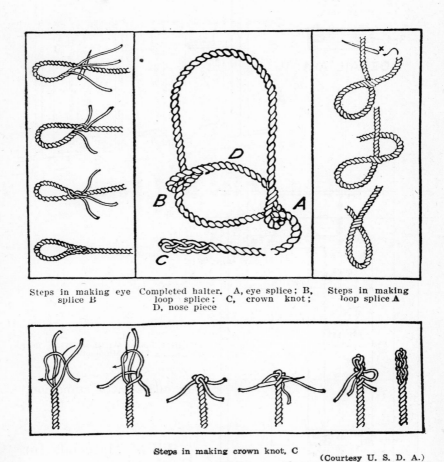

Steps in making eye splice B

Completed halter. A, eye splice; B, loop splice; C, crown knot; D, nose piece

Steps in making loop splice A

Steps in making crown knot, C

(Courtesy U. S. D. A.)

Fig. 409—A completed rope halter, and steps showing method of making.

Equipment for Beef Cattle

■ ■ ■

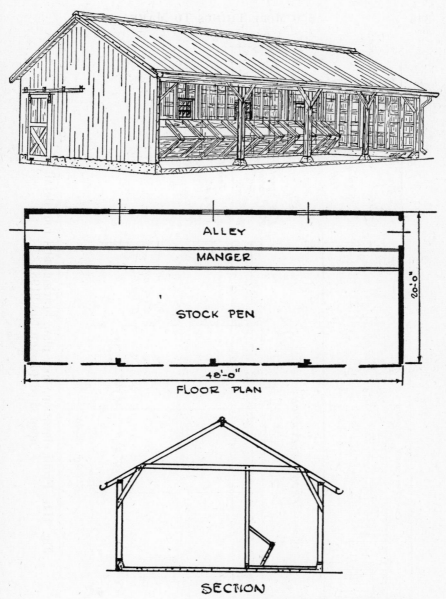

ALLEY

MANGER

STOCK PEN

20'-0"

48'-0"

FLOOR PLAN

SECTION

(Courtesy Continental Steel Corporation)

Fig. 410—Cattle shed.

347

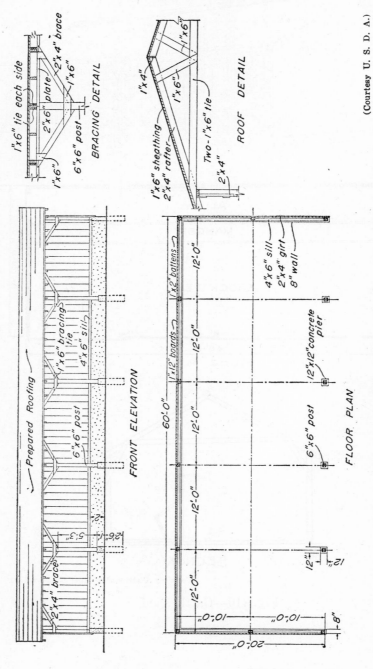

(Courtesy U. S. D. A.)

Fig. 411—Front elevation, floor plan, bracing, and roof detail of open shed (design No. 2198).

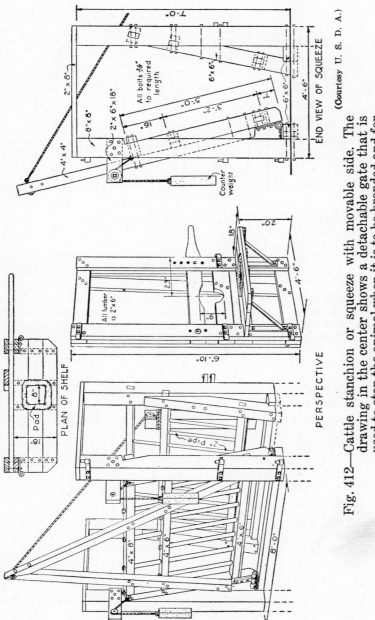

Fig. 412—Cattle stanchion or squeeze with movable side. The drawing in the center shows a detachable gate that is used to stop the animal when it is to be branded and for holding the head firm when dehorning. The padded hole for the nose is shown at the top.

(Courtesy U. S. D. A.)

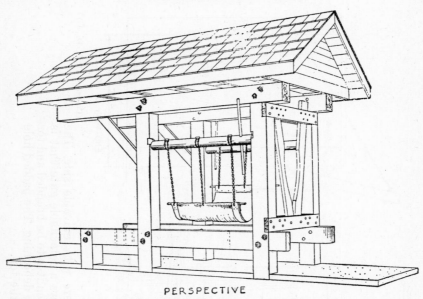

PERSPECTIVE

Fig. 413—Cattle stocks used in handling exhibition animals or valuable breeding stock where it is necessary to get the animal off its feet. The roof reduces deterioration from rain and sun (design No 3133).*

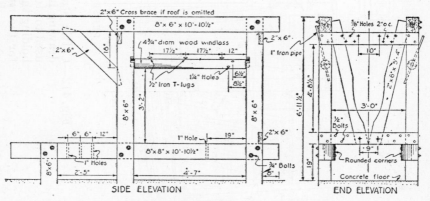

SIDE ELEVATION   END ELEVATION

Fig. 414—Details of the construction of the cattle stocks shown in Fig. 413 (design No. 3133).

* Figures 413 and 414 courtesy U. S. D. A.

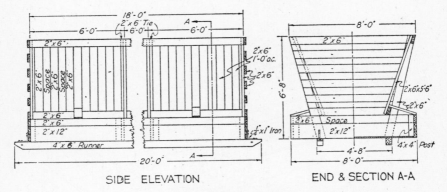

SIDE ELEVATION

END & SECTION A-A

(Courtesy Extension Division, University of Minnesota)

Fig. 415—A good type of portable rack for feeding hay to cattle.

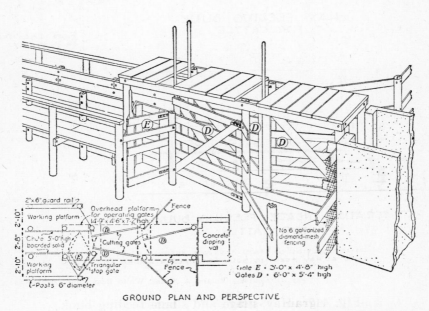

GROUND PLAN AND PERSPECTIVE

(Courtesy U. S. D. A.)

Fig. 416—Ground plan and perspective of a cutting chute with overhead and working (side) platforms, triangular stop gate, and cutting gates (design No. 3132).

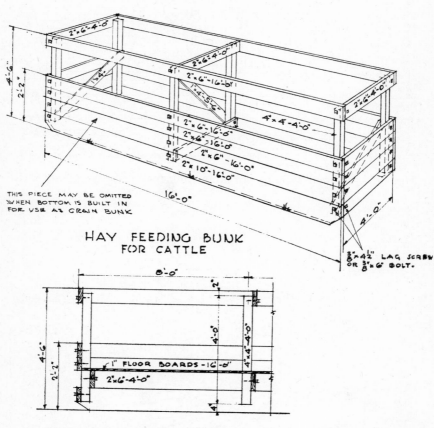

2"×6"-4'-0"

4'-0"

2'-2"

2"×6"-4'-0"

4'×4'

2"×6"-16'-0"

4'×5'-2

4"×4-4'-0"

2"×6"-16'-0"

2"×6"-16'-0"

2"×6"-16'-0"

2"×6"-16'-0"

2"×6"-4'-0"

2"×10"-16'-0"

16'-0"

4'-0"

THIS PIECE MAY BE OMITTED
WHEN BOTTOM IS BUILT IN
FOR USE AS GRAIN BUNK

⅜"×4½" LAG SCREW
OR ⅜"×6" BOLT.

HAY FEEDING BUNK
FOR CATTLE

8'-0"

2"

4'-0"

4'×4-4'-0"

4'-6"

2'-2"

1" FLOOR BOARDS -16'-0"

2"×6"-4'-0"

GRAIN & SILAGE FEEDING BUNK.
FOR CATTLE

CONSTRUCTION OF GRAIN & SILAGE FEEDING BUNK
SAME AS HAY FEEDING BUNK WITH FLOOR ADDED.

(Courtesy Roland A. Glaze, White Bear Lake, Minnesota)

Fig. 417—Hay, grain and silage feeding bunk.

Bill of Materials for Hay, Grain and Silage Feeding Bunk

Item	Pieces	Size	Exact Length
Corner supports	6	4"x 4"	4'-0"
End and center boards	12	2"x 6"	4'-0"
Side boards	8	2"x 6"	16'-0"
Side boards	2	2"x10"	16'-0"
End braces	2	1"x 4"	4'-3"
Center braces	1	1"x 4"	5'-6"
Lag screws	60	3/8"	4½"
or bolts		3/8"	6"

Floor for Feeding Grain and Silage

Item	Pieces	Size	Exact Length
Floor	7	1"x 6"	15'-8¾"
Floor	1	1"x10"	15'-8¾"
Nails	½ lb. 6d		

✠✠✠✠

Bill of Materials for Cattle Feed Bunk

Item	Pieces	Size	Exact Length
Legs	4	4"x 4"	2'-6"
Cross pieces	6	2"x 4"	4'-3½"
Cross pieces	3	2"x 4"	4'-0"
Ends	2	2"x 4"	3'-8¼"
Ends	2	2"x 8"	3'-5"
Sides	2	2"x10"	10'-0"
Floor	5	1"x 8"	10'-0"
Floor	1	1"x 4"	10'-0"

6—10"x½" strap bolts   8—3/8"x4½" lag screws & washers
18—½"x3" bolts & washers   8—3/8"x3"   lag screws & washers
8—3/8"x6" bolts & washers   1 lb. 16d common nails
8—3/8"x8" bolts & washers   2 lb. 8d common nails

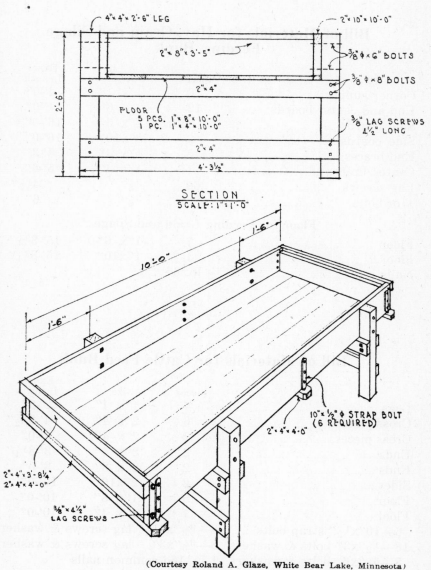

4"x 4"x 2'-6" LEG

2"x 10"x 10'-0"

2"x 8"x 3'-5"

3/8" φ x 6" BOLTS

3/8" φ x 8" BOLTS

2"x 4"

FLOOR
5 PCS. 1"x 8"x 10'-0"
1 PC. 1"x 4"x 10'-0"

3/8" LAG SCREWS
4 1/2" LONG

2"x 4"

2'-6"

4'-3 1/2"

SECTION
SCALE: 1"=1'-0"

1'-6"

10'-0"

1'-6"

10"x 1/2" φ STRAP BOLT
(6 REQUIRED)

2"x 4"x 4'-0"

2"x 4"x 3'-8 1/4"
2"x 4"x 4'-0"

3/8"x 4 1/2"
LAG SCREWS

(Courtesy Roland A. Glaze, White Bear Lake, Minnesota)

Fig. 418—Cattle feed bunk.

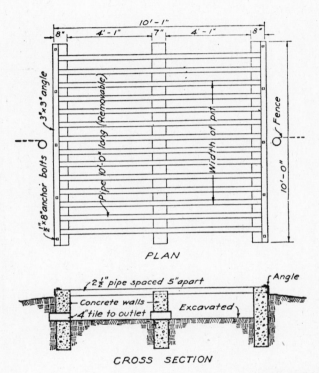

PLAN

CROSS SECTION

(Courtesy U. S. D. A.)

Fig. 419—Plan and cross section of cattle guard (design No. 1951).

Equipment for Sheep

∙ ∙ ∙

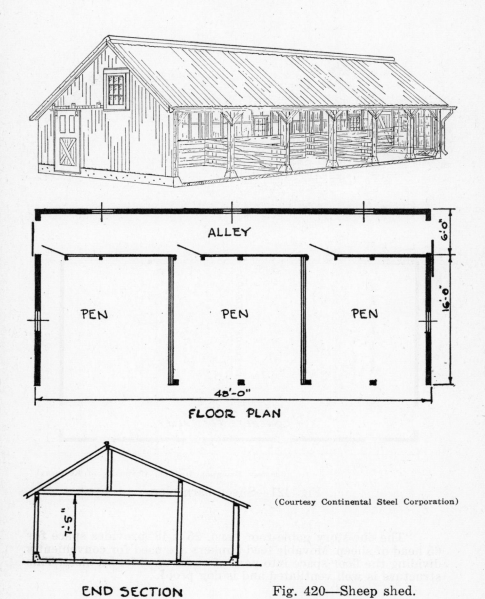

ALLEY

PEN   PEN   PEN

6'-0"

16'-6"

48'-0"

FLOOR PLAN

7'-5"

END SECTION

(Courtesy Continental Steel Corporation)

Fig. 420—Sheep shed.

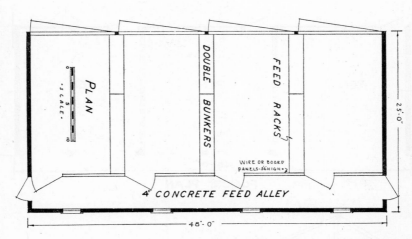

PLAN

DOUBLE BUNKERS

FEED RACKS

WIRE OR BOARD
PANELS-36"HIGH

4' CONCRETE FEED ALLEY

25'-0"

48'-0"

(Courtesy Extension Division, University of Kentucky)

Fig. 421—Sheep barn plan.

"The one-story gable-roof barn, 25' x 48' provides space for 65 head of sheep. Movable feed bunkers are used for conveniently dividing the floor space into pens of equal or different sizes. This structure is well ventilated and is dog proof."

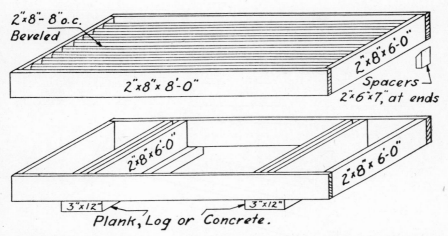

Fig. 422—This cattle or sheep guard set in a road leading to pastures allows a vehicle to pass over without opening gates but will keep the sheep in. Top section rests on bottom section.*

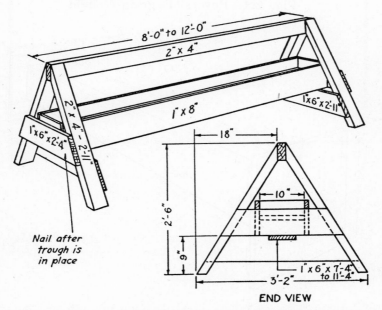

Fig. 423—A movable type of reversible feeding trough.

* Figures 422 and 423 courtesy Extension Division, Univ. of Minnesota.

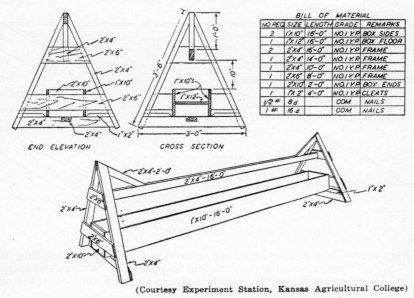

BILL OF MATERIAL

NO REQ	SIZE	LENGTH	GRADE	REMARKS
2	1"x10"	16'-0"	NO.1 Y.P.	BOX SIDES
1	1"x12"	16'-0"	NO.1 Y.P.	BOX FLOOR
2	2"x4"	16'-0"	NO.1 Y.P.	FRAME
1	2"x4"	14'-0"	NO.1 Y.P.	FRAME
1	2"x4"	10'-0"	NO.1 Y.P.	FRAME
1	2"x6"	8'-0"	NO.1 Y.P.	FRAME
1	2"x10"	2'-0"	NO.1 Y.P.	BOX ENDS
1	1"x2"	4'-0"	NO.1 Y.P.	CLEATS
1/2 #	8 d		COM.	NAILS
1 #	16 d		COM.	NAILS

END ELEVATION   CROSS SECTION

(Courtesy Experiment Station, Kansas Agricultural College)

Fig. 424—Reversible grain trough.

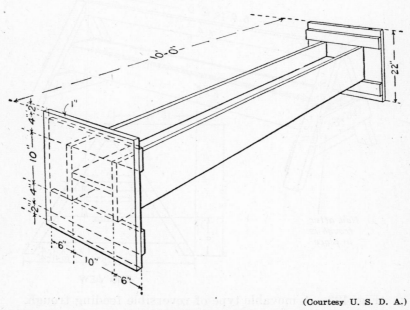

(Courtesy U. S. D. A.)

Fig. 425—A reversible movable grain trough with square ends.

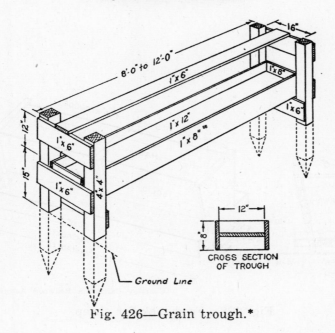

6'-0" to 12'-0"
16"
1"x 6"
1"x 8"
1"x 6"
12"
1"x 12"
1"x 8"
1"x 6"
15"
4 x 4
1"x 6"

12"
8"

CROSS SECTION
OF TROUGH

Ground Line

Fig. 426—Grain trough.*

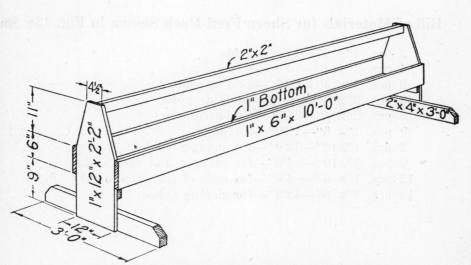

2"x 2"
4½
1" Bottom
2"x 4"x 3'-0"
1" x 6" x 10'-0"
9"—6"—11"
1"x 12"x 2'-2"
12"
3'-0"

Fig. 427—Single non-reversible grain trough.

* Figures 426 and 427 courtesy Extension Division, Univ. of Minnesota.

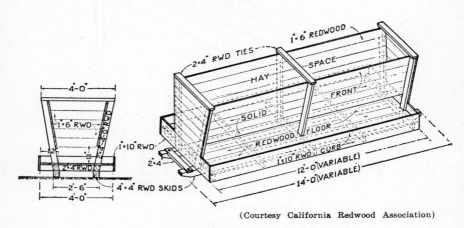

(Courtesy California Redwood Association)

Fig. 428—Feed-rack for sheep.

Bill of Materials for Sheep Feed-Rack Shown in Fig. 428

 2 pcs. 4"x 4"—14'0"—skids
 5 pcs. 2"x 4"— 4'0"—joists
 2 pcs. 2"x 4"— 2'6"—skid spreaders
 6 pcs. 2"x 4"— 4'0"—studs or posts
 3 pcs. 2"x 4"— 4'0"—ties across top
 8 pcs. 1"x 6"—12'0"—for floor
 2 pcs. 1"x10"—12'0"—for manger curbs
 2 pcs. 1"x10"— 4'0"—for manger and rack ends
12 pcs. 1"x 6"— 4'0"—for ends of rack (to be cut to fit)
10 pcs. 1"x 6"—12'0"—for sloping sides

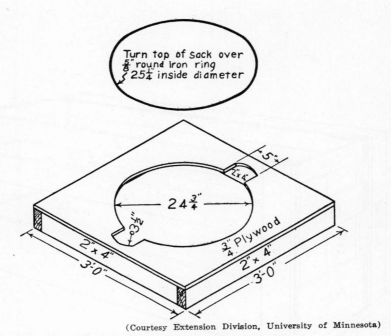

Turn top of sack over
$\frac{5}{8}$" round iron ring
$25\frac{1}{4}$" inside diameter

(Courtesy Extension Division, University of Minnesota)

Fig. 429—Wool sack holder.

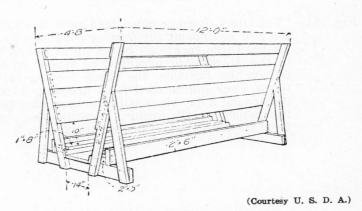

(Courtesy U. S. D. A.)

Fig. 430—The self-feeder hayrack.

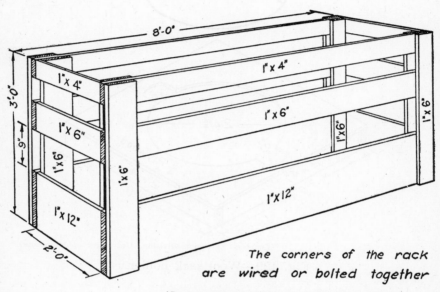

The corners of the rack
are wired or bolted together

(Courtesy Extension Division, University of Minnesota)

Fig. 431—"The knock-down or panel feed rack is an economical
      piece of equipment for feeding roughage to fattening
      lambs. These racks can be set up as bunks, as shown
      in the drawing or arranged as fences with the hay
      fed on the far side, the sheep feeding through the
      fence. They can be used for a breeding flock by plac-
      ing around a hay stack with the hay being fed against
      the panels on the inside. Locating the stack away
      from the shed forces the ewes to exercise."

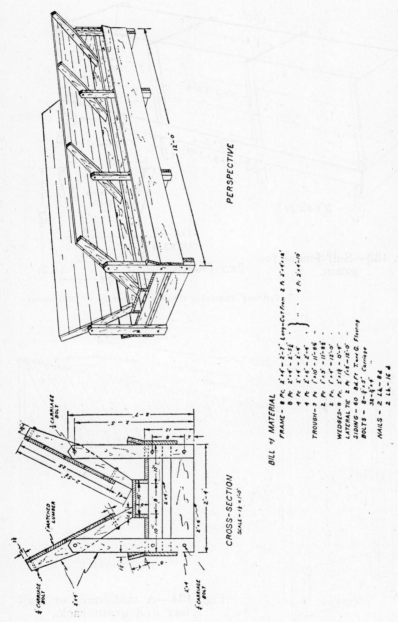

PERSPECTIVE

CROSS-SECTION
SCALE = 1½"=1'-0"

BILL of MATERIAL

FRAME—8 Pc. 2"×4"—2'-7" Long—Cut from 2 Pc. 2'-4"×14'
        }   "   "   1 Pc. 2"×4"-10'
        8 Pc. 2"×4"—2'-5⅝"
        1 Pc. 2"×4"—2'-4"
TROUGH—3 Pc. 1"×10"—11'-8½"
        2 Pc. 1"×3"—11'-8½"
WEDGES—8 Pc. 2"×4"—12'-0"
LATERAL TIE 2 Pc. 1¼"-12'-0"
SIDING—60 Bd. Ft T and G. Flooring
BOLTS—8—⅜"×5" Carriage
        32-⅜"×4"
NAILS—2 Lb.—8d
        2 Lb.—16d

(Courtesy Extension Division, Michigan State Agricultural College)

Fig. 432—A feeding rack that is easily cleaned and protects the fleeces from chaff and straw.

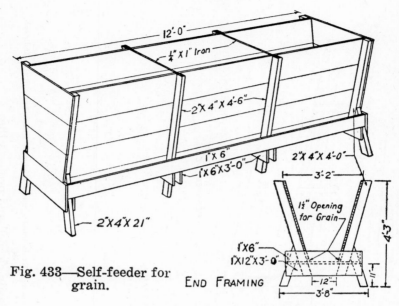

Fig. 433—Self-feeder for grain.

END FRAMING

(Courtesy Extension Division, University of Minnesota)

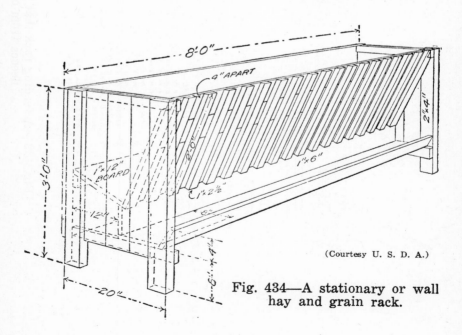

(Courtesy U. S. D. A.)

Fig. 434—A stationary or wall hay and grain rack.

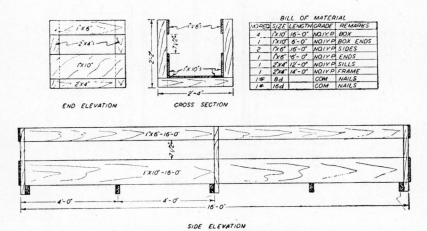

Fig. 435—Combination feeder.*

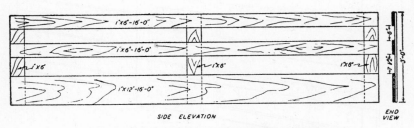

Fig. 436—Fence and feeding panel.

* Figures 435 and 436 courtesy Experiment Station, Kansas Agricultural College.

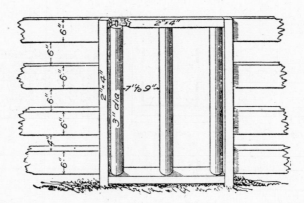

Fig. 437—Lamb creep with rollers for uprights.*

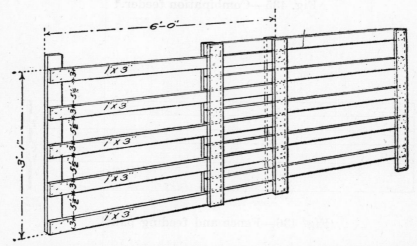

Fig. 438—Extension hurdle. May be closed up to 6 feet 4 inches or extended to 11 feet 4 inches.

* Figures 437 and 438 courtesy U. S. D. A.

PART IV

FARM CONCRETE

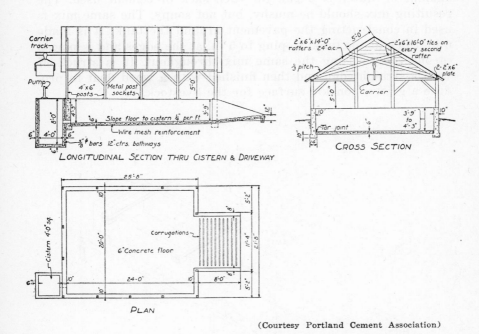

(Courtesy Portland Cement Association)

Fig. 439—Concrete manure pit for 20 cows.

Mixtures for Tanks and Troughs

"The recommended mix for watering tanks and troughs is 1 part portland cement, 2¼ parts clean sand and 3 parts gravel or crushed stone (not over ¾ in. in size). The correct amount of water is 5 gal. for each sack of cement used. The resulting mix should be mushy, but not soupy. The same mix is used in constructing the pavement around the tank. It is made 6 in. thick at the tank, sloping to 5 in. at the edges and is placed in one course using the same mix throughout. It is struck-off with a straightedge and then finished with a wood float to produce a gritty, nonskid surface for the livestock."

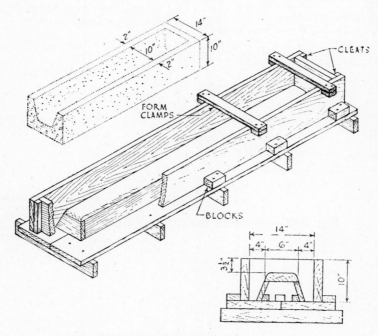

Fig. 440—Concrete hog trough form.*

* Figures 440 to 444 inclusive, and quotations courtesy Portland Cement Association.

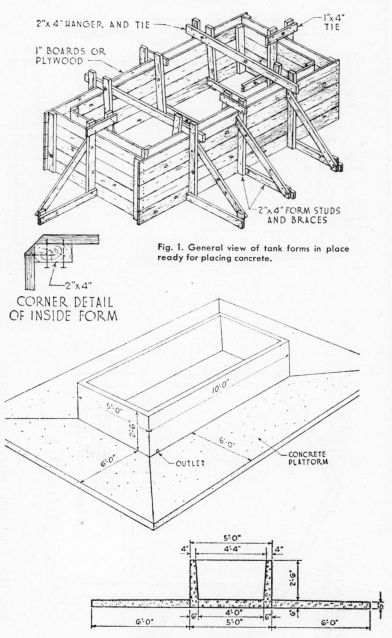

2"x4" HANGER AND TIE

1" BOARDS OR PLYWOOD

1"x4" TIE

2"x4" FORM STUDS AND BRACES

Fig. 1. General view of tank forms in place ready for placing concrete.

2"x4"

CORNER DETAIL OF INSIDE FORM

10'-0"

5'-0"

2'-6"

6'-0"

6'-0"

OUTLET

CONCRETE PLATFORM

5'-0"

4"

4'-4"

4"

2'-6"

6'-0"

6"

4'-0"

6"

9"

6'-0"

5'-0"

Fig. 441—Concrete tank.

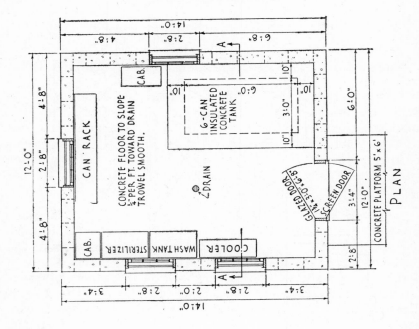

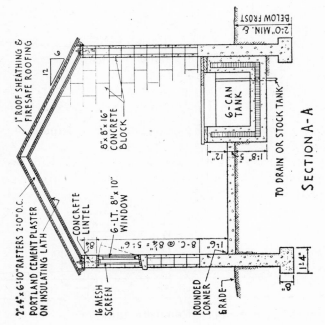

Fig. 442—One-room concrete milk house.

Suggestions for Constructing Concrete Milk House*

"*Footings and foundations.* Footings are 16 in. wide and 8 in. thick and extend to firm soil and below frost. The 8-in. foundation walls are carried up 2 ft. above ground level. A mix of 1 part portland cement to 2¾ parts sand to 4 parts gravel or crushed rock is used in constructing footings and foundation walls. The proper amount of water for this mix is 5½ gal. per sack of cement, using average damp sand.

"*Floors and walls.* Concrete floor is made 5 in. thick and is placed in one course using the same quality of concrete throughout. The recommended mixture is 1 part portland cement, 2¼ parts sand and 3 parts gravel or crushed rock, using 5 gal. of water for each sack of cement when sand is in a moist condition. Gravel or rock should not be larger than 1½ in. The floor is sloped ¼ in. per ft. toward the drain. A simple way to get proper slope on the floor is to drive a number of pegs in the ground, the tops of which will be at the desired floor level; then place concrete even with the top of the pegs and remove pegs as concreting progresses. All corners and angles at junctions of wall and floor may be rounded with a bottle to make sanitary joints. The floor is first floated with a wood float to a uniform surface. After the concrete has become quite stiff it is finished with a steel trowel. Cure the floor by keeping it moist for about five days.

"Walls are constructed of plain smooth-faced concrete blocks laid in a mortar of 1 part portland cement, 1 part lime putty or hydrated lime, and 6 parts mortar sand. Sufficient water is added to obtain a workable mortar. The interior may be given 2 coats of portland cement paint or 2 coats of portland cement plaster."

---

* Courtesy Portland Cement Association.

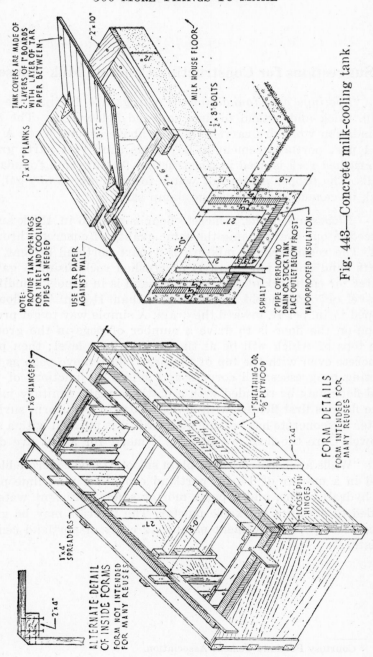

TANK COVERS ARE MADE OF
2 LAYERS OF 1" BOARDS
WITH LAYER OF TAR
PAPER BETWEEN

2" x 10"

2" x 10" PLANKS

3'-2"

2'-6"

MILK HOUSE FLOOR

½" x 8" BOLTS

12

NOTE:
PROVIDE TANK OPENINGS
FOR INLET AND COOLING
PIPES AS NEEDED

USE TAR PAPER
AGAINST WALL

3'-0"

1'-8"

12

27

4½"

21

2" PIPE OVERFLOW TO
DRAIN OR STOCK TANK
PLACE OUTLET BELOW FROST

ASPHALT

VAPORPROOFED INSULATION

Fig. 443—Concrete milk-cooling tank.

1" x 6" HANGERS

1" SHEATHING OR
⅝" PLYWOOD

LENGTH A
WIDTH B

2" x 4"

1" x 4"
SPREADERS

27

3'-0"

FORM DETAILS
FORM INTENDED FOR
MANY REUSES

LOOSE PIN
HINGES

2" x 4"

ALTERNATE DETAIL
OF INSIDE FORMS
FORM NOT INTENDED
FOR MANY REUSES

Dimensions of Insulated Milk-Cooling Tanks*

Tanks are 36 in. wide, 27 in. deep inside

Number of 10-gal. cans tank holds	Inside length A	Outside length B
4	4' 0"	5' 8"
6	6' 0"	7' 8"
8	8' 0"	9' 8"
10	10' 0"	11' 8"
12	12' 0"	13' 8"

"Mixing and placing concrete. A 1:2¼:3 mixture of concrete is recommended. This means 1 part portland cement, 2¼ parts sand and 3 parts of gravel or crushed rock. None of the coarse material should be larger than ¾ in. in size. The proper amount of water for this mix is 5 gal. per sack of cement, using average moist sand. The mixture should be mushy, but not soupy. In placing tank walls, take care to fill the inner and outer walls to the same depth so that insulation will not be moved out of position. Concrete should be spaded carefully and thoroughly to produce smooth walls and dense concrete"

Suggestions for Concrete Farrowing Pen*

"In a well-tamped fill of gravel, cinders, or crushed rock 6 to 12 in. thick place a 1½-in.-thick base course of concrete. After it hardens lay asphalt roll roofing or tough waterproof building paper over the base, lapping and carefully sealing all joints with roofing cement. Over this place a top course of concrete about 3 in. thick.

"For both courses of concrete use a 1:2¼:3 mix, meaning 1 part portland cement to 2¼ parts sand to 3 parts gravel or crushed stone not over 1 in. in size. The proper amount of water for this mix is 5 gal. per sack of cement, using average damp sand."

---

* Courtesy Portland Cement Association.

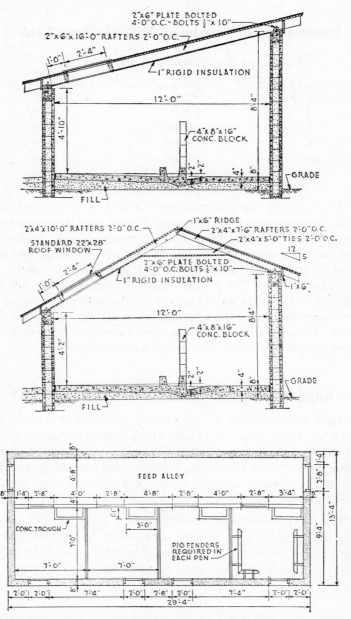

Fig. 444—Farrowing pen. Either the shed roof or the gable roof
may be used.

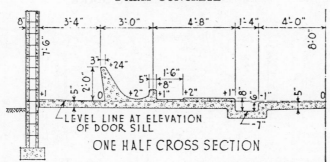

ONE HALF CROSS SECTION

Fig. 445—Standard cow stall. Elevations of finished surfaces are indicated by + or − figures. Top of curb is thus 8 in. above the level line which is established at the elevation of the door sills.*

"Concrete mix. The recommended mixture for dairy barn floors and mangers is 1:2¼:3, which means 1 part portland cement, 2¼ parts sand and 3 parts of gravel or crushed stone. The largest piece of gravel should not be over 1½ in. The proper amount of water is 5 gal. per sack of cement when average moist sand is used. After thorough mixing, this should result in a mushy mix which will place the finish readily."

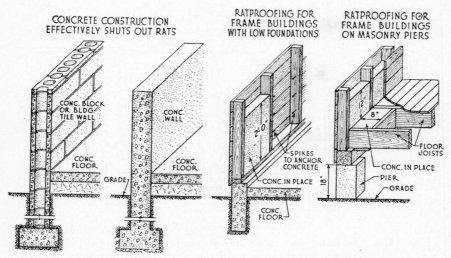

Fig. 446—Principal methods of ratproofing buildings.

* Figures 445 and 446 courtesy Portland Cement Association.

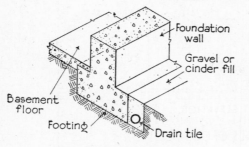

Fig. 447—Footing for
foundation wall.*

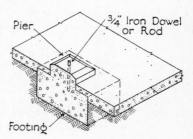

Fig. 448—Footing for
column.

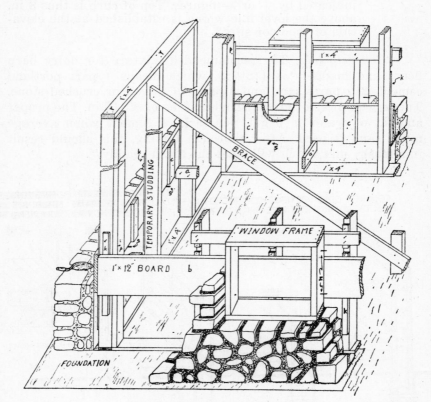

(Courtesy Extension Division, Oklahoma A. and M. College)

Fig. 449—Showing construction of adjustable form for laying
a rock wall and holding door and window frames
in place.

* Figures 447 and 448 courtesy Weyerhaeuser Sales Company.

Oklahoma Circular No. 317 states that "There is no better building material in existence than native rock. It makes a neat permanent wall. It is fireproof and needs no painting or upkeep. Where rock and sand are abundant and can be had practically for the hauling, native rock is a natural building material.

"One bag of cement and about 450 pounds of sand will make mortar for about seven to ten square feet of wall, 12 inches thick, depending on how careful one is to fill in small rock and whether sand or sand and gravel mixed is used. There is no exact method of determining the amount of cement and sand, but data from a number of buildings show that about half the wall is rock and half concrete. So for a 12-inch cobblestone wall the amount of concrete required will be figured as though it were a six-inch concrete wall."

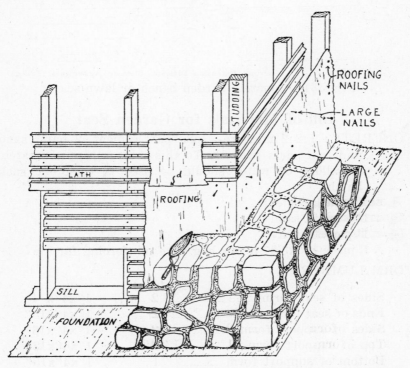

Fig. 450—Showing how to build rock against studding in permanent forms.

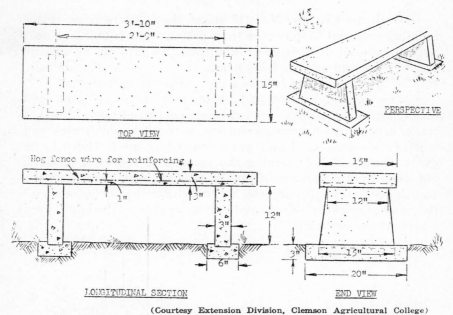

TOP VIEW

PERSPECTIVE

Hog fence wire for reinforcing

LONGITUDINAL SECTION

END VIEW

(Courtesy Extension Division, Clemson Agricultural College)

Fig. 451—Concrete garden bench or lawn seat

Bill of Materials for Garden Seat

CONCRETE: 1:2:2 mixture—(one part cement, 2 parts sand and two parts gravel). To this mixture approximately 4 gallons of water should be used to each one sack batch.

¾ sack cement.

1½ cu. ft. sand

1½ cu. ft. gravel

1 piece 12"x3'8" heavy hog wire reinforcing for top

FORM LUMBER:

Use	No. Pieces	Size
Sides of seat form	2	1"x4"x 4'
Ends of seat form	2	1"x4"x15"
Sides of support form	2	1"x4"x13"
Top of support form	1	1"x4"x12"
Bottom of support form	1	1"x4"x15"
Common nails for placing form together—small quantity		6d

Bill of Materials for Frost Proof Drinking Fountain for Swine

	Cost		Cost
½ yd. gravel	$0.70	Float and check valve	$2.00
5 sacks cement	4.00	Pipe	.20
½ sack hydrated lime	.35	Reinforcement	1.50
	Total		$8.75

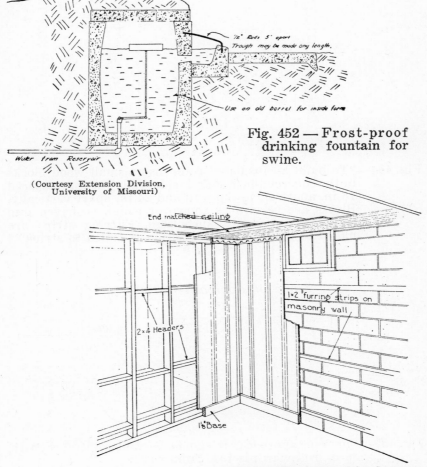

Fig. 452 — Frost-proof drinking fountain for swine.

(Courtesy Extension Division, University of Missouri)

(Courtesy Weyerhaeuser Sales Company)
Fig. 453—Preparation of walls for vertical panels.

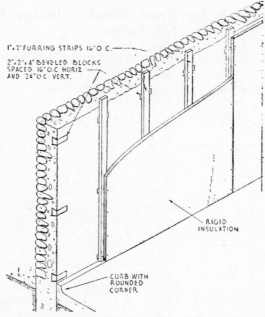

Fig. 454—"To build an insulated wall, insert small wood blocks in the concrete flush with inside wall. These are spaced 16 in. apart along the wall and 24 in. apart vertically. Blocks are beveled as shown or a nail is driven into each side to insure anchorage. Furring strips are nailed to blocks, rigid insulation is nailed to strips."*

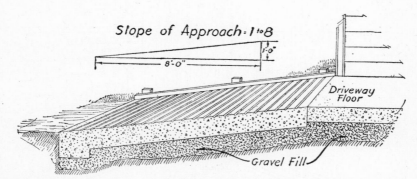

Fig. 455—Concrete approach. It should be well reinforced with ½-in. rod which is free from rust.

---

* Figures 454 and 455 courtesy Portland Cement Association.

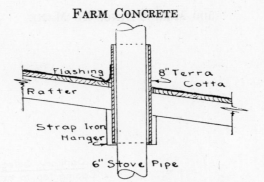

TERRA COTTA FLUE DETAIL

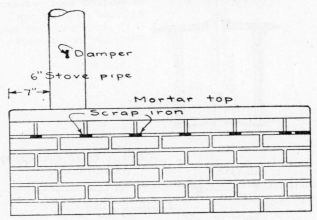

Side View

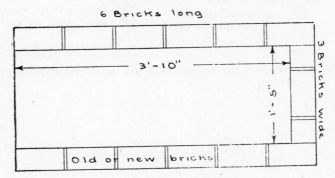

Floor Plan

(Courtesy Extension Division, University of Georgia)

Fig. 456—Brick brooder. One part cement and three parts sand
with just enough lime added to make it work well
used for mortar in laying the brick.

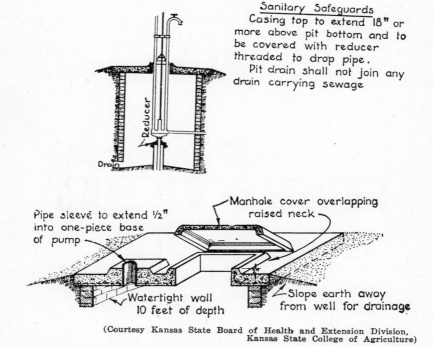

Sanitary Safeguards
Casing top to extend 18" or
more above pit bottom and to
be covered with reducer
threaded to drop pipe.
Pit drain shall not join any
drain carrying sewage

Reducer

Drain

Pipe sleeve to extend ½"
into one-piece base
of pump

Manhole cover overlapping
raised neck

Watertight wall
10 feet of depth

Slope earth away
from well for drainage

(Courtesy Kansas State Board of Health and Extension Division,
Kansas State College of Agriculture)

Fig. 457—A three-way pump and pit and reinforced concrete
well top.

PART V

FARM PLUMBING

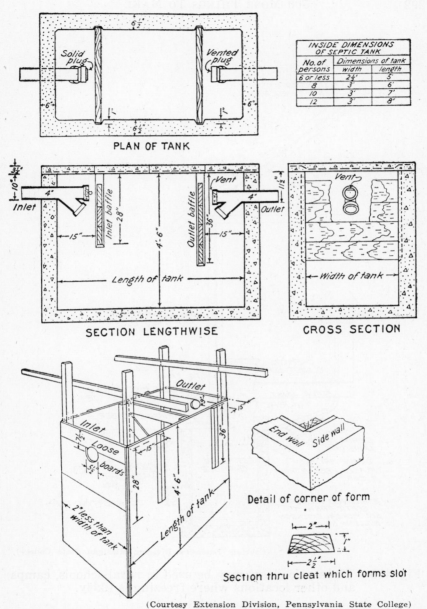

(Courtesy Extension Division, Pennsylvania State College)

Fig. 458—Septic tank. Dimensions are for nailed form. For bolted one with extra strips for community use, deduct 2 inches from the length and 3½ inches from the width in cutting lumber. Standard size has pieces 5 feet 10 inches and 2 feet 8½ inches, respectively, which makes a 3 by 6-foot tank holding 475 gallons.

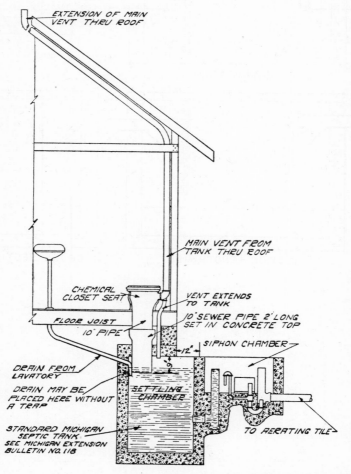

EXTENSION OF MAIN
VENT THRU ROOF

MAIN VENT FROM
TANK THRU ROOF

VENT EXTENDS
TO TANK

CHEMICAL
CLOSET SEAT

10" SEWER PIPE 2' LONG
SET IN CONCRETE TOP

FLOOR JOIST

10" PIPE

12"

SIPHON CHAMBER

DRAIN FROM
LAVATORY

DRAIN MAY BE
PLACED HERE WITHOUT
A TRAP

SETTLING
CHAMBER

STANDARD MICHIGAN
SEPTIC TANK
SEE MICHIGAN EXTENSION
BULLETIN NO. 118

TO AERATING TILE

(Courtesy Extension Division, Michigan State College)

Fig. 459—The septic closet may be used in rural schools, camps, and other locations where freezing is likely.

"The septic closet has been developed to meet a special condition where running water is not practical. In some cases running water is not available owing to a lack of power or because of limited quantities. There are other locations where it is not practical to have running water because of the danger of freezing. This is especially true in rural schools and camps.

"It is necessary to use some water with the septic closet. Water from the lavatory will be beneficial to the operation of the septic tank. Also it is necessary to pour a pail of water occasionally (daily in most cases) into the closet in order to wash down the drop tube and keep it in a sanitary condition."

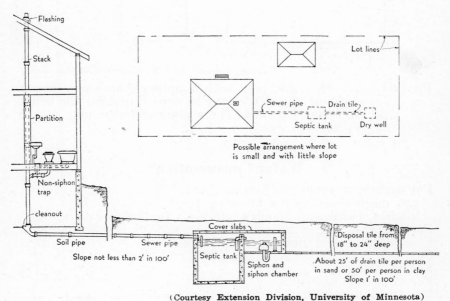

(Courtesy Extension Division, University of Minnesota)

Fig. 460—Complete sewage disposal system.

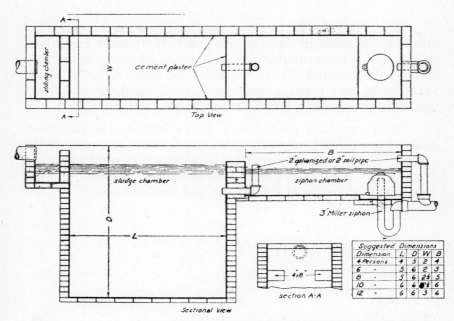

(Courtesy Extension Division, University of Minnesota)

Fig. 461—A brick septic tank with a siphon chamber. Concrete blocks or glazed tile may be substituted for the brick. No form is needed. The stilling chamber may not be necessary.

Water Consumption*

For each member of the family (average daily consumption allowing for kitchen. bathroom, laundry, etc.)	(gallons per day)	35
For each cow	" " "	30
For each horse or mule	" " "	15
For each hog	" " "	2
For each sheep	" " "	1½
For each 100 chickens	" " "	4
For sprinkling with ½-inch hose	(gallons per hour)	200
For sprinkling with ¾-inch hose	" " "	300

10 gallons will sprinkle 100 sq. ft.; 20 gallons will soak 100 sq. ft.

---

* From Georgia Extension Bulletin 483, "Electric Water Systems for the Farm."

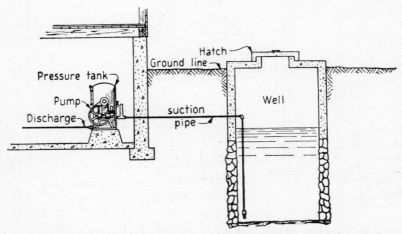

Fig. 462—A shallow well pump installed in basement.*

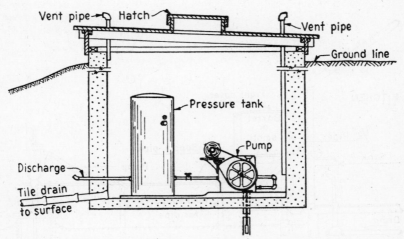

Fig. 463—A deep well pump in pit of good construction.

---

* Figures 462 and 463 courtesy Extension Division, Univ. of Georgia.

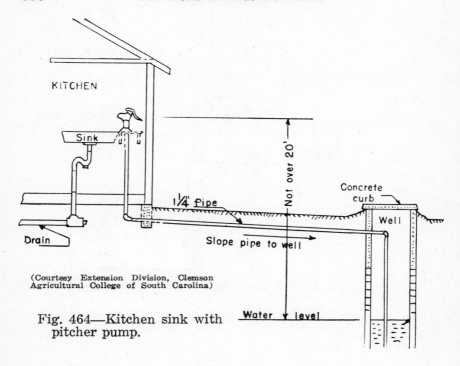

(Courtesy Extension Division, Clemson
Agricultural College of South Carolina)

Fig. 464—Kitchen sink with
  pitcher pump.

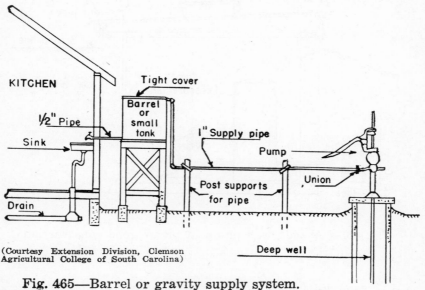

(Courtesy Extension Division, Clemson
Agricultural College of South Carolina)

Fig. 465—Barrel or gravity supply system.

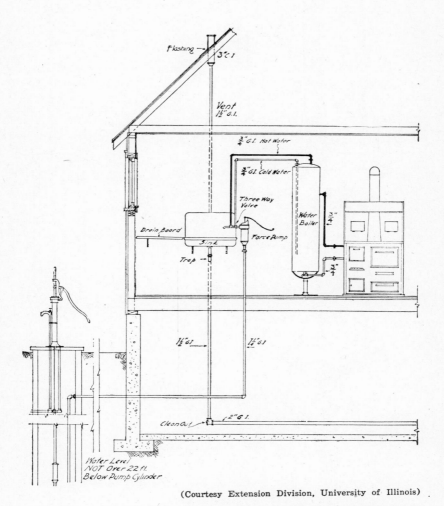

Fig. 466—An inexpensive hot and cold water system.

PART VI

ELECTRICITY
FOR THE FARM

Fig. 467—This drawing of a farm wiring distribution system shows how feeders should be planned for maximum efficiency. Separate feeders serve each main building.*

* Figures 467 and 468 courtesy General Electric.

Fig. 468—Cutaway view of house showing how "feeder wiring"
    assures convenient and efficient use of electricity.
    Note the heavy feeders going to control units on the
    first and second floors and the circuits starting at the
    control units. Note also the ample lighting outlets and
    many convenience outlets. Future as well as present
    needs are provided for.

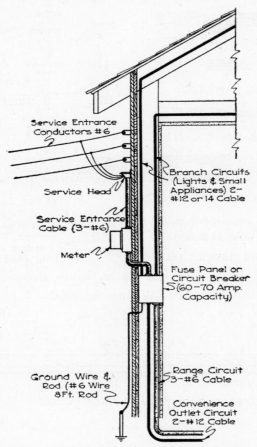

Service Entrance
Conductors #6

Service Head

Service Entrance
Cable (3-#6)

Meter

Branch Circuits
(Lights & Small
Appliances) 2-
#12 or 14 Cable

Fuse Panel or
Circuit Breaker
(60-70 Amp.
Capacity)

Ground Wire &
Rod (#6 Wire
8 Ft. Rod

Range Circuit
3-#6 Cable

Convenience
Outlet Circuit
2-#12 Cable

(Courtesy Extension Division, Iowa State College of Agriculture)

Fig. 469—Cross section of a typical installation showing service entrance and load center equipment. Main load center must have 60 or 70-ampere capacity in order to supply sufficient energy for the need of the average family.

"Cable or conduit for entrance wiring must be run in open or exposed locations either on the inside or outside of wall construction. A new type of fire and moisture-resistant, armored entrance cable is used in many present installations. Connections between service conductors and meters are made by the service entrance cable. These connections are called the meter loop."

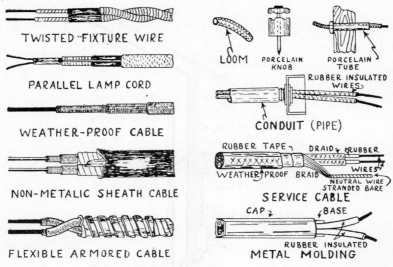

TWISTED FIXTURE WIRE

PARALLEL LAMP CORD

WEATHER-PROOF CABLE

NON-METALIC SHEATH CABLE

FLEXIBLE ARMORED CABLE

LOOM   PORCELAIN   PORCELAIN
        KNOB   TUBE

RUBBER INSULATED
WIRES

CONDUIT (PIPE)

RUBBER TAPE   DRAID   RUBBER

WEATHER PROOF BRAID   WIRES

NEUTRAL WIRE
STRANDED BARE

SERVICE CABLE

CAP   BASE

RUBBER INSULATED
METAL MOLDING

(Courtesy Extension Division, University of Kentucky)

Fig. 470—Wiring materials.

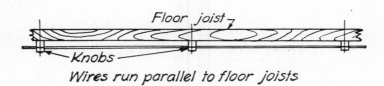

Floor joist

Knobs

Wires run parallel to floor joists

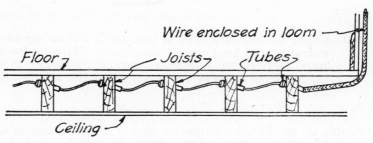

Wire enclosed in loom

Floor   Joists   Tubes

Ceiling

Wires run through floor joists

(Courtesy Extension Division, Kansas State College of Agriculture)

Fig. 471—Knob and tube wiring as used in the floor joists of a frame building.

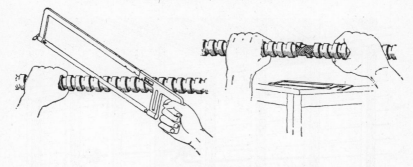

Cutting armored cable material.

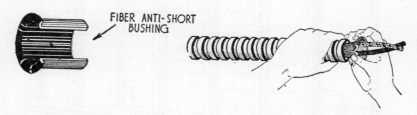

FIBER ANTI-SHORT
BUSHING

A fiber anti-short bushing should be used on end of cable.

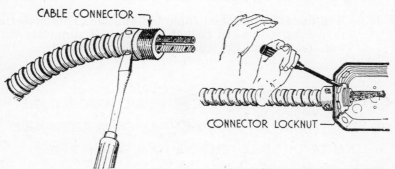

CABLE CONNECTOR

CONNECTOR LOCKNUT

(Courtesy Extension Division, Kansas State Agricultural College)

Fig. 472—Armored cable outlet box installation.
Fastening cable connector to cable with set screw.
Fastening cable to outlet box with locknut.

(Courtesy Extension Division, Iowa State College of Agriculture)

Fig. 473—Non-metallic sheathed cable installation. This material is moisture, fire and rodent-resistant. It simplifies wiring and reduces fire and electric shock hazard.

CEILING OUTLET   SPECIAL PURPOSE OUTLET

WALL FAN OUTLET   PULL CHAIN RECEPTACLE
                                                P.C.R.

S_1 LOCAL SWITCH - SINGLE POLE S_3 LOCAL SWITCH 3 - WAY

S_2 LOCAL SWITCH - DOUBLE POLE S_4 LOCAL SWITCH 4 - WAY

DOUBLE CONVENIENCE OUTLET

(Courtesy Extension Division, Kansas State Agricultural College)

Fig. 474—Wiring symbols used on house floor plans.

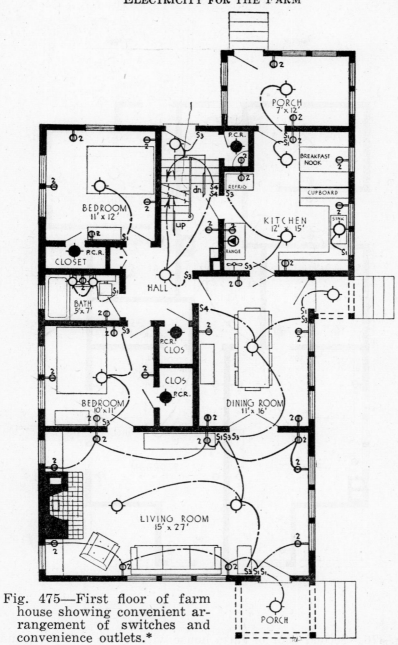

Fig. 475—First floor of farm house showing convenient arrangement of switches and convenience outlets.*

* Figures 475 to 477 courtesy Extension Division, Kansas State College of Agriculture.

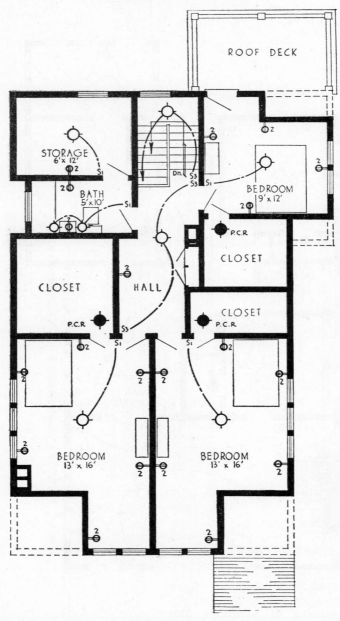

Fig. 476—Second floor of farm house with lights, switches, and convenience outlets as indicated.

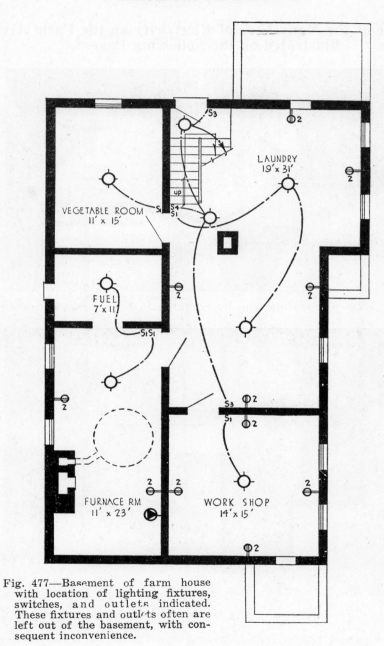

Fig. 477—Basement of farm house with location of lighting fixtures, switches, and outlets indicated. These fixtures and outlets often are left out of the basement, with consequent inconvenience.

Some of the Many Uses of Electricity on the Farm Are Illustrated on the Following Pages*

Fig. 478—Grindstone run by portable ¼-horsepower motor.

Fig. 479—Corn sheller run by portable 2-horsepower motor.

* Figures 478 to 484 courtesy Westinghouse Electric and Manufacturing Company.

Fig. 480—Meat grinder run by ¼-horsepower motor.

Fig. 481—Small grinder run by ¼-horsepower motor. Larger grinders need a ½-horsepower motor for best farm use.

Fig. 482—One-hole corn sheller run by ¼-horsepower motor.

Fig. 483—Fanning mill run by ¼-horsepower motor.

Fig. 484—Post drill run by ¼-horsepower motor.

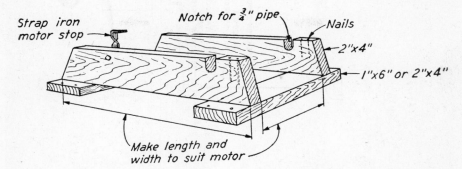

Strap iron motor stop

Notch for ¾" pipe

Nails

2"x4"

1"x6" or 2"x4"

Make length and width to suit motor

(Courtesy Extension Division, University of Tennessee)

Fig. 485—Homemade swing type motor base.

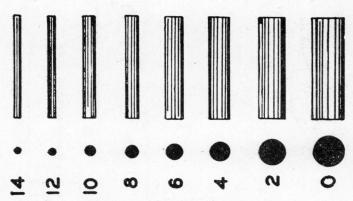

14   12   10   8   6   4   2   0

Fig. 486—Actual wire sizes.*

"The wire size to use depends upon the load in amperes and the length of the circuit. Wire sizes for the farm range from No. 0 to 14. The larger the number, the smaller the size of the wire. No. 14 wire is used for light and small-appliance circuits in the home, but the larger sizes are needed for the large-sized motors and heating equipment. No. 12 wire should be used for lighting with 32-volt farm electric plants. For circuits used exclusively for appliances in kitchen, laundry, or dining room, No. 12 wire is required. The greater the distance from the transformer to the equipment, the larger the size of wire required."

* Figures 486 to 495 with bill of materials from Bulletin 209, Building Electrical Equipment for the Farm, published by the Vocational Division, U. S. Office of Education in cooperation with the Rural Electrification Administration.

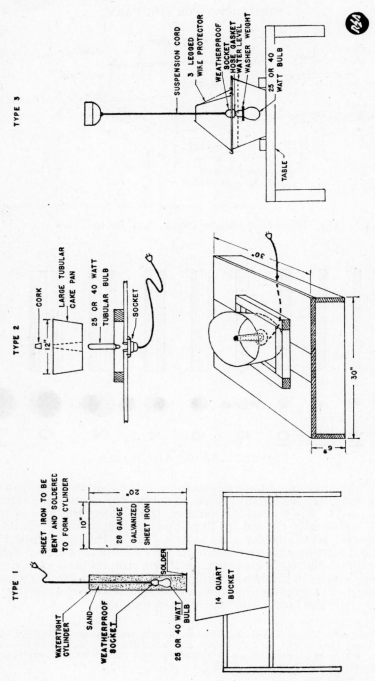

Fig. 487—Poultry water warmers.

Materials Needed for Poultry Water Warmers

Type 1

1 10′ rubber-covered extension cord with cap.
1 weatherproof socket.
1 25- or 40-watt bulb.
1 14-quart bucket.
1 piece 28-gauge galvanized sheet iron, 10″x20″.
1 piece 28-gauge galvanized sheet iron 4″x4″.

Type 2

1 1″ cork.
1 large tubular cake pan with solid bottom.
1 25- or 40-watt tubular bulb.
1 conduit box receptable and box.
1 10′ extension cord with cap.
1 1″x6″x14′ board.

1 1″x12″x5′ board.
1 lb. 6d nails.
2 No. 6 ¾″ screws.
Saw from stock lumber:
 3 1″x6″x30″ pieces.
 2 1″x6″x28″ pieces.
 2 1″x12″x30″ pieces.
 4 1″x1″x12″ pieces.

Type 3

6 to 8′ of suspension cord.
1 waterproof socket.
1 25- or 40-watt bulb.
1 1½″ washer.

1 large cake pan or dishpan.
4′ No. 9 steel wire.
1 ¾″ hose gasket.

Materials Needed for Ultra-Violet Reflectors

For 250-watt size

1 250-watt CX Mazda lamp.
1 15″ round aluminum dishpan.
1 conduit box receptacle similar to Bryant lampholder No. 9411.
2 1″x$\frac{3}{16}$″ round-head stove bolts.

1 roll electricians' rubber tape.
1 roll friction tape.
4′ to 6′ heavy-duty 2-wire suspension cord.
1 outlet box.
1 rosette cover.

For 60-watt size

1 60-watt CX Mazda lamp.
1 8″ round aluminum piepan.

Other materials the same as for 250-watt size above.

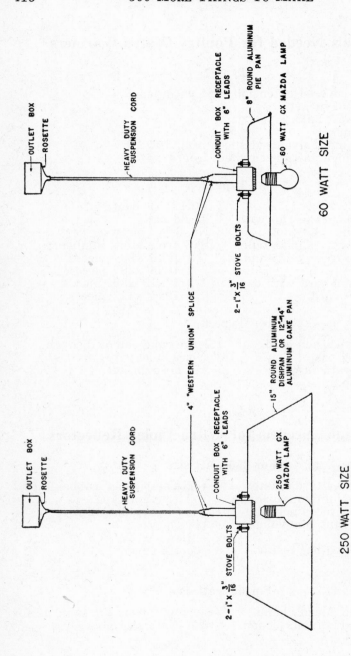

OUTLET BOX

ROSETTE

HEAVY DUTY
SUSPENSION CORD

CONDUIT BOX RECEPTACLE
WITH 6" LEADS

8" ROUND ALUMINUM
PIE PAN

60 WATT CX MAZDA LAMP

2 – 1"x $\frac{3}{16}$" STOVE BOLTS

60 WATT SIZE

4" "WESTERN UNION" SPLICE

15" ROUND ALUMINUM
DISHPAN OR 12"–14"
ALUMINUM CAKE PAN

CONDUIT BOX RECEPTACLE
WITH 6" LEADS

250 WATT CX
MAZDA LAMP

2 – 1" x $\frac{3}{16}$" STOVE BOLTS

250 WATT SIZE

Fig. 488—Ultra-violet reflectors.

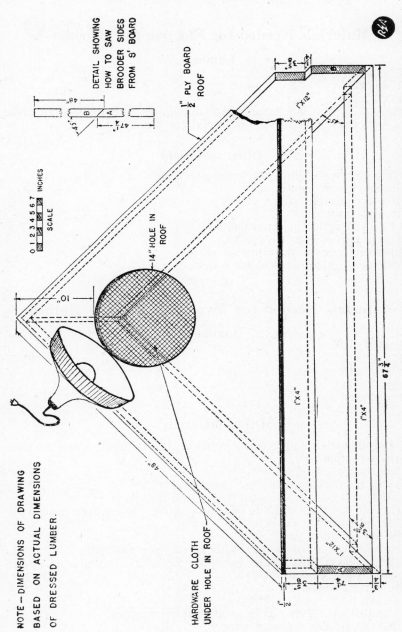

DETAIL SHOWING
HOW TO SAW
BROODER SIDES
FROM 9' BOARD

48"

45°

47¼"

B

A

0 1 2 3 4 5 6 7 INCHES

SCALE

½" PLY BOARD ROOF

1" PLY BOARD ROOF

14" HOLE IN ROOF

10"

NOTE—DIMENSIONS OF DRAWING BASED ON ACTUAL DIMENSIONS OF DRESSED LUMBER.

HARDWARE CLOTH UNDER HOLE IN ROOF

49"

1"X12"

1"X4"

1"X4"

1"X12"

67¾"

½"

5"

3½"

7¼"

3½"

⅝"

Fig. 489—Electric pig brooder. (⅜" plywood should be substituted for the ½" ply board roof.)

Materials Needed for Electric Pig Brooder
Lumber
1 1"x12"x8'.
1 1"x4"x12'.
1 1"x6"x12'.
1 piece ⅜" plywood, triangular shaped, 48"x48"x67¾" (a piece
    ⅜"x4'x8' will provide material for 4 roofs).

Other materials
1 strip hardware cloth, ½"mesh, 18"x18".
½ lb. 8d common nails.
½ lb. 6d common nails.
½ lb. wire staples.
1 14" RLM reflector, enameled.
1 weatherproof electric socket.
1 10' rubber-covered extension cord.
1 100-watt or 150-watt electric lamp.

Materials Needed for Two Sash Electric Hotbed
Lumber
2 2"x12"x12'.
1 2"x 6"x12'.
5 1"x 2"x12'.
1 1"x 4"x12'.
1 2"x 4"x 8'.

Other materials
60' lead sheathed soil-heating cable or 120' rubber sheathed soil-
    heating cable.
1 weatherproof plug.
1 strip hardware cloth, ½" mesh, 36"x12'.
1 weatherproof duplex outlet box and outlet.
1 thermostat with outside manual control (25-ampere capacity).
3 lbs. 8d common nails.
1 lb. 6d common nails.
8 corner braces for sashes with screws for fastening.
2 strips glass substitute for sash 36"x72" (should carry at
    least 2-year guarantee).
½ lb. carpet tacks.
8 screen door hooks and eyes.
6" conduit or service drop cable and connectors.
4" No. 12 rubber covered wire.

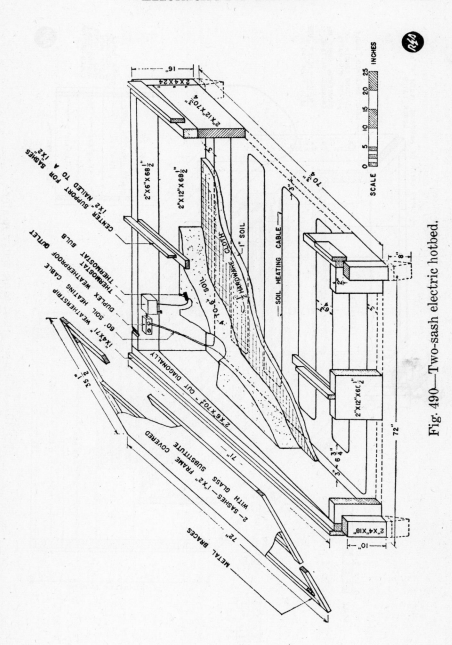

Fig. 490—Two-sash electric hotbed.

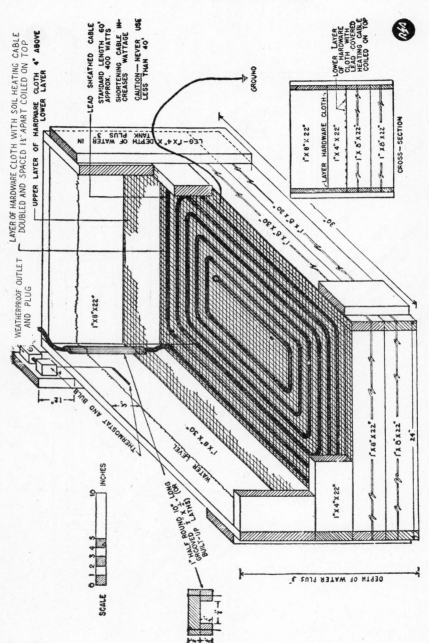

Fig. 491—Electric stock tank water heater.

Materials Needed for Electric Stock Tank Water Heater

Lumber

(A water depth of approximately 25″ in the tank is assumed.)
1 1″x4″x10′ sides and ends enclosing heating unit when assembled.
1 1″x4″x3′ additional support for lead heating cable.
1 1″x8″x8′ ends.
2 1″x8″x10′ (or 12′ if preferred) sides and ends.
1 10″ piece of half-round or 20″ of quarter-round or 1 lath.
1 1″x4″x10′ (estimate) leg.
1 1″x8″x4′ leg.

Other materials

1 strip ½″ mesh hardware cloth 24″x60″.
60′ lead or 120′ rubber sheathed soil-heating cable.
Insulated ground wire, about 6′.
1 weatherproof outlet.
1 weatherproof plug.
1 thermostat with outside manual control.
1 ¾″x8′-6″ galvanized iron pipe.
2 lbs. 6d nails.
1 lb. ½″ wire staples.
4″ galvanized conduit and connectors.
3′ No. 12 rubber sheathed wire (or service drop cable or waterproof connectors in place of wire and conduit).

Materials Needed for Portable Electric Motor

1 piece of No. 10 rubber-covered wire 36″ long.
2 pieces ¾″ galvanized gas pipe, lengths equal to over-all width of motor.
4 ¼″x1½″ flat-head stove bolts.
4 locknut washers to fit bolts.
4 plain washers to fit bolts.
1 piece rubber-covered extension cord equipped with plug, federal bushing for ½″ knockout and, if desired, a combination switch and thermal cutout.
1 5″ 4-step V-pulley with shaft opening same size as shaft of motor.
1 standard with bearings and shaft. See speed reducers, Fig. 492.
1 12″ V-pulley to fit shaft of standard.
1 2″ V-pulley to fit shaft of standard.
2″x12″ plank for holder and speed-reducer bases.
2 ¾″ pipe straps.

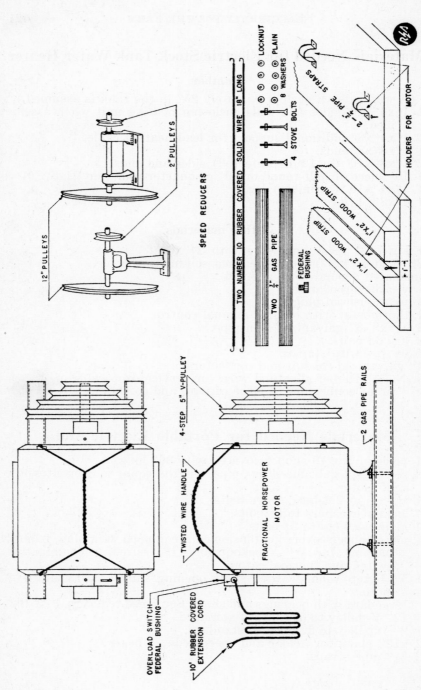

Fig. 492—Electric portable motor.

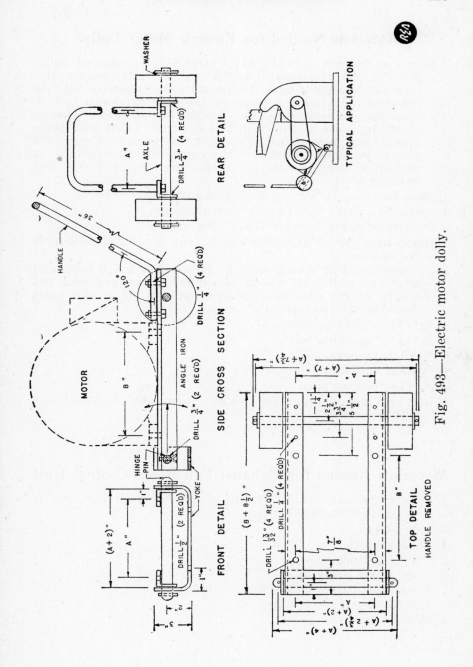

Fig. 493—Electric motor dolly.

Materials Needed for Electric Motor Dolly

2 pieces angle iron $\frac{1}{4}$"x1$\frac{1}{2}$"x1$\frac{1}{2}$"x(B+8$\frac{1}{2}$)" frame of dolly. See Fig. 493. The dimensions "A' and "B" refer to measurements on the motor base. A represents the crosswise distance between the mounting holes on the base as shown in this drawing. B represents the lengthwise distance between mounting holes as shown in this drawing. These measaurements must be accurate. Frequent reference to Figure 493 should be made throughout the construction, especially to determine exact points for measuring, boring holes, and bending pieces.

1 piece bar iron $\frac{1}{4}$"x2"   (A+8")long for yoke.

1 cold rolled shaft $\frac{3}{4}$"x(A+4)" for hinge pin.

1 cold rolled shaft $\frac{3}{4}$"x(A+7$\frac{3}{4}$)" for axle.

1 round iron rod $\frac{5}{8}$"x(A+85)" or 1" iron pipe of same length for handle.

2 5" bag-truck iron wheels with 2" face width, a $\frac{3}{4}$" bore, and 2$\frac{3}{8}$" hub width. (If wheels of a different size are used, the length of the axle and distance between cotter pin holes might need to be altered.)

4 $\frac{3}{8}$"x1$\frac{1}{2}$" machine bolts.

4 $\frac{1}{4}$"x1$\frac{1}{4}$" machine bolts.

8 $\frac{3}{8}$" flat washers.

2 $\frac{3}{4}$" flat washers.

4 $\frac{3}{16}$"x1$\frac{1}{2}$" cotter pins.

If iron pipe is used for handle, two 90° elbows and two 45° elbows will be needed.

Materials Needed for Exhaust Fan Room Cooling Unit

1 piece of lumber 1"x12" x width of window plus 12", oak or similar quality preferred.

2 door pulls.

1 4" barrel bolt.

2 3"x3" butt hinges.

2 6"x8" shelf brackets.

1 8" non-oscillating electric fan.

4 doz. No. 6 screws, $\frac{3}{4}$" long.

4 8d nails.

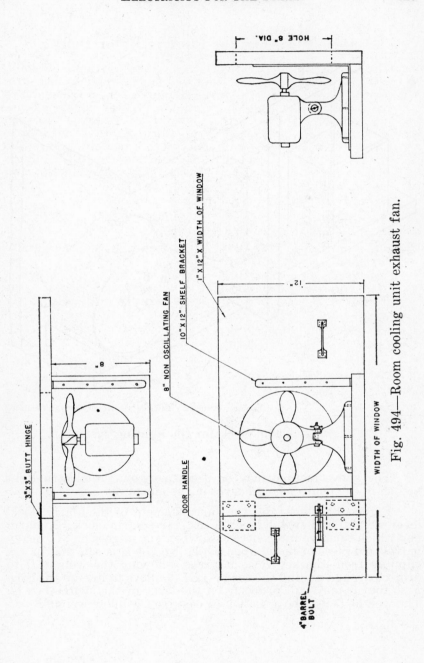

Fig. 494—Room cooling unit exhaust fan.

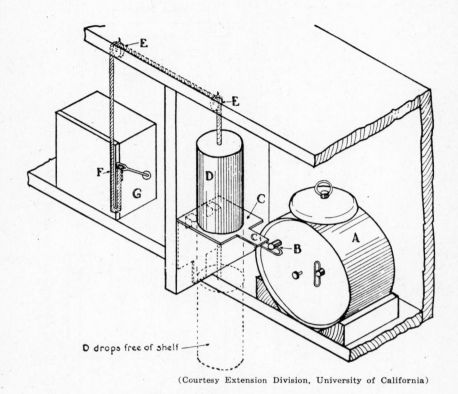

D drops free of shelf

(Courtesy Extension Division, University of California)

Fig. 495—Alarm clock for the lighting system.

The above method may be used to throw the electric-light switch in the poultry house early in the morning.

Figure 495 illustrates the "arrangement of the alarm clock, lever weight, and switch box: A, ordinary alarm clock; B, alarm key which turns counter clockwise when alarm goes off; C, heavy galvanized piece of metal upon which weight D is set, the tip. C_1, slipping from the key B as it turns, allowing the weight D to drop clear, and pulling the cord F; EE, pulleys to line up the cord F so that it may pull properly on the lever of the switch box G. The weight D may be a section of cast-iron window weight."

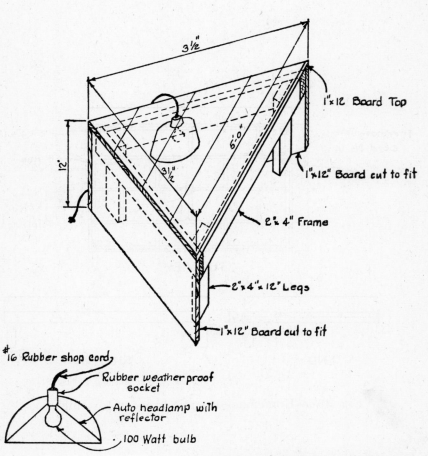

3½"

1"x12 Board Top

1"x12" Board cut to fit

6'-0"

12'

3½"

2"x 4" Frame

2"x4"x12" Legs

1"x12" Board cut to fit

#16 Rubber shop cord,

Rubber weather proof
socket

Auto headlamp with
reflector

100 Watt bulb

(Courtesy V. J. Morford, Seward, Nebraska)

Fig. 496—Lamp type electric pig brooder.

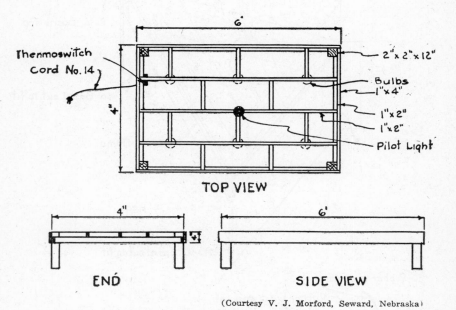

(Courtesy V. J. Morford, Seward, Nebraska)

Fig. 497—Homemade electric brooder for chicks.

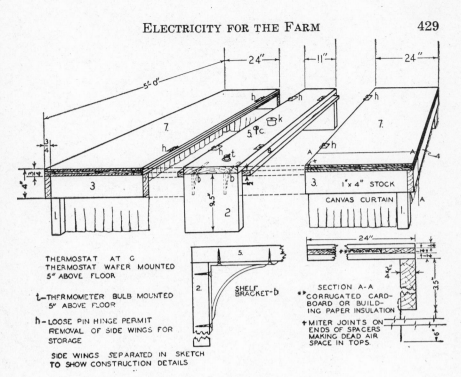

THERMOSTAT AT c
THERMOSTAT WAFER MOUNTED
5" ABOVE FLOOR

t—THERMOMETER BULB MOUNTED
5" ABOVE FLOOR

h—LOOSE PIN HINGE PERMIT
REMOVAL OF SIDE WINGS FOR
STORAGE

SIDE WINGS SEPARATED IN SKETCH
TO SHOW CONSTRUCTION DETAILS

SHELF
BRACKET-b

SECTION A-A
**CORRUGATED CARD-
BOARD OR BUILD-
ING PAPER INSULATION

+MITER JOINTS ON
ENDS OF SPACERS
MAKING DEAD AIR
SPACE IN TOPS.

SPECIFICATIONS: ALL LUMBER NO. 1 COMMON

	NAME OF PIECE	NO. PIECES	SIZE T	W	L	MATERIAL	COST PER FOOT	TOTAL COST
1	CORNER LEG	4	0-2	0-2	0-9.5	FIR	0.025	0.03
2	CENTER LEG	2	0-3/4	0-11	0-9.5	"		0.10
3	END RAIL	4	0-3/4	0-4	1-10.25	"		0.06
4	SIDE RAIL	2	0-3/4	0-4	5-0	"		0.08
5	CENTER TOP	1	0-3/4	0-11	5-0	"		0.11
6	CENTER RAIL	2	0-3/4	0-8	4-8.5	"		0.04
7	SIDE TOP	4	0-1/4	2-0	5-0	PLYWOOD		0.60
	SPACER STRIPS	6	0-1/4	0-11/2	5-0			
h	HINGES	2 PAIR		0-3	0-3	LOOSE PIN, IRON, BUTT	0.20 PAIR	0.40
b	SHELF BRACKET	2 PAIR		0-5	0-6	IRON	0.20 PAIR	0.40
	SCREWS		3/4" FLATHEAD	7 GAGE		IRON	FURNISHED WITH*	
	NAILS, TACKS		6 PENNY BOX.	CARPET TACKS				
	CANVAS	3 YARDS (APP.)	0-8	18-0		WATER-PROOFED	0.55 YARD (APP.)	1.50
k	ELECTRICAL KIT							17.50
							TOTAL COST	20.22

(Courtesy Agricultural Engineering Department, Oregon Agricultural College)

Fig. 498—Home built fan-type electric brooder. 500-chick capacity.

PART VII

HANDY FARM HINTS

(Courtesy Extension Division, Pennsylvania State College)

Fig. 499—Water container for poultry.

"A device commonly used is an enamel kitchen sink filled by a faucet conveniently located over the sink. It may be set in the partition so as to furnish water for two pens. An overflow pipe that can be unscrewed at the bottom of the sink will permit easy cleaning and flushing out. Even when water must be carried this type of water container is practical."

433

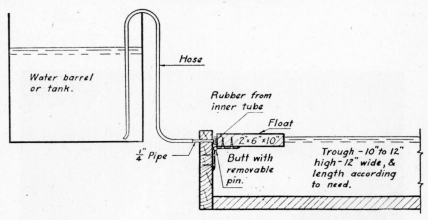

Water barrel or tank.

Hose

Rubber from inner tube

Float

2"x6"x10"

¼" Pipe

Butt with removable pin.

Trough – 10" to 12" high – 12" wide, & length according to need.

(Courtesy Extension Division, University of Minnesota)

Fig. 500.

"Frequently it is necessary to pasture sheep where water is not available. This requires the hauling of water. A wagon tank or barrel, according to capacity needed, may be used for this. The water trough illustrated with a float to control the flow makes an inexpensive self-watering piece of equipment when connected to the wagon tank or barrels."

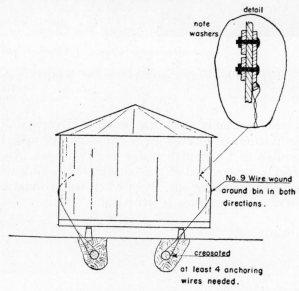

detail

note washers

No. 9 Wire wound around bin in both directions.

creosoted

at least 4 anchoring wires needed.

(Courtesy Extension Division, North Dakota Agricultural College)

Fig. 501—A method of anchoring metal bins.

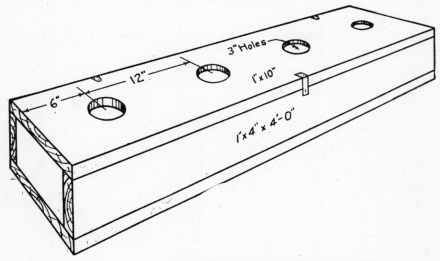

(Courtesy Extension Division, University of Minnesota)

Fig. 502—"Prevention is the only control for grub in the head. Pine tar on the noses repels the fly causing the infestation. A salt box with pine tar smeared around the hole the sheep reach through for salt applies the tar where needed. Pads of gunny bagging around these holes hold the pine tar. This salt box is 3 or 4 inches deep and has openings 3 inches across."

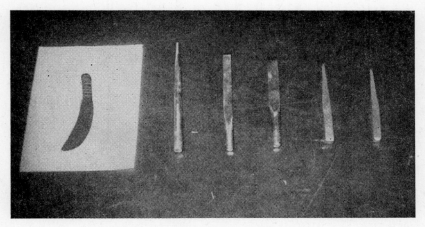

Fig. 503—Chisels, punches and rivet cutters may be made from old cylinder teeth.

Fig. 504—Punches made from hay rake tooth.

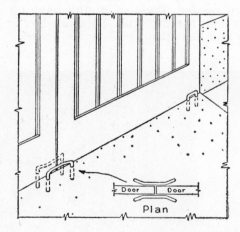

(Courtesy U. S. D. A.)

Fig. 505—Homemade sliding door stay made from 1″ iron rod.

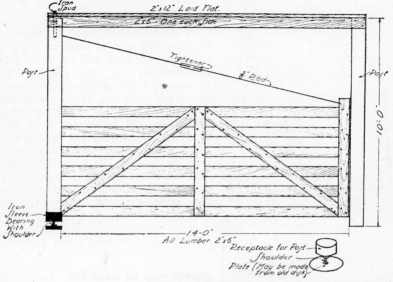

(Courtesy Extension Division, University of Wyoming)

Fig. 506—Stock gate.

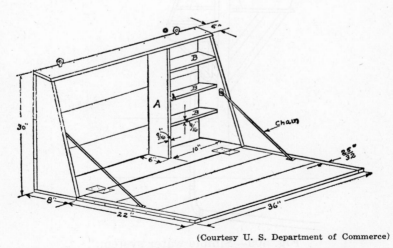

(Courtesy U. S. Department of Commerce)

Fig. 507—Wall desk (1-inch lumber may be used).

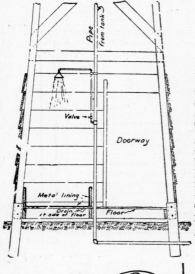

Fig. 508—Shower bath in tank tower.

A shower bath such as shown in Figure 508 can be built at very little expense, and will be very much appreciated on the farm. This shower is built on the tower for the elevated tank so as to save pipe. The pipe from the tank is tapped and a cut-off valve set in a small pipe which carries the water overhead. The small pipe may be ½-inch or ¾-inch in size. The sprinkler on the pipe may be omitted if desired. The floor under the shower may consist of boards, covered with galvanized iron.

(Courtesy Extension Division, Texas A. and M. College)

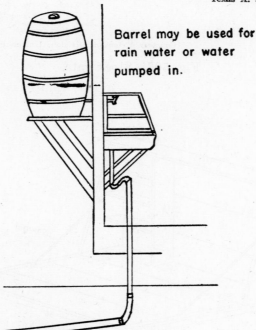

Barrel may be used for rain water or water pumped in.

Fig. 509—Simple water system.*

* Figures 509 to 511 courtesy U. S. Office of Education, Education and Training of NYA Project Workers.

A sink embedded in cement with drain pipe connection.

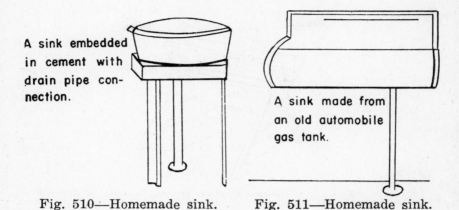

A sink made from an old automobile gas tank.

Fig. 510—Homemade sink. Fig. 511—Homemade sink.

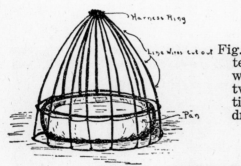

Fig. 512—Drinking fountain protector made from electric lawn weld fence with the line wires twisted off to permit hens puttings their heads through to drink.

(Courtesy Experiment Station, University of Maryland)

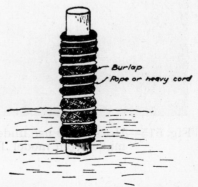

Fig. 513—A homemade rubbing post for hogs.

(Courtesy Extension Division, University of Missouri)

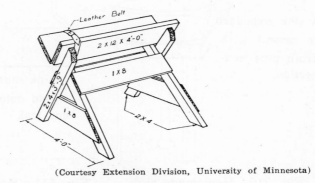

(Courtesy Extension Division, University of Minnesota)

Fig. 514—Castrating trough for hogs.

Fig. 515—Horses for use under cars, trucks and the like may be made from model T Ford differential housings.

Fig. 516—Homemade garbage container made from scrap pieces and old grease bucket. Made by metal working class at Fargo, North Dakota.

"To make scalding easy, you need plenty of hot water at the right temperature. Here are several suggestions. A galvanized tank, set so a fire can be built under it, is an ideal arrangement. Beside it build a heavy solid table for scraping. Or, there's nothing much better than a big, old bathtub for scalding. Fire can be built under it. It's heavy and lasts indefinitely. It makes it easy to slide the hog in and out. Many farmers use a tight barrel, leaned at a 45° angle, at one end of the scraping table. Water can be heated in a large kettle or old wash boiler and emptied into the barrel. A little lye or wood ashes added to the water makes scraping easier. The water should be heated to around 150°."

Fig. 517—Scalding equipment.*

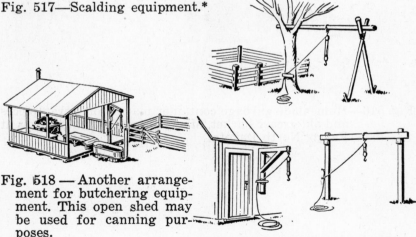

Fig. 518 — Another arrangement for butchering equipment. This open shed may be used for canning purposes.

Fig. 519—Hoisting arrangements for butchering.

* Figures 517 to 519 courtesy Morton Salt Company and Agricultural Leaders Digest.

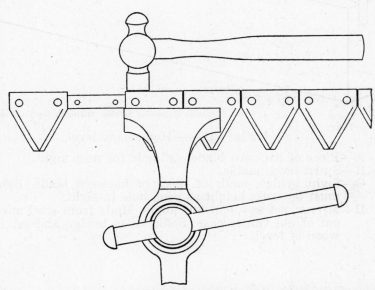

(Courtesy Extension Division, University of Kentucky)

Fig. 520—"In removing sections place the knife in a horizontal
position with the sections between the jaws of a vise
so that the bar rests on the edge of the jaw and the
sections will slide down between the jaws when the
rivets are sheared. Shear the rivets by striking the
edge of the section with a hammer."

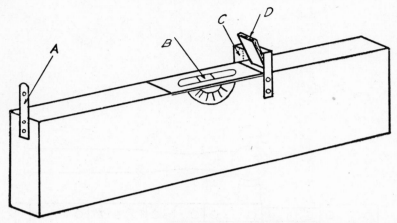

(Courtesy Extension Service, Michigan State College)

Fig. 521——Homemade level.

A—Piece of hacksaw blade, $\frac{1}{16}''$ hole for peep sight.

B—Spirit level bubble.

C—Sight bridge, made of piece of hacksaw blade. Bridge must be exact height as peep hole in sight.

D—Mirror, set at about 30° angle. Made from steel mirror out of old vanity case. Soldered to bridge and set into wood of level.

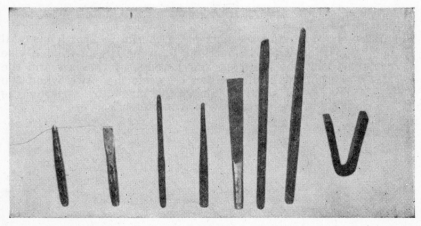

Fig. 522—Punches and chisels made from a magnet in metal working class at Monroe City, Indiana.

Fig. 523—Punches, chisels and scribers made from re-enforcing
steel in the metal working class at Fargo, N. Dakota.

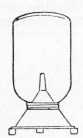

Fig. 524—Fly trap.*

"A dandy flytrap made with funnel and a fruit
jar. Put bait under the jar and empty by pouring
water down the funnel and simply throwing out
the flies. Set the jar down on three little pieces of
wood."

"Take two old tire rims, like
those used on a '29 Chevrolet,
and heat them in the middle to
bend them open as illustrated in
the drawing. Then bore holes in
them, so they can be bolted onto
a stand. Fifty-gallon barrels will
set in these rims tightly and
there will not be any danger of
the barrels falling off."

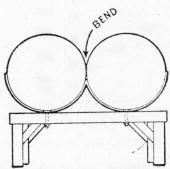

Fig. 525—Barrel holder.

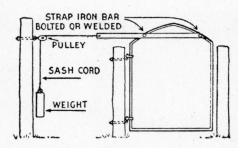

Fig. 526—Method of keeping a gate shut.

"This method of always keeping the gate shut works well where children forget to shut the gate, and chickens and dogs keep coming into the yard. The gate works as as well both ways and will stay shut even in a high wind. The change can be made easily with little labor and materials. Four feet of sash cord, a small pulley, an old weight, and a piece of strap iron are all that is needed."

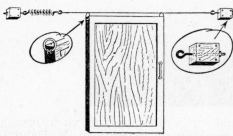

Fig. 527—Hanging light weight doors.

"Lightweight d o o r s, such as those made of plywood or light panel material, can be hung on tightly stretched wire instead of a track. The wire is fixed above a door in place of a regular track, stretched tightly between blocks of wood through which eyebolts pass. A good, strong, spring from a plow or cultivator may be used to keep wire constantly taut. Place a ring on each upper corner of door and let these rings slide over wire."

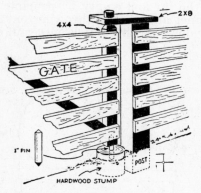

Fig. 528—Hingeless gate.

"A 'hingeless' gate can be constructed easily by nailing a four-by-four on the hinge end of the gate and rounding it on the top. On this is fitted a two-by-eight with a three-inch hole in it. The two-by-eight is nailed to the gatepost top. In the bottom of the four-by-four a one-inch hole is bored, and one also in a hardwood stump which is set next to the post. A pin is placed in the holes, permitting gate to turn freely either way."

* Figures 524 to 538, inclusive, and quotations, courtesy Successful Farming.

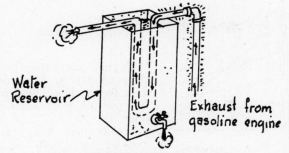

Fig. 529—Heating hot water.

A tank may be built in the milkhouse so that the exhaust pipe from a pump engine can be run through the water in the tank. By the time the engine has done its job of pumping water, running the separator, and so on, hot water for washing the utensils is ready.

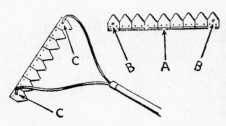

Fig. 530—Dandelion eradicator.

"One can take a short scrap of an old mowing-machine sickle and make a good dandelion eradicator. To do this, get a piece of sickle with the sections slightly longer than the width of the yoke of an old worn-out garden rake. Now take the old rake and cut off the head, leaving the yoke prongs only, and bend each of these ends down as shown at C. About an inch and a half should be bent. Then mark and drill a hole in each end of the sickle pieces at B so the ends of the yoke which have been turned down can be set in the holes and riveted lightly on the underside. The bar should be down, below the sections. Front edge of bar may be beveled."

"Nail two horseshoes on a block of wood opposite each other. Place the boards or sticks in the claw of the horseshoe on the block of wood. Then the boards or sticks do not fly around while being chopped."

Fig. 531—Method of holding wood while chopping.

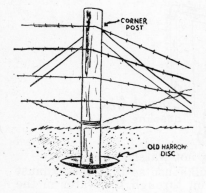

Fig. 532—Corner post anchor.

Corner posts may be anchored very solidly by fastening an old disk to the lower end of the corner post. A good-sized lag screw does the trick. This absolutely prevents the post from being heaved by frost—or anything else, in fact.

"To repair old, worn-out rollers on binders or headers, nail a strap of leather or webbing about two inches wide around the end of the roller, as shown. Set the pin in the center of the worn-out pin hole and fill the hole with babbitt. If the cracks are

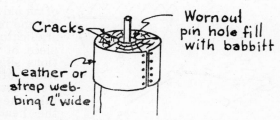

Fig. 533—Worn-out roller repaired.

very deep, wrap a newspaper tightly over the rollers so the babbitt cannot run out the sides."

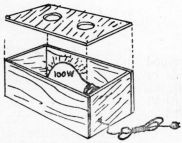

Fig. 534—Egg candler.

An egg candler may be made from a box 12 inches long and 5 inches wide. Two holes are drilled in the top, which is placed as shown in the diagram. A 100-watt bulb is used in the box.

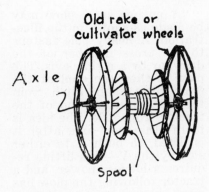

Fig. 535—Barbed wire reel.

"A barbed-wire reel may be made with two old, high rake or cultivator wheels about 45 to 50 inches high, set about 30 inches apart on an axle. The axle is one-inch iron long enough to extend beyond the hubs of the high wheels. On this same axle, between the two high wheels, put two smaller cultivator wheels, about 28 or 30 inches high, and set them about two feet apart. By placing six-inch boards between spokes of small wheels and drawing small wheels tight against ends of boards with a wire, this "spool" will be held in place. This will hold 180 to 240 rods of wire, and wire can be wound onto spool quickly. If a regular wire spool is handy, it can be swung onto the axle between the large wheels as shown in the drawing."

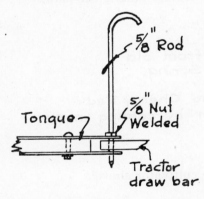

Fig. 536—Tractor draw-bar pin.

A pin of this type is easily made and can be pulled out of the tractor draw-bar without getting off the seat.

Old sickle blades can easily be driven into the earth to use as fence anchors. Simply take a piece of inch pipe four feet long and slot it at one end. Inside it drop a one-half-inch rod four and one-half feet long to tap the blade out of the slot when in the ground. Drill one-half-inch holes in the sickle sections for the heavy-gauge anchor wires. The pipe and rod are easily pulled out of the ground, but the sickle blades remain as excellent anchors for the fence.

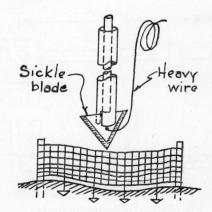

Fig. 537—Fence anchors.

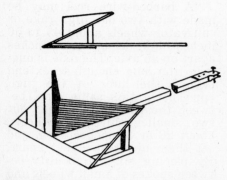

Fig. 538—Homemade snow plow.

"A pusher snow plow may be made as shown in the illustration. A heavy pole fastens to the cross member of the drawbar by a rigid clevis. The plow is then centered at the front by a chain hitch from the pole to either end of the tractor front axle. The idea is to lift the snow and, after it is lifted, to push it to either side by the V—this lifting requires a lot less power, and a tractor following the plow has much better traction than a tractor pulling the plow."

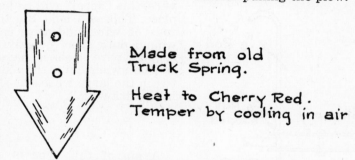

Made from old Truck Spring.

Heat to Cherry Red. Temper by cooling in air

Fig. 539—Homemade cultivator shovel.

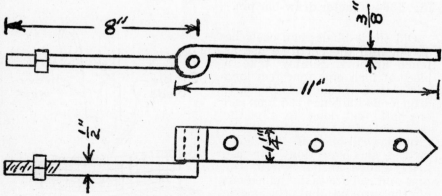

(Courtesy Justin R. Tucker, Arkansas Division of Vocational Education)

Fig. 540—Homemade gate hinge made from old rod and a car spring.

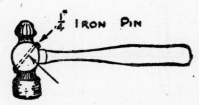

Fig. 541—Hammer head
tighten er.*

"We have all seen nails, staples, wood and metal driven into
the end of hammer handles to
prevent the head from coming
off. None is equal to the method
shown. A quarter inch pin placed
at an angle through both hammer head and handle will keep
the head from working loose and
flying off."

"Here is a way to make
hog slopping a little easier
and safer. Take an old milk
or cream can, cut the bottom
out and bolt the can firmly to
a strong post at the end of
the hog trough as shown in
the illustration."

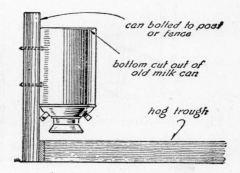

Fig. 542—Hog slopper.

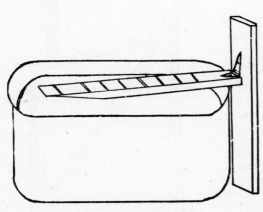

Fig. 543—Chicken saver.

"For one reason or
other chickens will in-
sist on drinking out of
livestock tanks, and
each year a large num-
ber of chickens are
drowned.

"The board shown in
the drawing rises and
falls with the water in
the tank and can al-
ways be reached by
the chickens. The
board should be a strip
that is about three
inches wide. The cleats
can be ½ by one-inch
pieces."

* Figures 541 to 577, inclusive, and quotations, courtesy American Farm
Youth magazine.

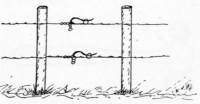

"To make a handy gate in a temporary fence fasten a harness snap to one end of the wire and a few links of chain to the other end."

Fig. 544—Temporary gate.

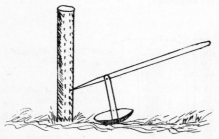

Fig. 545—Steel post puller.

"This is a low cost easily carried post puller. Sharpen the end of a buggy axle, making the front small enough to fit into a steel post, or into the link of a log chain. The axle is fastened six inches back from the point where the fulcrum is bolted. This fulcrum is made of two pieces of one-half inch by one-fourth inch iron bent at the bottom and fastened to a disc that spreads the load on the ground. By applying the body weight or force on the axle the post will lift out of the ground."

"A good method to anchor a fence corner is to dig a hole two feet in diameter, three or more feet deep. Two holes are bored in the butt of the post about four or five inches from the bottom. In these holes are inserted iron rods in shape of a cross. The post is put in the hole, which is filled with dirt up to the rods and well tamped. Then fill with rocks and dirt, tamping it well. The posts should be wired tightly together. This corner will not pull out and makes a neat looking job."

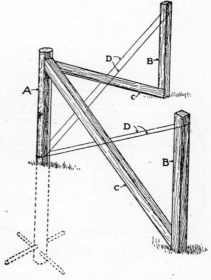

Fig. 546—Anchor for fence corner.

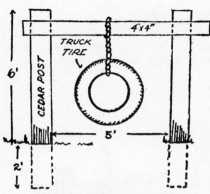

Fig. 547—Bull exerciser.

"Here is a farm experience that has been proven and found to be well worth the cost and time to construct. As shown in the accompanying illustration, the rig is used to keep a bull busy in the pen. The bull can hook and play with the tire as much as he wishes without damage to his horns; it also keeps him from pushing on the fence.

"Use a heavy discarded truck tire and suspend it from the cross bar so that it will swing free. Strong cedar posts are suggested for use as they last longer."

"An old tire casing fitted with a board and attached to the pulley as shown provides a convenient seat from which the hay carrier in a barn may be repaired. Quite often, when hay is pulled up, the plunger does not release the carrier as it should. With this device the farmer can be safely pulled up to make the repairs."

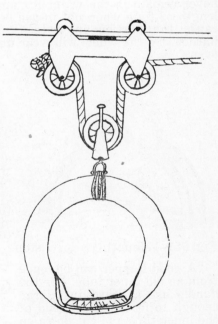

Fig. 548—Handy seat for hay carrier repairing.

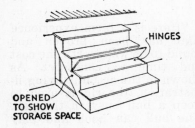

Fig. 549—Step cupboard.

"The hinged step as shown in the illustration with a cupboard space beneath keeps over-shoes out of sight and is always handy."

"As a means of keeping plenty of water on a grindstone, a simple, yet effective method is shown. A section of an old water-tight tire is used. The tire should be fastened in such a manner as to be easily removed or dropped away from the grindstone wheel. The wheel should never remain in the water for any length of time when not in use because the portion in water will harden and the wheel will wear uneven."

Fig. 550—Water trough for grindstone.

Fig. 551—Mounting a grindstone.

"Saw a felloe of an old wagon wheel in two. To keep the two semi-circles the right distance apart use a wooden block as illustrated. By placing four wooden blocks, a little longer than the stone is wide, between the felloe they will keep their shape and allow the foot paddle to be fastened with a strap hinge."

"A good slapper can be made from an old inner tube. For the handle use a board just large enough to fit inside one end of the inner tube and cut down on the other end to fit the hand. The inner tube is nailed securely to the handle, and the harmless slapper is ready for use."

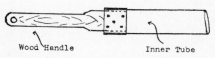

Fig. 552—Animal persuader.

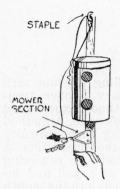

Fig. 553—Twine holder.

"Considerable twine is used around the farm throughout the year for many purposes and a suitable holder is very desirable. Remove the twine box from a discarded binder and attach it to the wall of the shop or barn. Then screw a sickle section to the studding to be used for a cutter. This method of handling twine will not only be handy but it will also keep the twine in good condition."

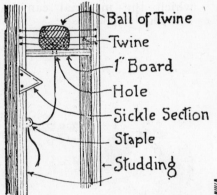

Ball of Twine
Twine
1" Board
Hole
Sickle Section
Staple
Studding

Fig. 554—Twine holder.

"Take a one-inch board and cut it to fit between the studding in the shop. A hole bored through the board, allows the twine to pass through while the ball is held in place by strips on either side. The twine passes through a staple in one stud while just above is fastened a sharpened sickle section."

"When pouring a liquid through an ordinary funnel into a bottle, the funnel usually fails to work properly on account of the air back-pressure in the bottle. A simple remedy for this difficulty is to bend a small piece of tubing to the shape of a funnel and solder it in place, as indicated in the drawing."

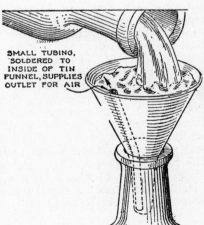

SMALL TUBING, SOLDERED TO INSIDE OF TIN FUNNEL, SUPPLIES OUTLET FOR AIR

Fig. 555—Air vent funnel.

Fig. 556—Sack funnel.

"When filling a grain sack in the ordinary manner, trouble is sometimes experienced when the sack sags. A method of overcoming such difficulty is shown in the illustration. A funnel is made by removing the bottom of a pail and inserting the pail into the mouth of the grain sack. The pail is held in the sack by a helper and makes a rigid opening into which the material can be scooped."

"A farmer recently engaged in drainage work on a rather extensive scale had several loads of 36-inch concrete tile to distribute through waterlogged territory. In some places the ground was so soft that it was impossible to haul the tile on wagon or motor truck close to where they were to be used. It was anticipated that much hand labor

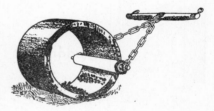

Fig. 557—Device for hauling heavy tile over soft earth.

would be involved in pushing the tile distances which ranged from 200 to 600 feet from the unloading points to the main ditches. Finally a scheme was evolved of utilizing a six-inch wooden roller which was a little wider than the average tile, the ends of the roller being stationary end terminals of the iron axle on which the roller revolved. The roller ends were fastened by means of short lengths of chain to a single-tree to which a horse was hitched and used as motive power to haul the tile to the place where they were to be used."

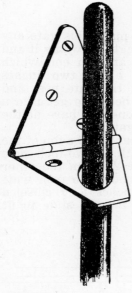

"The illustration shows how an ordinary strap hinge can be made into a very effective holder for the broom. One wing of the hinge is screwed to the hole drilled in it to receive the handle of the broom. The handle is then pushed into the hole from beneath, and when released, the weight of the broom clamps it after the manner of most other types of holders."

Fig. 558—Hinged holder for a broom.

Fig. 559—Gate fastener.

"There are many good methods of fastening gates and here is another.

"An old three-inch strap hinge is fastened to the slanted post top and to a length of oak or any other hard wood which serves as a handle. As the handle is raised the wire loop can be removed. To close the gate one merely has to place the loop over the end of the handle and press it down and the gate is taut."

"The gate arrangement pictured in the illustration provides a desirable means of separating the hogs from the cattle or allowing the hogs access to the cattle pasture."

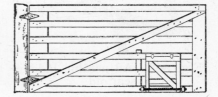

Fig. 560—Double purpose gate.

Fig. 561—Two-way gate.

"One can make this gate any height or length he wants it and have a 2x4 at each end which extends up about two inches higher than the gate post and far enough below to get into a hole in a stone you have at the foot of the gatepost.

"Nail a board at the top of the gatepost with a two-inch hole in it for the 2x4. On the other side have a hole one inch wide and three inches long chiseled in the post for the slide to fit into."

"To stop a small sliding door on a barn or shed from rubbing and scratching the side of the building, marring the wood or removing the paint, insert the shanks of two bed casters in the wall where the rub occurs as indicated by the drawing."

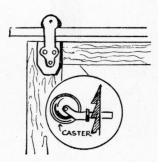

Fig. 562—Door slide.

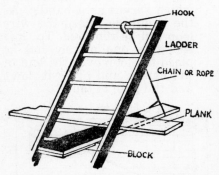

Fig. 563—Adjustable ladder scaffold.

"When painting or repairing a building it is sometimes inconvenient to build a regular carpenter's scaffold. This is especially true where there is only a short job to do.

"A quickly constructed scaffold is shown by the drawing. Two ladders are placed as indicated and a plank is used for the walk between the brackets on the ladders."

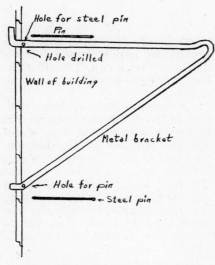

Fig. 564—Bent pipe makes strong brackets for scaffold.

"Wooden scaffold brackets are cumbersome to handle and slow to bolt to the building besides taking considerable time and money to make. Sturdy and inexpensive brackets which are easily stored and quickly attached to buildings can be made from 6 foot lengths of one-half inch galvanized iron pipe. The pipe is bent as shown and a hole drilled in each arm to take thin steel pins which serve as stops and also prevent the brackets from swinging to the side. Two holes are drilled through the wall of the building and the top arm of the bracket is inserted first."

"The diagram of a barrel cooler illustrated should be located in the corner of a building or under some cover which will protect it from dust, and the direct rays of the sun.

"Immerse the milk or cream cans to the neck in fresh water as near 50° F. as possible and hold it at that temperature until delivered. It may be cooled in about ten minutes if it is stirred frequently."

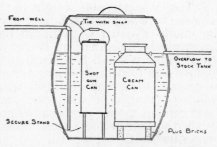

Fig. 565—Milk and cream cooler.

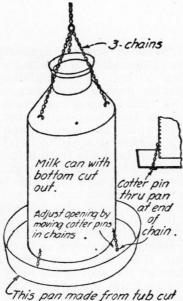

Milk can with bottom cut out.

Adjust opening by moving cotter pins in chains .

Cotter pin thru pan at end of chain .

3-chains

This pan made from tub cut down to 4 inches from bottom. Hang pan to can with 3 chains.

Fig. 566—Poultry feeder.

"A handy and good size poultry feeder can be made from a discarded milk can. The illustration will give one the idea of the design.

"A discarded tub or large dish pan is used for the bottom and a few pieces of old tire chain for the support of the bottom. The cotter pins through the pan bottom can be adjusted to give the feed a chance to feed down into the pan at whatever rate the user desires. Usually the pan should hang about two inches below the bottom of the milk can."

"A very serviceable weight to tie a horse to when left standing, may be made of concrete with an old horse-shoe imbedded in it for a ring. Make a small box six inches square and four or five inches deep to answer for a mold. Fill this with concrete mortar made from one part cement to two parts sand, and push the horseshoe, heels down, into the soft mortar till only a semi-circle large enough to tie the rein in shows. Smooth the mortar on top and slip the trowel around the edges between the mortar and the sides of the form."

Fig. 567—Concrete hitching post."

Hose Over Chain

Staple
Ends of Chain

Fig. 568—Slip proof ladder.

"By substituting a piece of chain and rubber hose for the top rung, a ladder can be prevented from slipping when used to climb trees and poles.

"The chain fits the curve of the pole or tree and the rubber hose prevents it from slipping. This arrangement also works very well when working around or painting corners of buildings."

"A wire bucket bail may hurt the hand if the bucket is carried a long way. This may be remedied with a piece of rubber hose. Just take one end of the bail off by straightening the hook, then slip the piece of hose on to the bail and put the bail back in its original position and the job is completed. It is surprising how much easier it will be to carry to pail long distances."

Fig. 569—Protector for wire bail

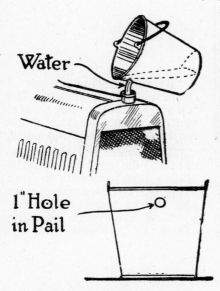

Water —

1" Hole in Pail

Fig. 570—Radiator filler.

"Often when one goes to fill the radiator of an automobile, the funnel has been misplaced. To use a pail usually means that most of the water is spilled over the radiator and hood. A combination pail that acts as a funnel as well is shown in the illustration.

"A one-inch hole is made in the side of a pail, near the top. When used to fill the radiator, this hole permits a stream to flow that is just about the size of the mouth of the radiator."

"To prevent large doors from swinging in the wind use the device shown in the sketch.

"The rod is a three-eighth inch material. The part fastened to the wall is a piece of oak or other hard wood through which a number of half-inch holes are bored to give the adjustment required. This device saves many broken doors and sagging hinges."

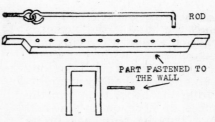

ROD

PART FASTENED TO THE WALL

Fig. 571—Door holder

"An automatic door stop is made out of a four-inch pipe which is placed in the ground and notched out at the top as shown in the illustration.

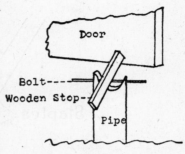

Fig. 572—Automatic door stop.

"The stop is pivoted on a bolt set across the notch. The holes in the opposite sides of the pipe make this possible. If a door is pushed past this stop, it will not come flying back as usual, but it is caught firmly behind this stop. The stop can be flipped into position to release the door instantly by lifting the extended part of the stop with the foot and can be done without stooping."

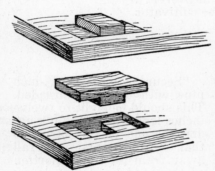

Fig. 573—Disappearing bench stop.

"A bench stop that is always at hand consists of a block of wood 2 by 6 by 12 inches cut to the shape shown and made to fit a hole of similar shape cut in the bench top. When the block is fitted in the hole, the bench presents a smooth surface, but when the block is lifted out and reversed here is a neat stop an inch high and six inches in width."

"When laying water pipe under a pavement or under a concrete floor, it is a good idea to place it inside of a larger pipe or strong tile considerably larger than the water pipe, sinking it into the concrete so that it will be well covered. Then the water pipe can be run through the tile or pipe. If it must be removed, it is quite a simple matter to

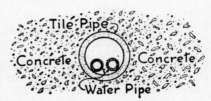

Fig. 574—Laying pipe under concrete.

take it out of the larger pipe, repair it and replace it without taking up the road or breaking up the floor."

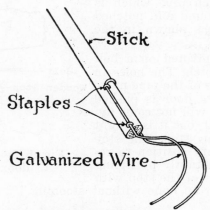

Fig. 575—Corn uncoverer to
be carried on the cultivator.

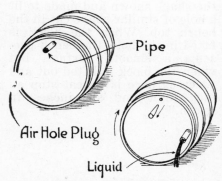

Fig. 576—Improvised barrel
faucet.

"Secure a piece of ¾-inch pipe with one end threaded. This should be eight to twelve inches long. Place a chunk under one end of the barrel so that the contents will fall away from the upper portion of the head near the chime. Then bore a hole through the head with a ⅞-inch bit. Now turn the threaded portion of the pipe into this hole.

"When ready to draw any of the contents just roll the barrel a little to the side until the liquid starts to run. When sufficient has been drawn roll the barrel back to a position where the pipe is uppermost and the contents will stop flowing. No hard work of lifting is needed. An air hole may be bored with a ⅜-inch bit about twenty inches from the pipe to allow the liquid to flow freely."

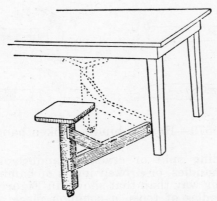

Fig. 577—Hinged stool for
kitchen table.

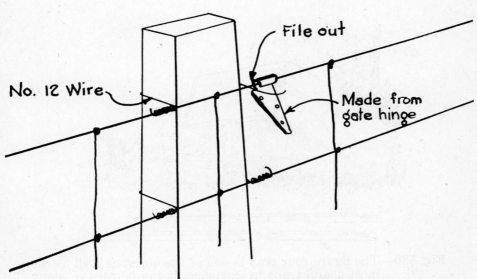

No. 12 Wire

File out

Made from
gate hinge

(Courtesy Agricultural Engineering Department, Michigan State College)

Fig. 578—Fence fastener.

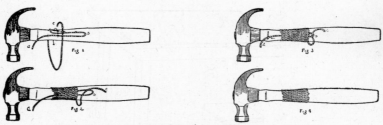

Fig. 579—How to bind a broken handle.*

"For mending split or cracked handles of tools such as hammer or ax handles, or broken joints of bamboo fishing rods, there is no better way than that shown in Figures 1, 2, 3, and 4. In mending handles of tools, a common piece of cord will do, although wax end is better. Do not use wire. It will not hold and it is likely to injure the hands. For bamboo fishing rods oiled silk or linen thread is best, but cotton thread treated with bees-wax will serve the purpose."

Fig. 580—The figure four trap is one of the oldest as well as the most useful traps in existence. It can be used in many different ways. It is light, easy to make, and costs practically nothing.

* Figures 579 and 580 courtesy International Harvester Company.

INDEX